AF887275

Computer Graphics: Systems and Applications

Managing Editor: J. L. Encarnação

Editors: K. Bø J. D. Foley R. A. Guedj
P. J. W. ten Hagen F. R. A. Hopgood M. Hosaka
M. Lucas A. G. Requicha

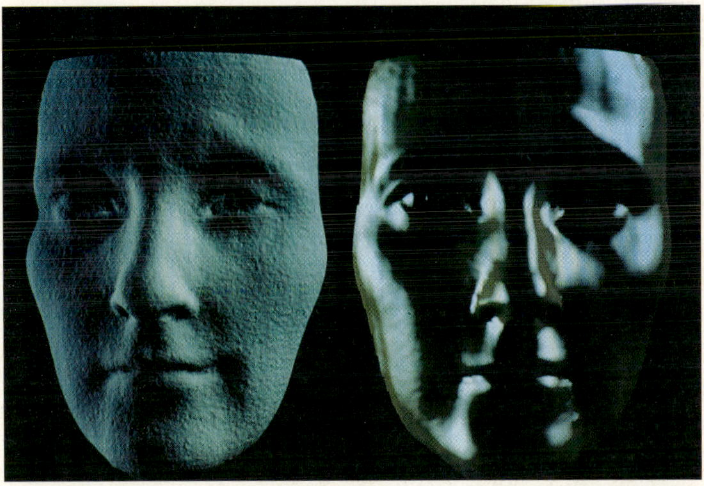

Markus Groß

Visual Computing

The Integration of Computer Graphics, Visual Perception and Imaging

With 207 Figures, 119 in Colour

Springer-Verlag
Berlin Heidelberg New York
London Paris Tokyo
Hong Kong Barcelona
Budapest

Markus Groß
Computer Science Department
Swiss Federal Institute of Technology
ETH Zürich
CH-8092 Zürich, Switzerland
and
Computer Graphics Center
(Zentrum für Graphische
Datenverarbeitung - ZGDV)
Wilhelminenstr. 7
D-64283 Darmstadt, FRG

ISBN 3-540-57222-8 Springer-Verlag Berlin Heidelberg New York
ISBN 0-387-57222-8 Springer-Verlag New York Berlin Heidelberg

CIP-Data applied for

This work is subject to copyright. All rights are reserved, whether the whole or part of the material is concerned, specifically the rights of translation, reprinting, reuse of illustrations, recitation, broadcasting, reproduction on microfilms or in any other way, and storage in data banks. Duplication of this publication or parts thereof is permitted only under the provisions of the German Copyright Law of September 9, 1965, in its current version, and permission for use must always be obtained from Springer-Verlag. Violations are liable for prosecution under the German Copyright Law.

© Springer-Verlag Berlin Heidelberg 1994
Printed in Germany

The use of general descriptive names, registered names, trademarks, etc. in this publication does not imply, even in the absence of a specific statement, that such names are exempt from the relevant protective laws and regulations and therefore free for general use.

Cover Design: Konzept & Design, Ilvesheim
Cover illustration by Ulrike Spierling, Darmstadt
Typesetting: Camera-ready by author
SPIN: 10122024 33/3140 - 5 4 3 2 1 0 - Printed on acid-free paper

For Lisa, Jana and Adrian

Foreword

Visual computing is an emerging discipline of increasing importance. Its content is based on the integration of technologies, methods, and concepts from computer graphics, visual perception, image processing, and imaging technology. This has become possible because of technological advances in microelectronics, raster technology, and software engineering. Visual computing is an enabling discipline for many new application domains, with an important market share.

Dr. Markus Gross, the author of this book, is one of the world's leading experts in visual computing. He has contributed to the development of this discipline over the last five years through his advanced research and development work in his department at the Computer Graphics Center (ZGDV) in Darmstadt, Germany, and through his lectures at the Darmstadt Technical University.

The content of the book represents a good mixture of basics and concepts on the one side, and of applications as case studies on the other. I am sure that it will attract a wide range of readers interested in the integration of the related technologies of computer graphics, visual perception, image processing, and imaging technology. The content is of very high technical quality and I am convinced that it will develop into an important textbook for this very interesting discipline.

Darmstadt, Germany *José L. Encarnação*

May 1994

Preface

This book does two things. It reflects the contents of a lecture series entitled *Visual Computing – Physiological and Technical Aspects*, which I gave in 1990, 1991, and 1992 at the Computer Science Department of the Technische Hochschule in Darmstadt. And it reviews the research I have done during the last few years since Jose Encarnação invited me to the Computer Graphics Center, Darmstadt to establish the Visual Computing Group. It presents an distillation of the rich and interesting work accomplished by this group. In particular, the large variety of different applications we investigated gave us many new insights that were only possible under the ideal working conditions available to us in Darmstadt. Many people contributed to this book in big and small ways. Some of them were former students who then became colleagues, providing important contributions to the topic; others were already established somewhere else but still connected in friendship. I have to thank them all.

In particular, I would like to thank Prof. Dr. Ing. Dr. h.c. J.L. Encarnação, our director, who was a fatherly figure as a teacher and advisor to me during this time and who made this book possible. Thanks are due also to the people who were involved in the neural network applications: Frank Seibert, Volker Abel, André Stork, Hartmut Luttermann, and Christoph Busch. Volker Kühn, Klaus Böhm, Christine Kullmer, Anke Schnabel, and Martin Zindler made the environmental simulation possible, and Ralf Winkel as well as Dirk Ahlmann wrote their theses in the context of this book. Salvador Clavé, Xavier Gomez, Tobias Richter, and Armin Berg investigated the rendering techniques for street lighting simulation. I also want to thank Maria Salazar and J. Andrew Ross for proofreading the English text in this book and in particular Chistiane Quanz for her persistence and patience, since she had to process every word and equation during numerous iterations.

Finally, I would like thank all of the industrial and institutional partners that supported us: DBP Telekom, Fraunhofer Gesellschaft, Dornier GmbH, Siemens AG, BMFT, Gesellschaft für Angewandte Fernerkundung, Technische Werke der Stadt Stuttgart, Gas- und Elektrizitätswerke Köln, Hellux GmbH, and others.

I enjoyed the time and I learnt much – it will always remain an unforgettable period of my life.

Darmstadt, Germany *Markus Groß*

May 1994

Contents

1. Introduction

2. Psychophysical Basics

Das Licht ist da und die Farben umgeben uns;
allein trügen wir kein Licht und keine Farben
in unserem Auge,
so würden wir auch außer uns dergleichen nicht
wahrnehmen.

(Johann Wolfgang von Goethe: Farbenlehre, 1824)

1. Introduction

1.1. The Concept of Visual Computing

"The purpose of (scientific) computing is insight, not numbers". This famous sentence by Richard Hamming expresses the request for an enrichment of existing scientific methods to get new insights through visual methods. Most of us have at one time or another heard the phrase, *"A picture is worth a thousand words",* and more likely than not we have all experienced its underlying significance.

This is simply because images provide huge amounts of iconic as well as symbolic information. During the course of evolution the human visual system has developed into a very sophisticated, real-time, broadband information processing unit. Among our sensory channels, the visual path is the most important one, and large parts of our brain are allocated to it. For this reason, visual representation and analysis of information is a natural process for human beings and thus extremely efficient on any kind of data base. Given the importance of human vision, discovering the main principles of its functionality has been, and remains, one of today's greatest research challenges. The research on human vision is interdisciplinary; included its realm is biology, neuroscience, psychology, human engineering and computer science. During the last decades, computer technology and information processing machinery have advanced enormously. Scientists have developed numerous methods for the artificial processing of visual information. In consequence of their different topics and goals, two major lines of research have been established, namely computer graphics and image processing or imaging.

According to James Foley's definitions [68] or [60], computer graphics deals with "*the pictorial synthesis of real or imaginary objects from their computer based models*" and covers workings areas like rendering, scientific visualization, animation, graphics in documents, or interactive user interfaces. As commonly understood, graphics can be interpreted as providing generic methods for the *representation path* of visual information processing by means of computers.

Image processing [80, 128], on the other hand, deals with the management, coding, and manipulation of images, the analysis of scenes, and the reconstruction of 3D objects from their 2D projectional presentations [209]. From the early paradigm of David Marr [165] to the neural network approaches of today, most methods developed try to implement basic features of human vision. For this reason image processing can be seen as the *perceptive* or as the *analytic element* of artificial visual information processing which describes the inverse pipeline of computer graphics.

This common understanding, first exemplified by Azriel Rosenfeld in the 1970s, can be represented as in Fig. 1. Basically, we can distinguish between two levels for the representation of visual information, namely the symbolic level and the iconic level. Whereas the symbolic level represents visual information in terms of attributed geometry stored and managed in a data base, the iconic level represents it via spatially and tempory discrete images. In order to accomplish interaction with the user we have to link these levels together. This can be performed by processing steps that define both inter-level transitions and intra-level transitions. These transitions are provided by computer graphics methods in addition to imaging methods.

Computer graphics provides methods for the intra-level transition in the symbolic layer, through symbolic processing on the geometry, for instance, geometric transformations, curve and surface design or manipulation, and any kind of CAD and geometric modeling. All of these are parts of this processing. Furthermore, computer graphics deals with the transition from symbolic to iconic information using visualization and rendering techniques. Attributed geometry can be mapped onto iconic image structures.

Image processing, on the other hand, defines methods for iconic processing that map images onto images, such as filtering, coding,

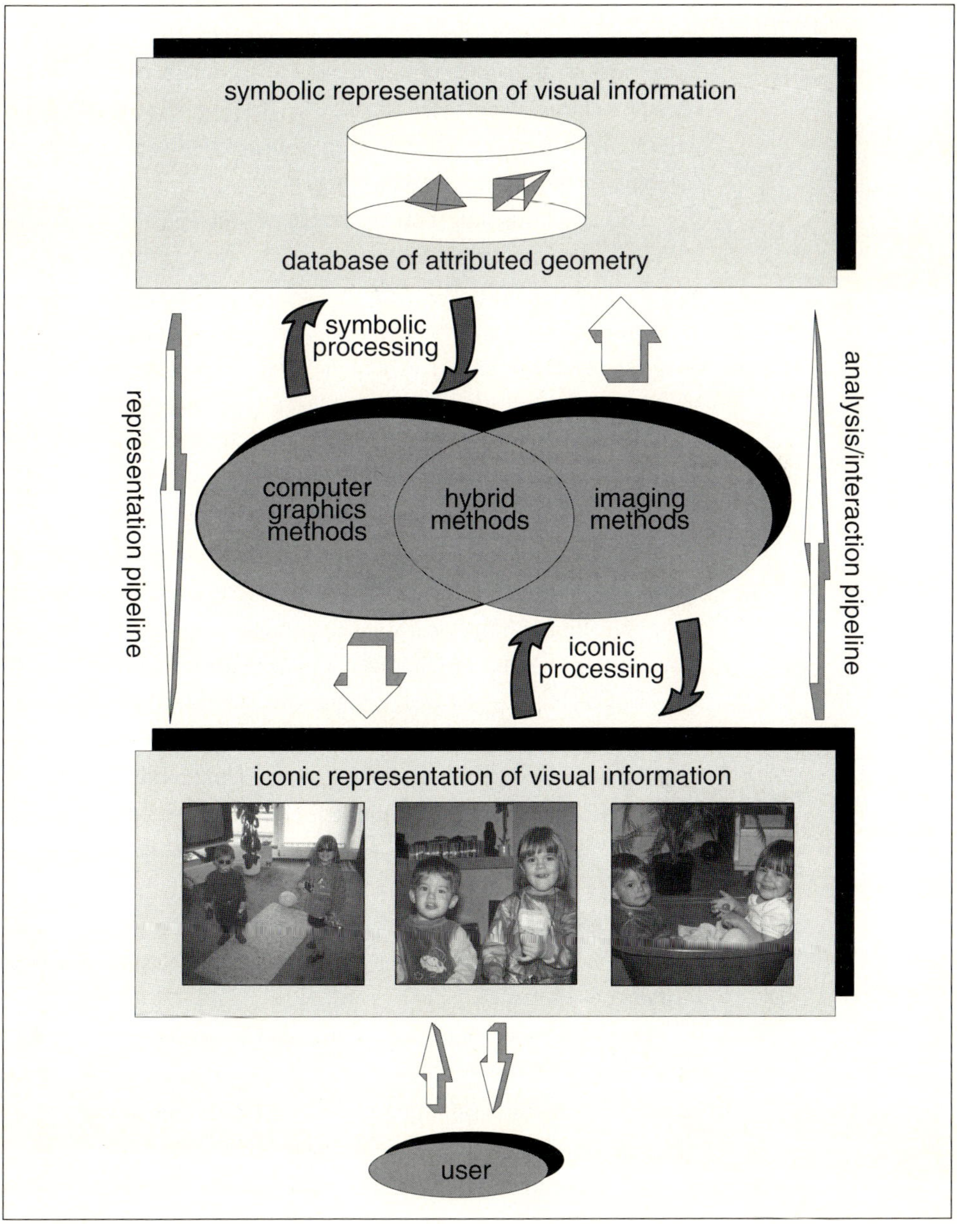

Figure 1: Computer graphics and imaging as commonly understood

or segmentation. The transition from the iconic pictorial representation to the symbolic level is accomplished by computer vision methods that allow for the recognition of shape and geometry from images. Therefore, imaging is often considered to be an essential working area in artificial intelligence [24]. This pictorial representation implies that we also must make use of both computer graphics and imaging methods in order to achieve interaction for the user. Since both areas provide opposite parts of the interaction cycle, according to Encarnação's definitions (see [61]) only hybrid methods will satisfy the request for a mapping from symbolic representations to iconic representations and vice versa.

This understanding corresponds to Kunii's vision of the integration of graphics and imaging in terms of data structures that have to be defined to perform this bidirectional mapping [146]. Both of them are part of this common concept and thus have to interact on the same data structures in both the symbolic and the iconic layer. Moreover, the hybrid methods that have to be defined to achieve such interaction are established on the basis of the same data organization.

Although during the past decades these two research lines have been separately organized, advanced visual information processing systems obviously require graphics and imaging techniques for various applications [61]. For instance, in medical imaging 3D reconstructions from MR- or CT-slices are computed based on volume rendering techniques. However, to perform this task they require sophisticated image segmentation and vectorization methods to transform iconic into symbolic representations. On the other hand, any kind of recognition and symbolic image understanding method strongly requires interpolation and geometric modeling to describe the objects extracted from images. Instead of learning vision systems and robots in real world scenarios, they can be even more successfully trained with computer graphics models in a simulation environment.

However, both computer graphics and imaging deal with pictorial information to be perceived, analyzed and interpreted by human beings. There is a basic requirement to take account of the results and the knowledge from human visual perception research in developing and generating the new generation of graphics and imaging systems [106]. For instance, in scientific visualization, where we map huge thematic data sets onto attributed geometry presented on a graphics display, we must decide which of the attributes are most appropriate: color, shape, transparency, shading, etc. Developers have to know where the limitations of human discrimination and perception lie. Any kind of interaction technique requires information regarding the temporal and spatial thresholds of human vision. In order to build adaptive vision systems we have to understand the basic principles of visual information processing in the human brain. Generally speaking, the development of computer graphics and imaging methods is deeply influenced by the principles of human visual perception.

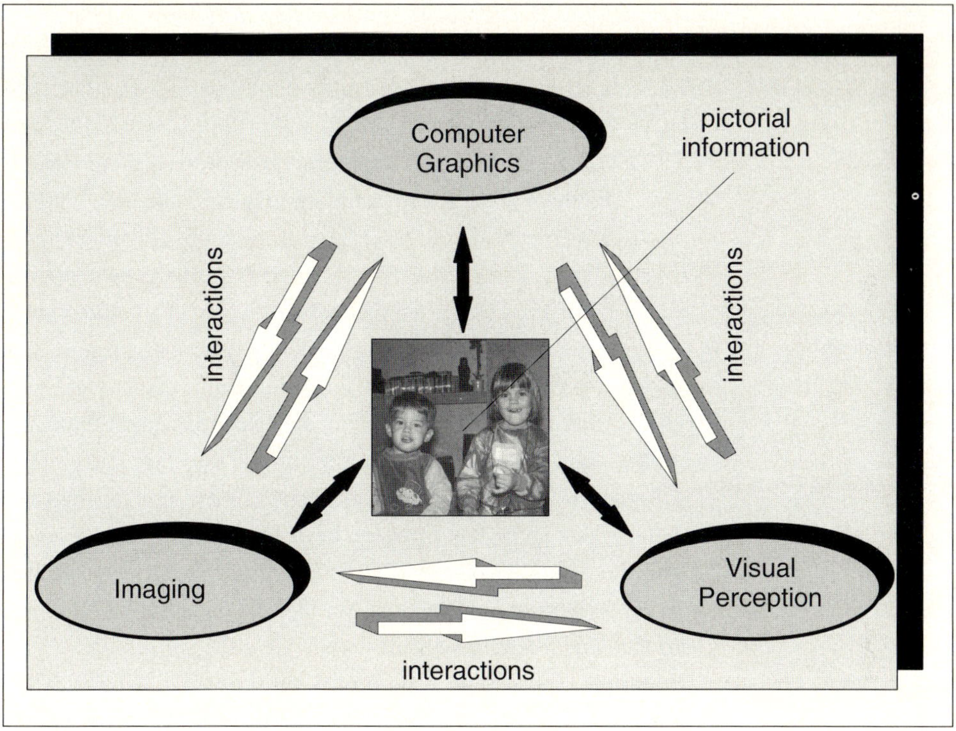

Figure 2: Pictorial reference for the interactions between computer graphics, imaging and visual perception

Another important step in this direction is the classic definition of scientific visualization [171] that states:

> Visualization embraces both image understanding and image synthesis. That is, visualization is a tool both for interpreting image data fed into a computer, and for generating images from complex multi-dimensional data sets. It studies those mechanisms in humans and computers which allow them in concert to perceive, use and communicate visual information. Visualization unifies the largely independent but convergent fields of:
>
> – Computer graphics
> – Image processing
> – Computer vision
> – Computer-aided design

- Signal processing
- User interface studies....

Based on the elucidations above there is an increasing demand for a common understanding of how to achieve this integration. To meet this demand, scientific conferences (e.g., Kunii, *Computer Graphics International 1992*; [146]) and journals (e.g., *The Visual Computer*, Springer) have been established and accomplished with great success. The expression ***visual computing*** has been born as a synonym for the integration of computer graphics and imaging techniques including the features and properties of human visual perception.

This concept of visual computing is expressed pictorially in Fig. 2. The three disciplines, computer graphics, imaging, and human visual perception, process visual information. The interactions and relationships among them are expressed by arrows symbolizing the transfer of knowledge and methods from one area to the other.

For instance, when defining rendering and imaging pipelines or color systems for the graphics display, it is important to take into consideration the ability of the human visual system to perceive brightness and color. Temporal sensitivity and thresholds are crucial for the construction of stereo workstations or eye-trackers that enable us to detect the line of vision in real time applications such as flight simulators. Generally, the thresholds of visual performance provide important information for the optimization of graphics hardware and software systems.

Image analysis and pattern recognition define algorithms for the classification of images as well as for the automatic recognition of underlying features, which is one of the very sophisticated properties of human perception. Other important tasks such as the recovery of shape information from stereo, shading, or motion are dealt with in computer vision.

Biological neural networks in the visual cortex and the basic principles of distributed information processing provide interesting ideas on how to code, manage and analyze large data sets. In particular, artificial neural networks that simulate the mechanisms of the nervous system represent a powerful tool for tasks such as clustering, classification, and subspace mapping, all of which are required for information coding and can therefore be used in both graphics and imaging.

1.2. Organization of the Book

This book aims to define a common understanding of computer graphics and imaging, as well as to provide an introduction to the concept of *visual computing*.

Since the topic dealt with in this book covers a huge range of research areas, however, it does not claim to be complete. The goal of the author is to give reasonable technical arguments in terms of foundations and applications for further worldwide work on this integration. The book is seen more as a technical and scientific introduction for computer scientists and engineers than as the ultimate framework on *visual computing*.

Foundations of visual perception and of psychophysics will be presented, as well as basic methods of imaging and computer vision. The relationship and the interaction with computer graphics is established by means of various examples and supported by applications. Most of them are included in the foundation chapters to illustrate the implications of the explained methods or features for computer graphics. The topics highlighted in this book extend from the sensitivity of visual channels, color perception, and early visual modeling to wavelet transforms, stereo matching, and neural networks. The applications represent research conducted by the author and others during the last years, ranging from environmental data analysis and driving simulation to medical imaging, remote sensing, and face recognition.

As suggested in Fig. 2, the author understands the three fields of research to be integrated as being symbolized by a 3-dimensional space where each one – graphics, imaging, and perception – defines one of the principal axes. This is illustrated in Fig. 3. As explained above, most advanced visual computing applications have to make use of methods provided by all of these areas. In the scheme the integration is performed by data structures and by hybrid methods that are realized in applications. Thus each hybrid method, algorithm, or common data structure can be thought of as a closed area or "cluster" in the space of Fig. 3. Each application, however, dependent on the methods required, unifies a group of these clusters in the sense of a "class" into statistical data analysis.

Finally, Fig. 4 gives the reader a detailed overview of the foundations and the applications treated in this book. It indicates

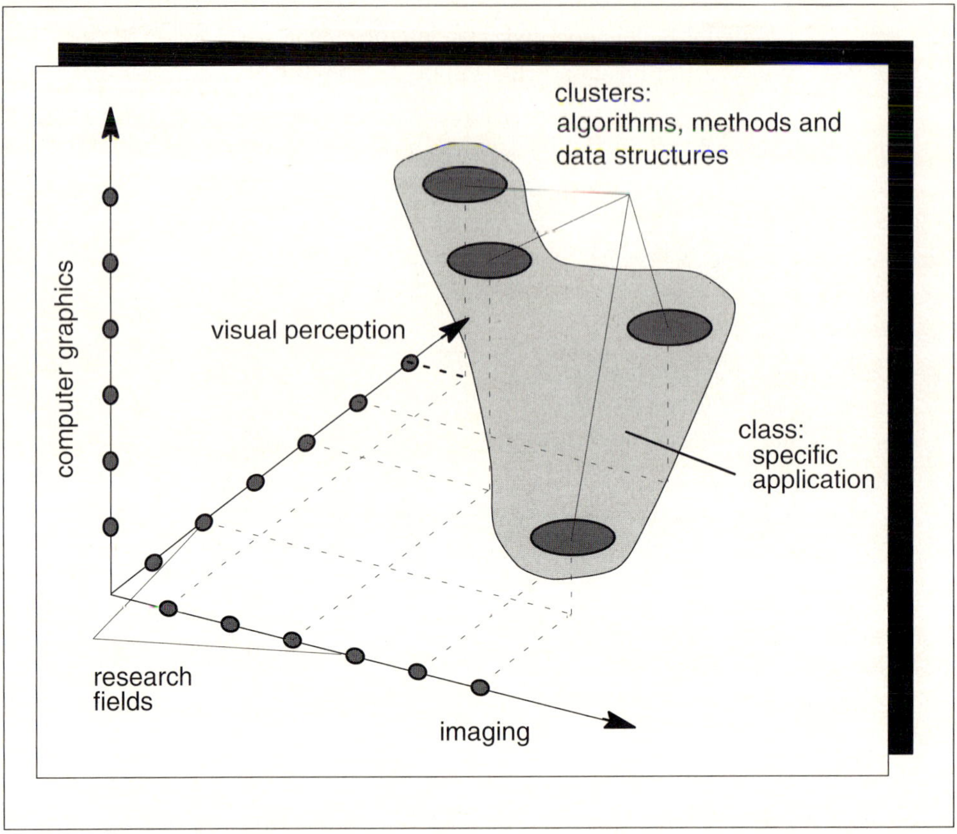

Figure 3:
Space defined by the research fields of computer graphics, imaging and visual perception

that the major working areas of computer graphics, imaging, and perception are addressed by the examples, such as rendering, scientific visualization, physically based modeling, human computer interaction or multimedia interfaces in graphics, filtering, coding, segmentation, image analysis and computer vision for imaging, as well as light and color for perception. Furthermore, the reader will be introduced to a wide range of generic methods adapted to the specific applications.

Since most equations are derived from the literature, all parameters are presented in their original notations, although this sometimes gives rise to ambiguities from one chapter to another.

The book itself is organized and structured into 8 chapters that deal with the following topics:

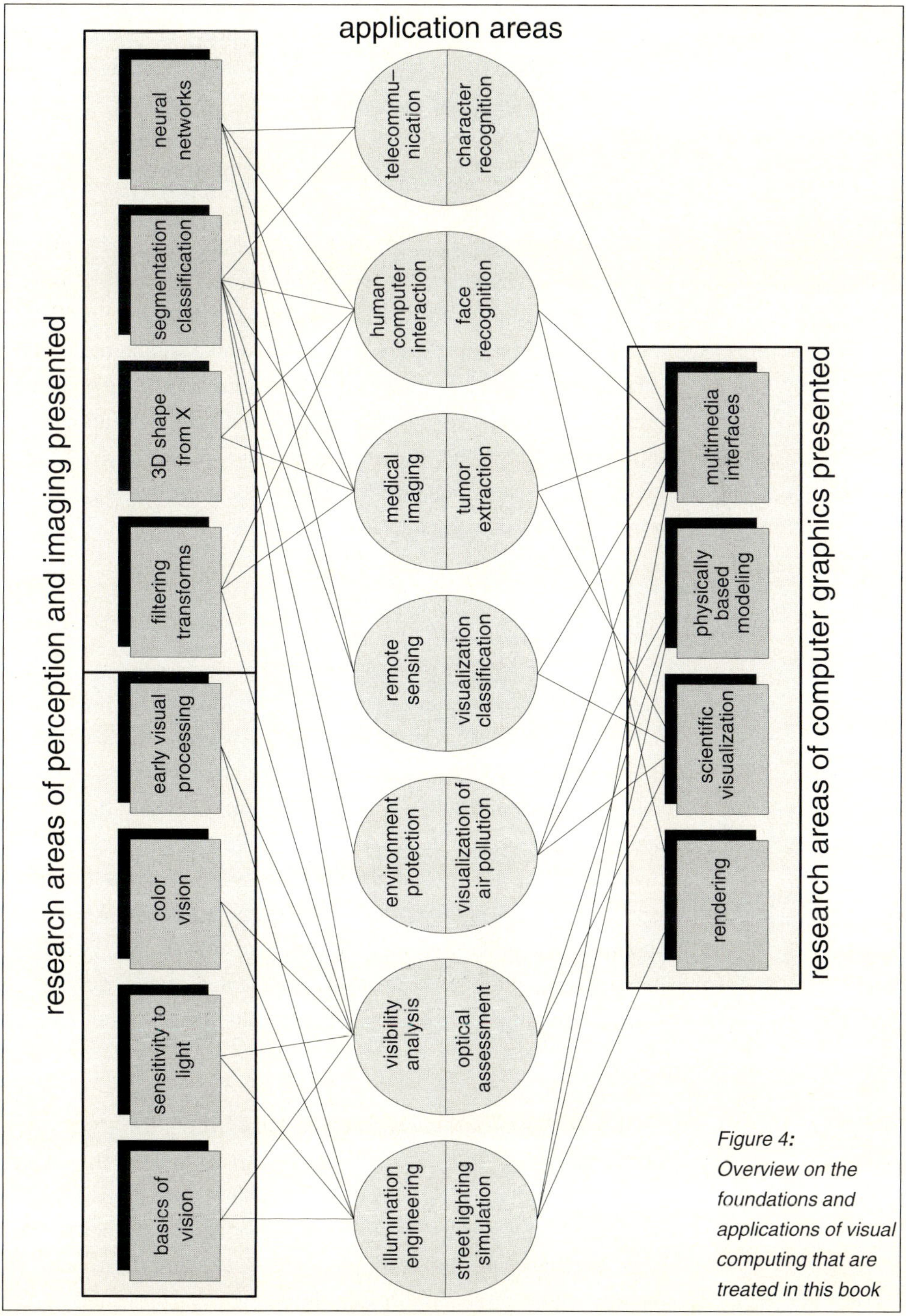

Figure 4: Overview on the foundations and applications of visual computing that are treated in this book

Chapter 1: Introduction

This chapter introduces the reader to the concept of *visual computing* and elucidates the request for a common understanding of graphics, imaging, and visual perception.

Chapter 2: Physiological and Psychophysical Basics

The second chapter introduces the reader to the basic principles of the human visual system. It provides an anatomical overview as well as biological aspects of visual neurons and ganglion cells. The chapter sheds light on the physics of the human eye and on basic measures for light and radiance, and it provides an explanation of the implications for rendering pipelines. Specifically, global illumination techniques, such as radiosity or ray-tracing, and the spectral treatment of light require detailed knowledge about the basics presented here. Applications from driving simulation and street lighting design are presented.

Chapter 3: Sensitivity to Light and Color

The third chapter contains detailed descriptions of psychophysical features and properties of human vision. It begins with an explanation of adaptation, contrast, luminance-brightness correction, visual acuity, and spatial resolution. Temporal visual channels, thresholds, and the perception of stereo are essential for any graphics application. Due to the numerous frameworks on color, this issue is treated from a perceptual point of view and emphasis placed on color measurements, color spaces, and higher-order colorimetry. Finally, a detailed description of the imaging pipeline in computer graphics is given, and optimal mappings of rendered images onto graphic displays are provided.

Chapter 4: Visualization and Visibility Analysis

The fourth chapter is dedicated to two major applications, namely the analysis of the visibility of objects in the landscape, and the simulation and visualization of air pollution. Both applications relate to environmental protection. Using the knowledge presented in the previous chapters, the reader will be able to understand the methods required in these applications. The first part of the chapter defines mathematical paradigms for the determination of the visibility of objects based on perceptual aspects and describes a method for the simulation of scenes, as well as an interpretation of the optical impression using ray tracing and image analysis. Examples are given from the field of overhead line design.

The second part of the chapter provides an example for the integration of interactive simulation and visualization for environmental data analysis. It explains how color and shape are used to visualize scientific data interpolation and coding techniques. This example requires our hybrid methods from graphics and from imaging for data acquisition and data processing.

Chapter 5: Computational Vision

Based on the psychophysical and biological topics of the previous chapters and on the requirements of the previous applications, the fifth chapter introduces the reader to computational models of vision in imaging. The Marr paradigm is explained and early models for retinal cells as well as for cortical cells are described. These models are exemplified by an analysis of the optical attractiveness of advertisement plates using both graphics and imaging methods. Furthermore, the recently developed wavelet transform is described and it is shown that it can be taken as an advanced model in early visual processing. Due to its promising results, 2D and 3D versions of this transform have been developed for volume rendering as well as for texture analysis. Finally, an example for generating shape from images is given, namely automatic modeling using matching of stereo image pairs.

Chapter 6: Image Analysis and Neural Networks

Chapter 6 is dedicated to statistical data analysis aimed at modeling basic features of symbolic information processing by the human mind, for instance decision making or grouping and ordering. Also, it provides useful algorithms for imaging and for scientific visualization. The chapter first explains generic tools for dimensionality reduction, ordering, clustering and classification. Principal axes transforms are illustrated as well as maximum likelihood estimation. An introduction to artificial neural networks is provided, and an outline is given of self-organizing structures such as Kohonen maps, Boltzmann machines, or competitive learning networks, as well as a description of supervised trained networks such as back-propagation.

Chapter 7: Neural Networks for Graphics and Imaging

Chapter 7 illustrates numerous examples for the application of artificial neural networks in graphics and imaging. The first application comes from telecommunications and illustrates the transmission, coding, and recognition of noisy characters with neural networks. The second topic is the analysis and visualization of multidimensional remotely sensed image data sets, where cluster analyses and subspace mappings are performed by means of Kohonen maps. A further example handles the identification and surface-reconstruction of brain tumors in magnetic-resonance images. This is achieved by combining both graphics and imaging techniques for use in the field of medicine. The last application stems from human–computer–interaction, where the automatic recognition of human faces becomes increasingly important. A face recognition algorithm is described using principal component analysis of face images, neural classifiers, and psychophysical experiments.

Chapter 8: The Way Ahead

The last chapter summarizes the book and aims to encourage the reader to work further in this area.

2. Psychophysical Basics

2.1. Anatomy of the Human Visual System

2.1.1. Overview

The human visual system presents an extremely complex architecture whose functionality has by no means been completely discovered. Several components participate in the processing of signals and are interconnected in specific ways. Figure 5 shows the structure of cerebral areas participating in the visual process by direct supply of signals according to [228]. The visual system consists of the eye, the optic nerve, the optic chiasma, the tractus opticus, the corpus geniculatum laterale, the colliculi superiores, and the visual cortex in areas 17, 18, and 19 of the brain. The visual information received and preprocessed by the retina of the eye is transmitted by the optic nerve separately for the nasal and temporal field of vision.

In the chiasma opticum half of the one million optical nerves cross over to the contralateral side and unite with the uncrossed part of the other eye, forming the tractus opticus, which then allocates the visual information of half of the visual field to each cerebral hemisphere. The optic ducts from the temporal part of the left eye retina and from the nasal part of the right eye run through the left tractus opticus and vice versa. The first switch after the crossing of the chiasma opticum is the corpus geniculatum laterale (CGL). It consists of a six-layered structure where three neuron layers dominate one eye. Color perception as well as contrast processes are attributed to the CGL. After this preprocessing the visual information is transmitted via the optic radiation to the main processing areas in the cerebral cortex, where early and higher-order visual processes, such as orientation-specific edge and motion detection are performed and complex shapes are analyzed. Furthermore, visual information from the retina arrives directly at the culliculi superiores, which among other things assumes the tasks of visual motoricity.

Figure 5: Schematic presentation of the structure and interconnections of the human visual system

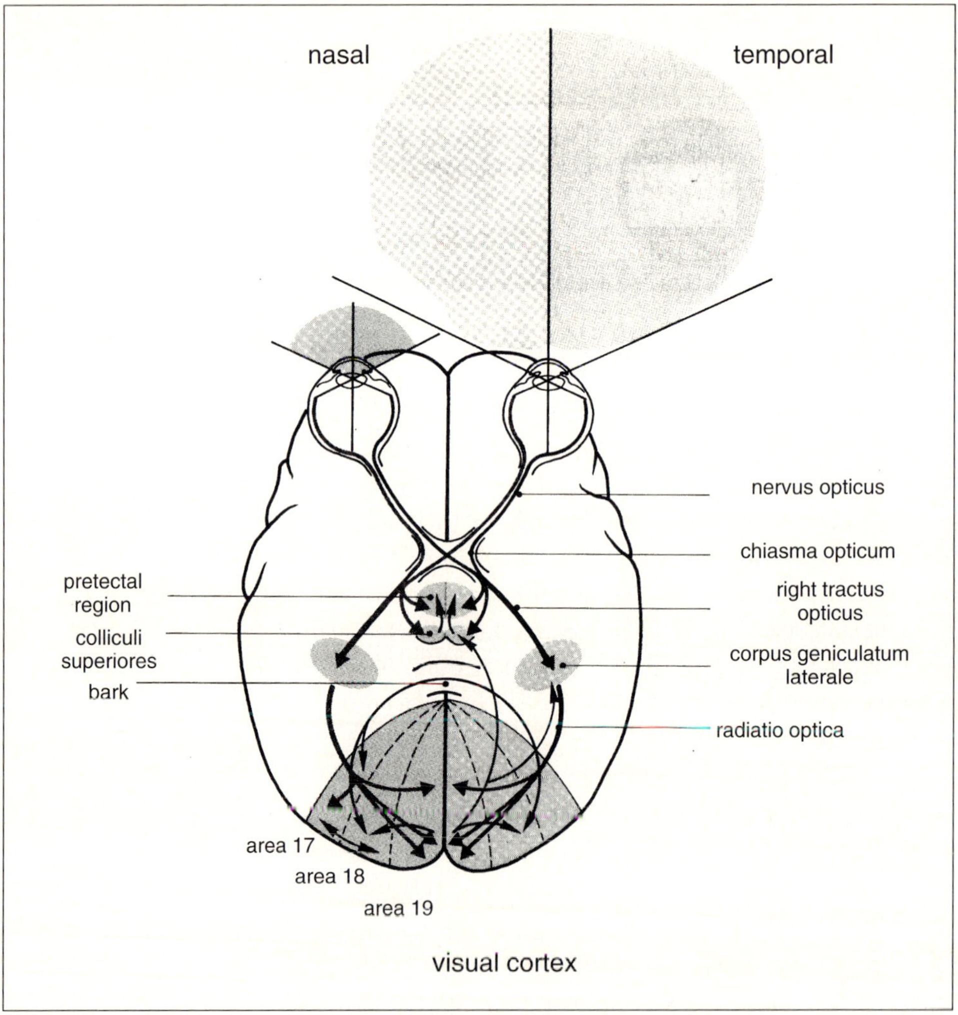

2.1.2. Biological Neurons

The basic biological information processing unit is the nerve cell or neuron. The human brain consists of more than 100 billion neurons. Neurons come in many different shapes and sizes depending on the job they are tailored for. Figure 6 shows the principal structure of a neuron according to [228, 54].

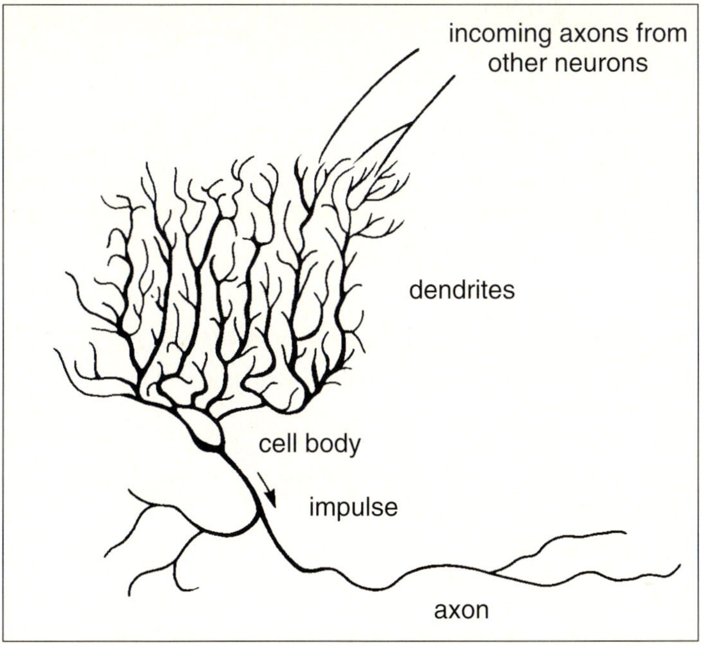

Figure 6:
Schematic drawing of a neuron and its components [54]

Four main parts can be distinguished: the axon, the dendrites, the synapses, and the cell body. The axon is a long branching output area of the neuron, which can transmit electrical impulses along the branches depending on the actual activity of the neuron. The input area of the nerve cell is a set of branching fibres called dendrites that are connected with the axons of other neurons. The connection between an axon and a dendrite is called synapse. The synapses represent an adaptive weight for the incoming information from other neurons, which means that the activity of a neuron depends not only on the activity of other neurons transmitted by the dendrites but also on their weights via the corresponding synapses. Cortical neurons are strongly interconnected with up to 10000 other neurons each. Since the weights may be either positive or negative, the incoming impulses may increase or decrease the actual activity of the cell.

Thus the frequency coding of the impulses sent through the axon represent the activity of the neuron. Figure 7 shows the electrochemical impulses for an active and an inactive neuron.

Figure 7: Impulse diagram of the electrochemical activity of a neuron

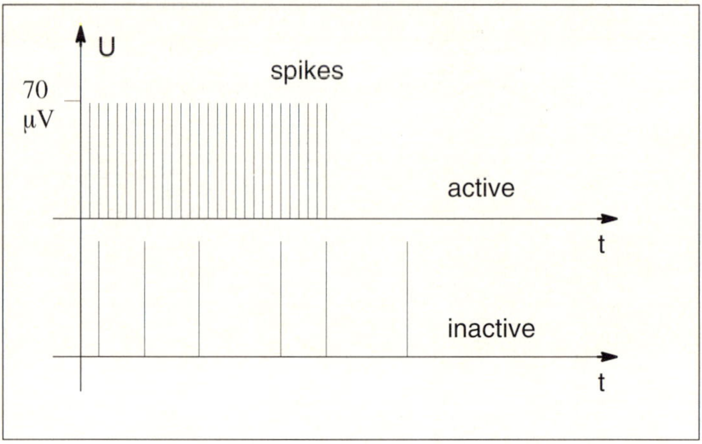

The evaluation of incoming impulses by the cell body is strongly nonlinear. In artificial neural networks this function is often described as sigmoid behavior [223]. Equation (1) expresses the characteristics of a sigmoidal response function *f*(*x*):

$$f(x) = \frac{1}{1 + e^{\sum_i w_i x_i}} \tag{1}$$

$\sum_i w_i x_i$: *weighted sum of incoming impulses* x_i

w_i: *weights*

This sigmoid function has the advantage of being continuously differentiable and allows for an efficient mathematical treatment.

2.1.3. Receptive Fields

The sum of spatially coherent receptors belonging to one ganglion cell is called its *receptive field* (RF). This is illustrated in Fig. 8. All the receptors in one receptive field feed their information into the dendrites of one nerve cell. The receptive fields of different cells usually overlap. Due to the information coding achieved with receptive fields, the spatial resolution of a stimulus is a priori limited to the size of the RF for the localization.

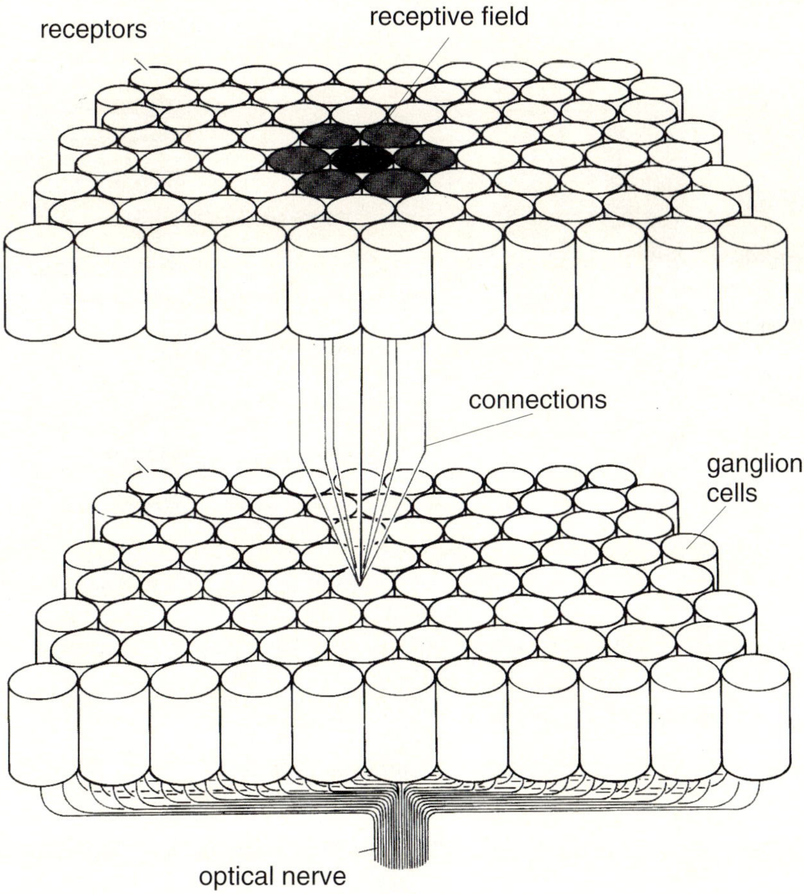

Figure 8:
Illustration of a receptive field that belongs to one ganglion cell [203]

2.1.4. The Human Retina

The retina of the eye contains the light-sensitive sensors of the visual system. After being focused, a scene is reproduced on its receptors. The structure of the retina is extremely complex. It consists of different types of cells functioning for different tasks within signal processing and control. The circa 6 million color-sensitive retinal cones for daylight vision (> 20 cd/m^2) as well as the 120 million retinal rods for night vision (< 1 cd/m^2) are of particular importance. Figure 9 shows the structure of the human retina schematically.

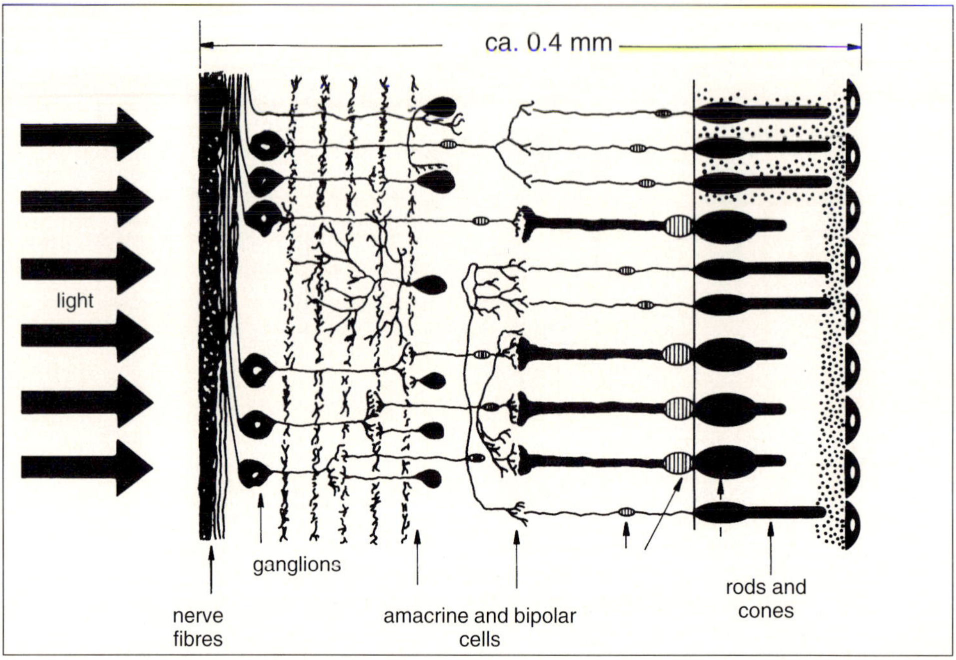

Figure 9: Structure of the retina according to [213]

In contrast to most artificial sensors, like cameras, the human retina consists of layers that are both horizontally and vertically interconnected. In addition to the receptors in the first layer, initial processing is done by horizontal cells, amacrines, bipolar cells, and ganglion cells. The horizontal cells of the second layer connect the bipolar cells of the third layer with the receptors and also average the signals of each cell's neighbors. The bipolar cell itself receives a signal from the receptor and from the horizontal cell and generates an output that is proportional to their difference. The control mechanism implemented by the first three layers allows a local adaptation of parts of the retina and a dynamic reduction. Due to the logarithmic behavior (Weber–Fechner–law, see also Chap. 3) of the cells, the reaction of the bipolars is proportional to the quotient of local brightness and background brightness. This lateral inhibition achieves a reinforcement of transitions from light to dark. The reaction achieved by the physiological behavior of retinal ganglion cells in the fifth layer is illustrated in Fig. 10 for a one-dimensional cut. Initial reaction to a locally limited light stimulus has its maximum in the area of transition from light to dark, i.e., the edges which are thus accentuated. From the point of view of signal theory this operation can be interpreted as an enhancement of high spatial frequencies.

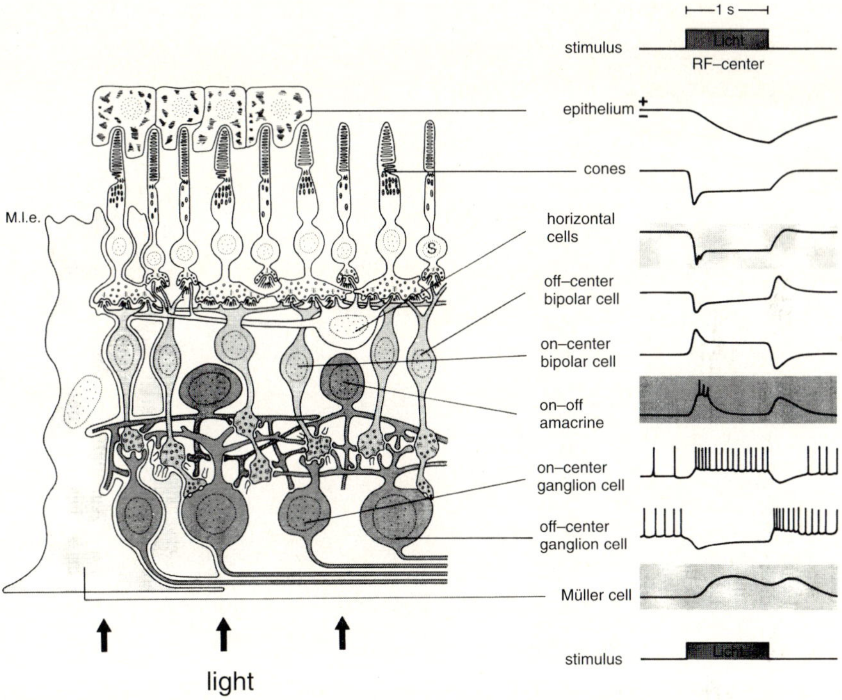

Figure 10:
Reaction of retinal ganglion cells to a locally limited light stimulus

Rods and cones are not evenly distributed over the retina surface. The cone density has its maximum at the fovea (point of sharpest focus) and decreases towards the periphery.

Each fiber of the optic nerve represents the axon of one ganglion cell, which is in turn connected functionally and anatomically with the retinal receptors of its receptive field. The totality of receptors directly or indirectly connected with a ganglion cell is called the visual receptive field (see also Fig. 8). The extent of these isotropic receptive fields also increases towards the periphery. For detailed presentations of these mechanisms see [228].

2.1.5. Organization of the Visual Cortex

The image received and preprocessed by the retinal receptors is projected into the visual cortex via the CGL. However, this projection is by no means linear: a disproportionately large part of the cortex is occupied by the area around the fovea, and a relatively small one by the periphery. An approximation of this nonlinear projection can also be attempted.

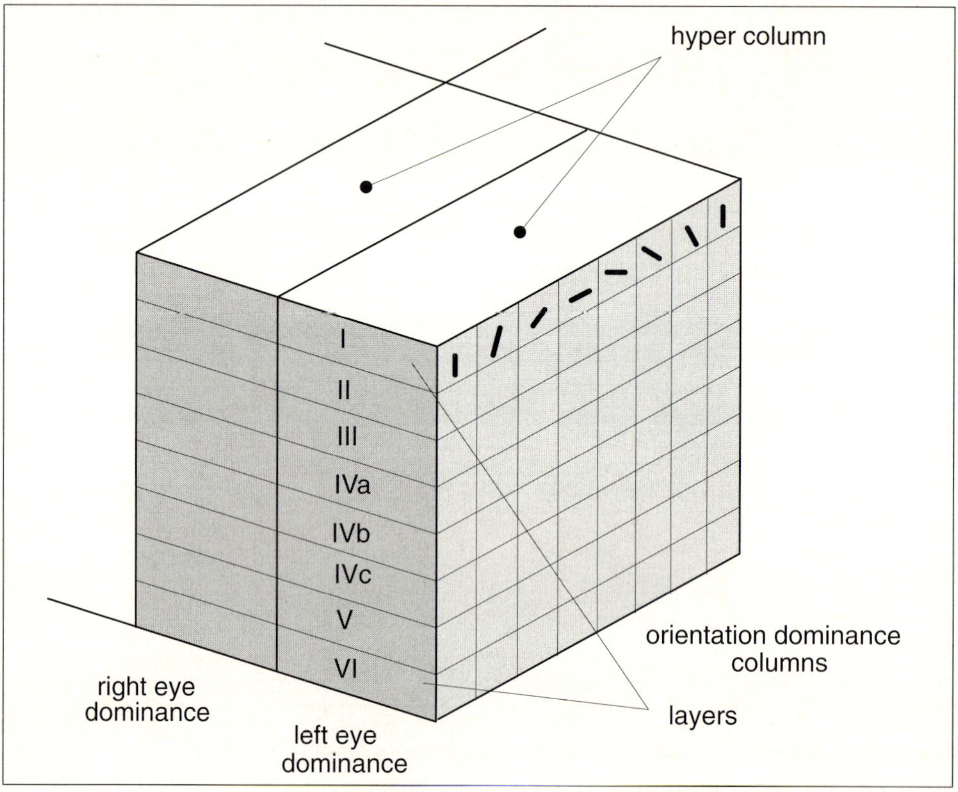

Figure 11: Schematic model organization of the visual cortex

We particularly owe basic detailed knowledge on the structure and functionality of the visual cortex due to the Nobel Prize winners Wiesel and Hubel [124]. Although we are far from knowing all the details of the visual system, in order to understand the model described, it is important to know that the primary visual cortex has a modular setup of individual columns, each column processing a small fraction of the visual field. Wiesel and Hubel found out by experiments with microelectrodes in the cerebral cortex of cats that these columns consist of neurons that are sensitive to the spatial orientation of lines presented in the visual field. Aside from this orientation preference these cells are also dominant to the signals stemming from one eye, either left or right. These so-called simple cells are organized in several horizontal layers where the orientation preference is preserved perpendicular to the layer. The only exception is layer IV that consists of cells with isotrope receptive fields of a pure monocular sensitivity. Figure 11 shows the schematic organization of the cortex according to [124]. Figure 12 illustrates the response of a simple cortical cell. The stimulation of the detector is highest when the orientation of the stimulating edge in the visual field coincides with its own orientation. The greater the deviation of a stimulating orientation the lesser the activity of the cell. These cells are combined in groups with orientation preferences staggered by about 10°.

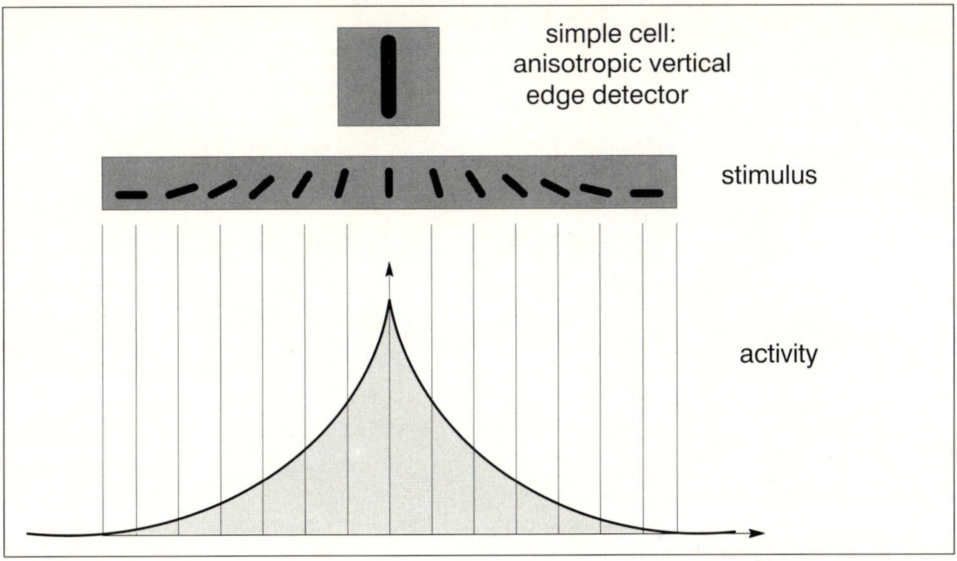

Figure 12:
Illustration of the reaction of an anisotropic simple cell in the visual cortex

From the point of view of signal theory these cells can be considered as oriented high-pass filters. In Chap. 5 we will demonstrate how to model this behavior. In addition to the simple cells of the visual cortex, other cells were discovered by experiment that process complex or hyper-complex receptive fields, the reactions of which depend for instance on movements in the visual field [124].

2.2. Physics of the Human Eye

2.2.1. Image Projection and the Field of Vision

Figure 13 shows the projection of an image onto the retina surface. The main angle describing the position of the object is denoted by α, where α is called the visual angle between two limiting rays from the object.

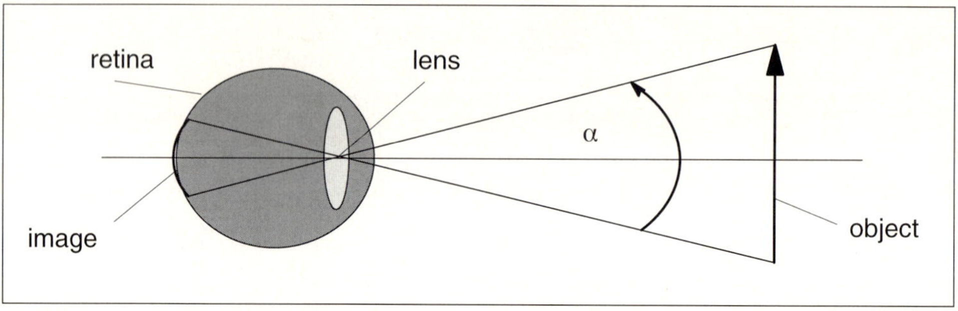

Figure 13: Projection of an image onto the retina surface

The optical projection of the image is indeed more complex than presented here because of the diameter of the lens, which depends on the amplitude of accommodation.

The visual field of the human eye is shown in Fig. 14 for achromatic stimuli and a fixed line of sight. The area of binocular vision is presented by the overlapping fields of the right and left eye. Hence, the total visual area is only limited by anatomical constraints.

It should be noted that for chromatic stimuli the blue-yellow channel has the largest extent. Detailed discussions of these classical features are presented in [230].

2.2.2. Accommodation

A target at a distance less than infinity causes the eye to change the focal length of its lens in order to project a sharp image on the retina. This change of focus is called accommodation. It is accomplished by an intraocular muscle. The accommodation is measured in diopters. A diopter is defined as the reciprocal of the distance r between the target and the eye. This is described by Eq. (2).

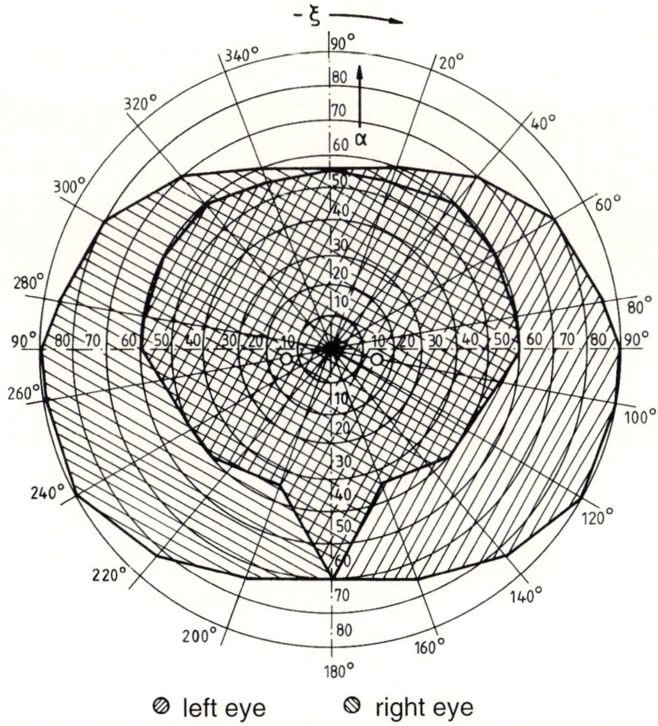

Figure 14: Visual field for achromatic light [230]

The accommodation depends strongly on the age of the person in question. Figure 15 shows the amplitude of accommodation as a function of age.

$$D = \frac{1}{r} \qquad (2)$$

D: *focus point in diopters*
r: *distance of an object from the eye*

The accommodation response times of several diopters are shown in Table 1 (see [230]):

diopters	3	4	5	6
from infinity	0.56	0.80	0.91	1.55 sec
to infinity	0.87	1.31	1.15	0.99 sec

Table 1: Response time for accommodation according to [230]

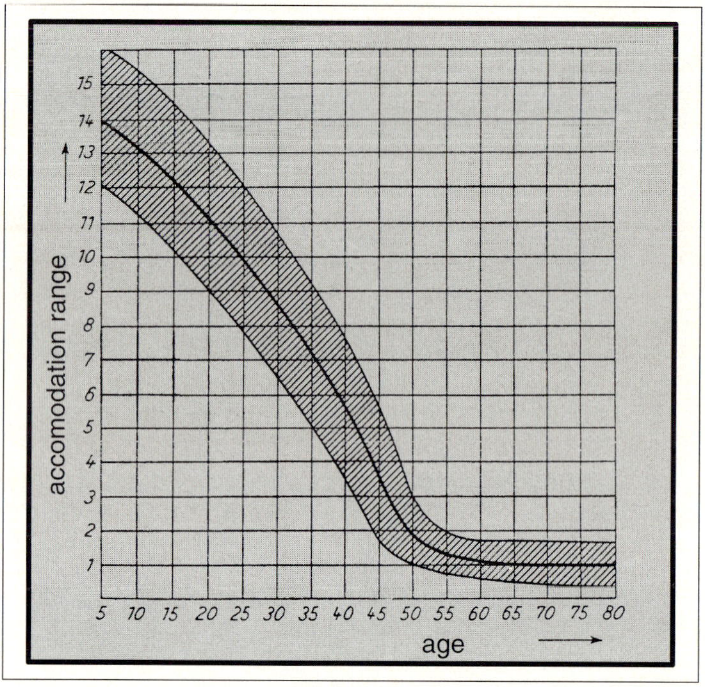

Figure 15: Amplitude of accommodation as a function of age [230]

2.2.3. Image Quality and Diffraction Effects

One of the most important effects of the wave nature of light is the limitation on optical resolution by diffraction effects at the aperture of the pupil. This is also expressed by Abbe's theory of light. Thus a point light source will be projected as a small disk on the retina. In fact the intensity of light arriving on the retina is described as in [123] by the point spread function in Eq. (3):

$$I(\alpha) = \left(\frac{J_1(\pi d \frac{\alpha}{\lambda})}{\pi d \frac{\alpha}{\lambda}} \right)^2 \qquad (3)$$

J_1 : *first–order Bessel function*
d : *pupil diameter*
α : *visual angle*
λ : *wavelength*

Figure 16 shows the point spread function or diffraction pattern in relative units for a wavelength of 555 nm. The central patch between the first zero on either side of the center represents the visual angle covered by a single point. To distinguish two points according to this theory, their point spread functions should not overlap at all, or if so, only a little. According to Fig. 16 this limit is about 1 arcmin. This seems to be a crucial optical limitation. Fortunately, the retinal and cortical image processing steps improve the resolution of the eye.

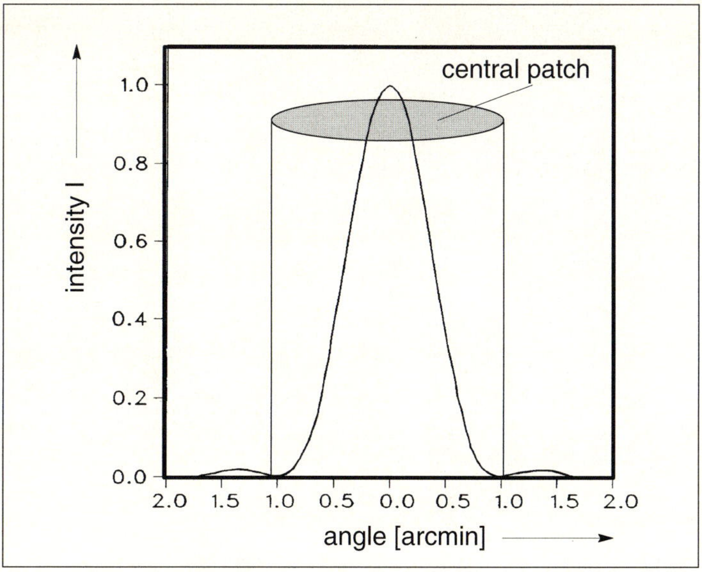

Figure 16:
Point spread function of the human eye [123]

2.3. Measuring Light

2.3.1. Spectral Sensitivity

Light is the part of the electromagnetic spectrum that can be perceived by the visual system. This is presented in Fig. 17.

The electromagnetic radiance is described by its energy E and its wavelength λ, where every quantum of light has the energy E:

$$E = \frac{hc}{\lambda} \tag{4}$$

h: *Planck's constant*
c: *speed of light*

The human observer, however, is not equally sensitive to all parts of the visible spectrum. Equal numbers of quanta differ greatly in their perceived brightness. Spectral sensitivity can be measured by several methods via visual stimuli. For computer graphics as well as for illumination engineering, the CIE curves [261], also called luminous efficiency curves, $V(\lambda)$ and $V'(\lambda)$ are of great importance (see Fig. 18).

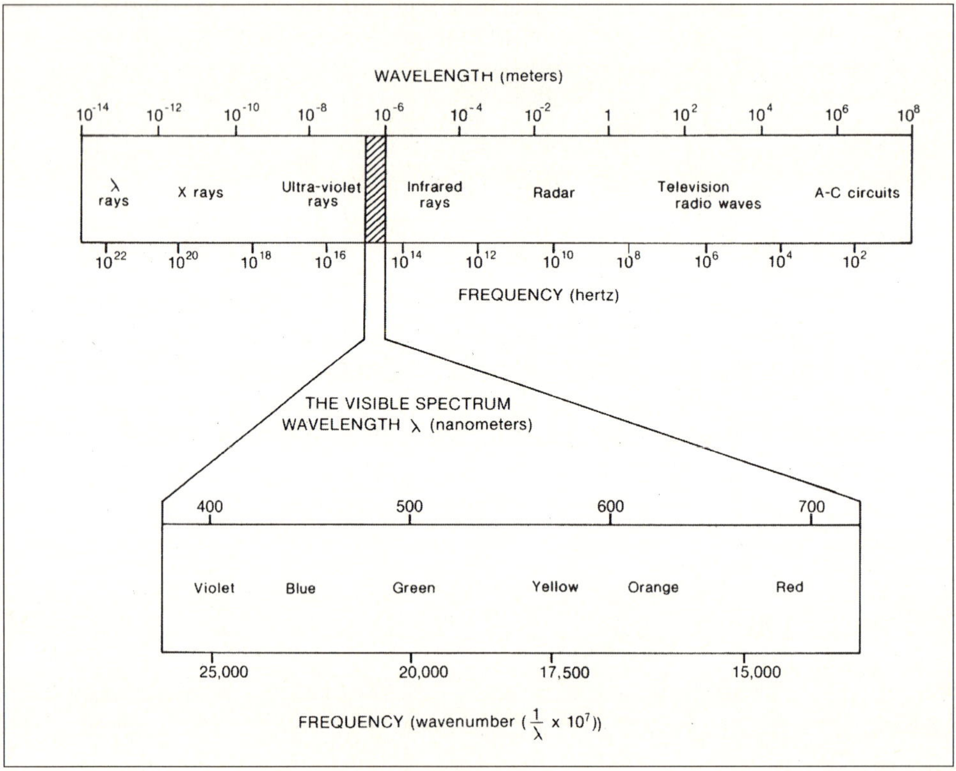

Figure 17: The electromagnetic spectrum (from [123])

The maxima of the curves differ for daytime (555 nm) $V(\lambda)$ and nighttime (507 nm) vision $V'(\lambda)$ but correspond to the energy distribution of sunlight.

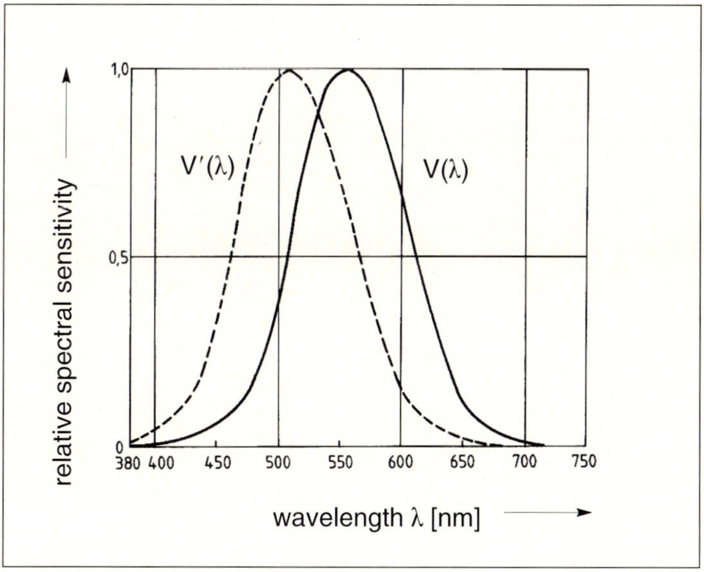

Figure 18:
Spectral sensitivity according to the CIE [261]

2.3.2. Basic Measurements

One of the basic tasks of illumination engineering is the measurement of light. Given the fact that the generated energy per unit time (its power) is not alone responsible for the perceived brightness, it becomes necessary to introduce additional measurements. They correspond to the physics of radiance but also take into account the spectral sensitivity shown in Fig. 18. The following section introduces four main measurements: luminous flux, illuminance, luminance, and luminous intensity [118, 111].

Luminous flux

Consider the light source from Fig. 19 and let $P(\lambda)$ be the spectral distribution of its power. The luminous flux describes the total amount of power weighted with the spectral sensitivity function $V(\lambda)$ and thus taking into account the effects discussed above.

$$F = const. \int_{380nm}^{780nm} P(\lambda)V(\lambda)d\lambda \qquad (5)$$

$$const.: 683\ \frac{lm}{W}$$

The unit introduced for luminous flux is the **lumen** (lm).

Luminous Intensity

If Ω describes the solid angle on the hemisphere surrounding the light source then the luminous intensity I for a certain direction is given by the luminous flux per unit solid angle in that direction according to Eq. (6):

$$I = \frac{dF}{d\Omega} \qquad (6)$$

Its unit is the **candela (cd)**.

The spatial distribution of the flux can be measured by special purpose hardware. The result is usually a goniometric diagram of the light source as in Fig. 19. The values for I are given in several planes, in this case the C-planes for street lighting and driving simulation.

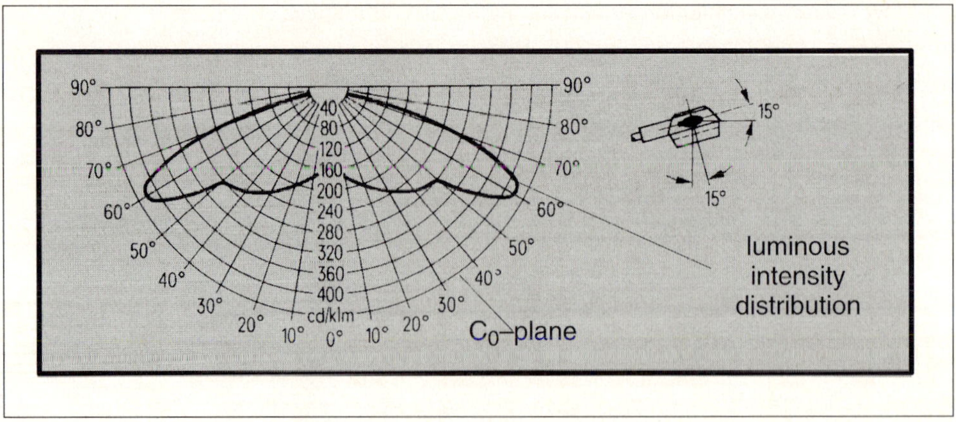

Figure 19: Light source and luminous intensity distribution/ goniometric diagram (from [118])

Illumination

The amount of luminous flux arriving on the surface A of a patch P is called illumination E_A and can be presented as:

$$E_A = \frac{dF}{dA} \tag{7}$$

The unit of illumination is the **lux (lx)**.

Luminance

Consider the patch illuminated by the light source and reflecting light into a certain direction $d\Omega$, where the angle between the light source and the patch is denoted by δ. Then according to Eq. (8) the luminance is defined as:

$$Y = \frac{d^2F}{dA\cos\delta d\Omega} \tag{8}$$

and its unit is the **candela/m^2 (cd/m^2)**.

2.3.3. Examples

Table 2 shows some characteristic values of the luminances and illuminances for particular situations (see also [230]).

It is easy to see that the variations of illumination in everyday life are very high, and the human visual system has to provide mechanisms that manage these value ranges.

situation	E_A [lux]	surface type	Y [cd/m^2]
clear sky in summer	$15 \cdot 10^4$	grass	2900
overcast sky	$16 \cdot 10^3$	grass	300
textile inspection	1500	light grey cloth	140
office work	500	white paper	120
heavy engineering	300	steel	20
good street lighting	10	concrete road surface	1.0
moonlight	0.5	asphalt road surface	0.01

Table 2: Luminances and illuminances for different situations

2.4. Rendering Physically Based Light Sources

2.4.1. A Rendering Pipeline

This section gives an example of how to make use of the basics in the field of physically based light modeling and rendering in computer graphics. In order to compute global illumination we have to find physical descriptions of light sources as well as laws that model the transport of the light. Since global illumination has been a generic problem in computer graphics, a great deal of work has been done in that area [68], for instance, the ray tracing techniques of [254] and the radiosity method derived from thermal engineering [81, 190] or combinations of these [234, 126]. Basic work on light sources is presented in [190] and a good framework for computer graphics is given by [111]. Particular consideration has to be given to Kajiya's [131] work on the rendering equation:

$$I(x,x') = g(x,x')\ [\varepsilon(x,x') + \int_A \varrho\ (x,x',x'')I(x',x'')dx'']\qquad (9)$$

$I(x,x')$ is related to the intensity of light passing from point x' to point x

$g(x,x')$ is a geometric term
$\varepsilon(x,x')$ is related to the intensity of emitted light from x' to x

Equation (9) generalizes the radiosity formulation and states that the transport intensity of light from one surface point x to another x' is the sum of the emitted and the total light intensity which is scattered towards x from all surface points x'' by reflection at x'. Then the integral has to be taken over all surfaces in the scene. The two elementary terms $g(x, x')$ and $\varrho(x, x', x'')$ describe the geometric arrangement and the physical reflection, respectively. It has been shown that both radiosity and ray tracing can be taken as approximations of this equation. Global illumination techniques can be used in many applications, for instance interior design [248] or driving simulation [184]. The following example stems from the field of street lighting simulation [46, 106]. This requires on the one hand a correct description of the light sources based on goniometric diagrams, as well as on spectral energy distributions and appropriate rendering methods based on spectral radiosity and spectral ray tracing. Furthermore, light has to be shed on the problems of mapping the image onto the limited dynamics of a graphics display.

In order to obtain a realistic image on the display, three different aspects have to be considered: a physically based model of the scene: a model for the light propagation, and the display of the results of the simulation.

According to this definition we can set up a pipeline including three steps (Fig. 20):

- *Modeling*
- *Spectral sampling renderer*
- *Display*

A correct physically based rendering has to provide spectral sampling methods. Thus in the preprocessing module the polygons of the scenery (street, buildings, street furniture, etc.) are defined with the spectral distribution of their reflection or transmission coefficients. Moreover, light sources are given by their spectral energy distribution and their luminous intensity surface, which is supposed to be independent of the wavelength. In addition, it is also necessary to define textures, especially the street textures influenced by light distribution. It is possible to simulate roughness using bump mapping techniques, fractals, or a combination of both [184].

The rendering method introduced uses spectral sampling, which is very expensive compared to the common rendering using the three primaries R, G, and B. Based on a spectral distribution of the energy of a light source, and the spectral distribution of the reflection coefficient, which is an attribute of the surface element, the corresponding illumination equation must be solved for each sample. The result is a function which describes the spectral distribution of light to be reflected or transmitted from the surface.

A detailed view of spectral sampling concerning color spaces is given in Chap. 3.

Figure 20:
Physically based rendering pipeline as used in [46]

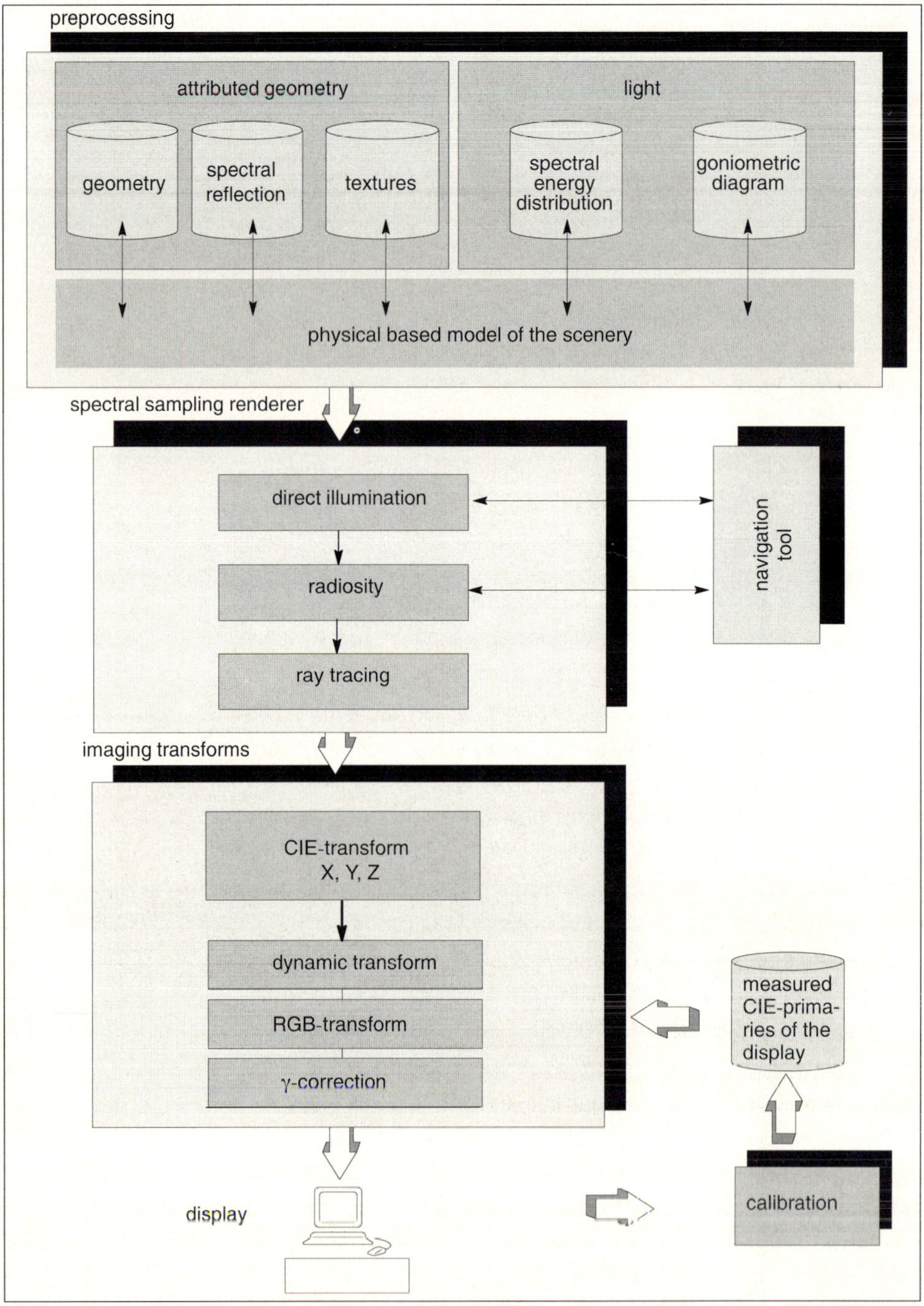

2.4.2. Modeling Light Sources

We saw previously that any physically based method has to take into account the spatial and spectral energy distribution of a light source. Both have been introduced in computer graphics, for instance in [248] or [89].

As we remember from Fig. 19, the diagram can be defined in terms of the C-plane system. The plane including the light center and the illumination axis is called C_0–C_{180} and all other planes are derived from this one by means of the angle θ_i between them (C_{20}–C_{200}, C_{40}–C_{220} ,..., C_{90}–C_{270}). The luminous intensity data for each plane is given by samples at different values of β (β_i = 0, 10°,.., 180°), where β describes the angle between the illumination axis and the light ray.

The complexity of the luminous intensity distribution depends not only on the geometry of the lamp but also on the lighting material (halogen, high-pressure sodium vapor, etc.), as well as on the material of the refractors and reflectors of the lamp.

An example for a spectral energy distribution of a physical light source is shown in Fig. 21.

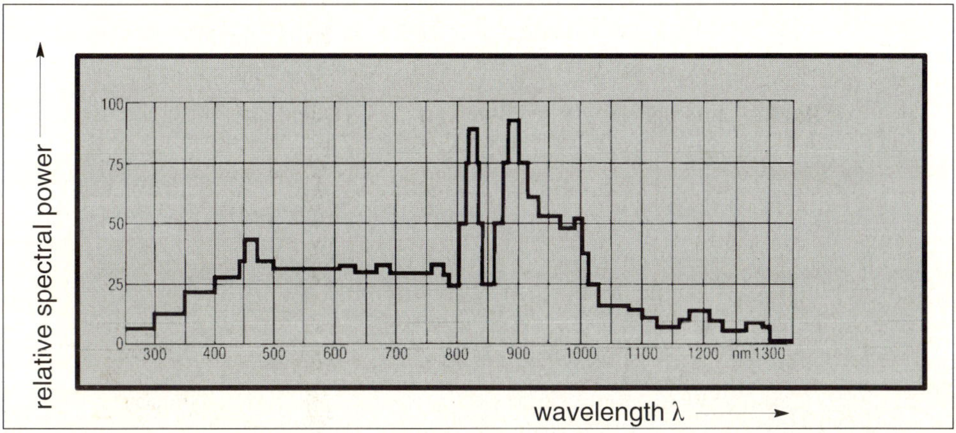

Figure 21: Example for a spectral energy distribution of a Xenon high-pressure bulb (see [118])

2.4.3. Direct Illumination

In order to compute the spectral energy arriving at a patch from a point light source, the luminous intensity distribution and the spectral distribution of the source must be combined. This can be done as described in [46].

Let P be the representative point of the patch that defines the plane $C_{\theta P}$ at θ_P degrees between the plane C_0 and the illumination axis. This plane is between the planes $C_{\theta i}$ and $C_{\theta i+1}$, where the curves of the luminous intensity are defined as in Fig. 22.

Figure 22: Calculation of the luminous intensity of the point P

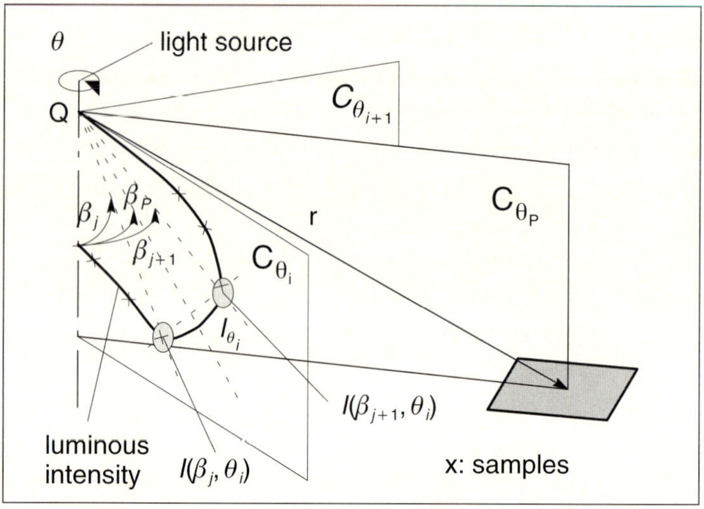

P also defines a light ray from the light point Q. This line is at β_P degrees from the illumination axis and is located between the line β_j and β_{j+1} where the samples of the luminous distribution at each plane $C_{\theta i}$ are given. We can now obtain the luminous intensity $I(\beta_P,\theta_P)$ by bilinear interpolation.

First, a linear interpolation is accomplished in the planes $C_{\theta i}$ and $C_{\theta i+1}$ between the given values at β_j and β_{j+1} degrees to obtain the $I_{\theta i}$ and $I_{\theta i+1}$ values:

$$I_{\theta_i} = I(\beta_j , \theta_i) + (I(\beta_{j+1},\theta_i) - I(\beta_j , \theta_i))w_1 \qquad (10)$$

where

$$w_1 = \frac{(\beta_P - \beta_j)}{(\beta_{j+1} - \beta_j)} \qquad (11)$$

Second, a linear interpolation is made between these two values to obtain the $I(\beta_P,\theta_P)$ assigned to the point P in the plane C_{θ_P}:

$$I(\beta_P, \theta_P) = I_{\theta_i} + (I_{\theta_{i+1}} - I_{\theta_i})w_2 \tag{12}$$

where

$$w_2 = \frac{(\theta_P - \theta_i)}{(\theta_{i+1} - \theta_i)} \tag{13}$$

The luminous energy per unit time T of a light source F_L that is equivalent to the luminous flux is defined by the integral over the spectral power distribution $P(\lambda)$ with the spectral luminous efficiency curve $V(\lambda)$ according to Eq. (5).

Second, the luminous intensity distribution $I(\beta,\theta)$ also describes the luminous flux distribution over the solid angle Ω of the hemisphere:

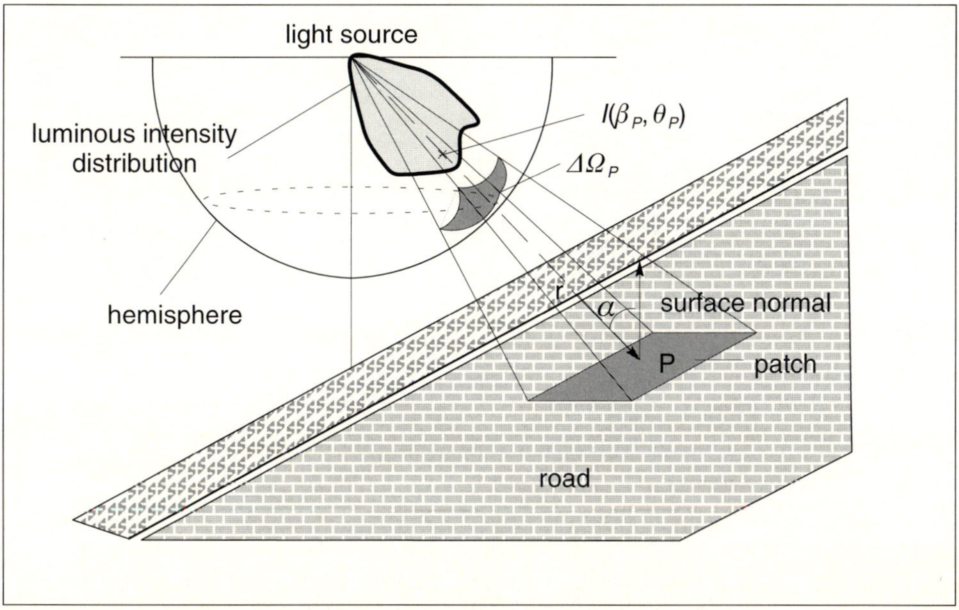

Figure 23: Luminous flux arriving at the patch P

$$F_L = \int_{\Omega(\beta,\theta)} I(\beta, \theta)\, d\Omega \tag{14}$$

This is illustrated in Fig. 23. If A is the area of the surface patch then F_P/A is the illuminance according to the definition of Eq. (15).

Consequently, the amount of luminous flux F_P from the light source arriving at the patch P is obtained by projecting the patch onto the hemisphere and multiplying the solid angle $\Delta\Omega_P$ covered with the luminous intensity $I(\beta_P, \theta_P)$. For small solid angles F_P this yields:

$$F_P = \Delta\Omega_P I(\beta_P, \theta_P) \qquad (15)$$

Considering spectral sampling methods, the part of energy $E_P(\lambda_K)$ for a sample λ_K per unit time may be calculated with the following equation:

$$\frac{E_P(\lambda_K)}{T} = P(\lambda_K)\Delta\lambda \frac{F_P}{F_L} \qquad (16)$$

T: *unit time*

$\Delta\lambda$: *resolution of the spectral samples.*

Thus, the values of $E_P(\lambda_K)$ describe spectral samples of the energy arriving at the patch. It is well known that the solid angle from a surface patch $\Delta\Omega$ is the area of the projection of this surface onto a hemisphere centered in the light source point divided by the square of the radius of the hemisphere.

Most of the time this projection is not easy to compute but can be approximated as the estimated area $A_{projected}$ in the direction of the lighting ray divided by the distance squared.

$$\Delta\Omega = \frac{A_{projected}}{r^2} = \frac{A\cos\xi}{r^2} \qquad (17)$$

ξ : *angle between the surface normal and the lighting ray*

The accuracy of this approximation is described in detail in [46].

2.4.4. Spectral Radiosity

During the direct illumination step in the rendering pipeline we have to distribute the energy from the point light sources to each patch in the scene combining the luminous intensity distribution curve of the light with its spectral distribution. Then interreflections have to be computed, where the radiosity formulation can also be defined as follows.

The light arriving from M light sources at a patch i at one sample λ_K is given by

$$\sum_{l=1}^{M} E_{il}(\lambda_K)$$

if the patch is visible from the source. Time is no longer considered in the following section, since we assume stationary processes with constant radiation.

Figure 24 expresses the energy model for the non-emitting diffuse surfaces and the mathematical expression is shown in Eq. (18). The amount of light $E_i(\lambda_K)$ emitted from the patch i at sample λ_K is the sum of the reflected direct illumination and the interreflected light from all other surfaces.

Such an equation exists for every surface patch in the scene which is expected to result from a subdivision process. The system of simultaneous equations is solved to determine the radiosity of each patch. The equation is solved at different samples.

$$E_i(\lambda_K) = \varrho_i(\lambda_K)\left(\sum_{l=1}^{M} E_{il}(\lambda_K) + \sum_{j=1, i\neq j}^{N} E_j(\lambda_K)\Gamma_{ij}\right) \qquad (18)$$

with

$E_i(\lambda_K)$: *Radiosity of the patch i (energy per unit area)*

$\varrho_i(\lambda_K)$: *Reflectivity of patch i*

$E_j(\lambda_K)$: *Radiosity of the non-emitting patch j*

Γ_{ij} : *Form-factor from patch i to patch j*

$E_{il}(\lambda_K)$: *Energy from the point light source l arriving at i*

N : *Number of patches*

The form-factor Γ_{ij} gives the fraction of energy leaving the patch i that arrives at the patch j. It can be calculated using the following equation:

$$\Gamma_{ij} = \int_{A_i}\int_{A_j} \frac{\cos\Theta_i \cos\Theta_j}{\pi r^2} H_{ij}\, dA_j\, dA_i \qquad (19)$$

H_{ij} : *visibility function*

The geometric relationships are illustrated in Fig. 24. The form-factors depend only on the geometric relationship between patches, and not on viewer positions or attributes of the surface. They are also constant over all spectral samples. Approaches such as the *Hemicube* technique [47] can be used to calculate them.

Figure 24: Geometry for the computation of form-factors [81]

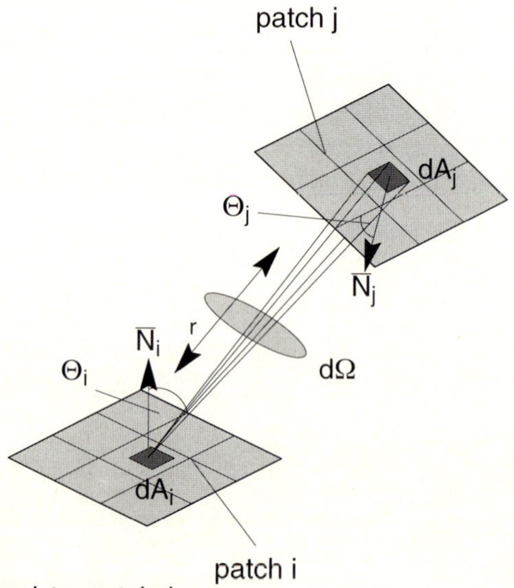

$\bar{N}_i$: *normal to patch i*

$\bar{N}_i$: *normal to patch j*

Unfortunately, radiosity only provides a solution of the rendering equation for the diffuse case. Specular interreflection that becomes important for wet streets has to be treated separately. There are different approaches for this including distributed ray tracing.

2.4.5. Spectral Ray Tracing

The final step in the rendering pipeline is image generation by a ray tracer.

Since the direct illumination and the radiosity approaches treat a scene by spectral sampling, any ray casting process for image generation will provide the spectral energy distribution for each pixel. This is shown in Fig. 25. The problem arising now is how to map this spectral image onto the RGB-graphics display. However, this is not only a computer graphics problem but also an imaging one. In particular the limited visual dynamics of a display forces us to find transformation methods based on human visual performance to display our results in the appropriate way. Furthermore, the treatment of color has not been touched so far. The next chapter will provide detailed information on these aspects.

Figure 25: Spectral sampling ray tracing

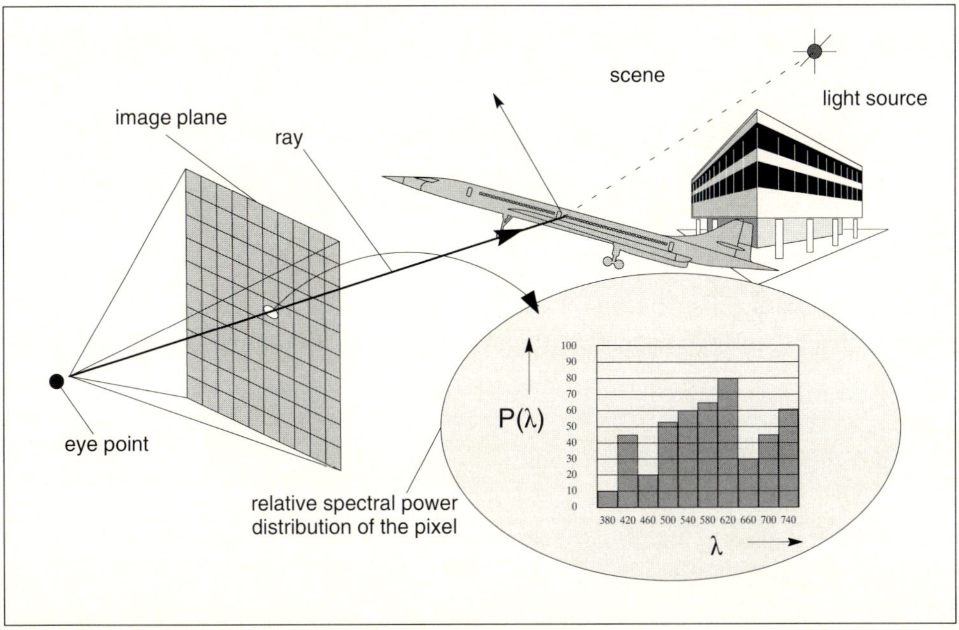

2.4.6. Examples

The following figures show an application of the methods introduced above from the field of illumination engineering. Light sources with different geometries and with different goniometric diagrams had to be compared regarding ambience and safety aspects. Figure 26a shows a top and side view of the geometry of the scene including the X/Motif user interface of a prototype system called LISA [106]. Furthermore, Fig. 26b shows the C-plane editor of LISA. The distribution of the direct illumination of the three light sources to be combined is shown by illuminating a plain road as in Fig. 26c.

Figure 27 shows bird views of the pedestrian zone compounding the effects of the different light sources. Figure 28 gives additional views of the scene.

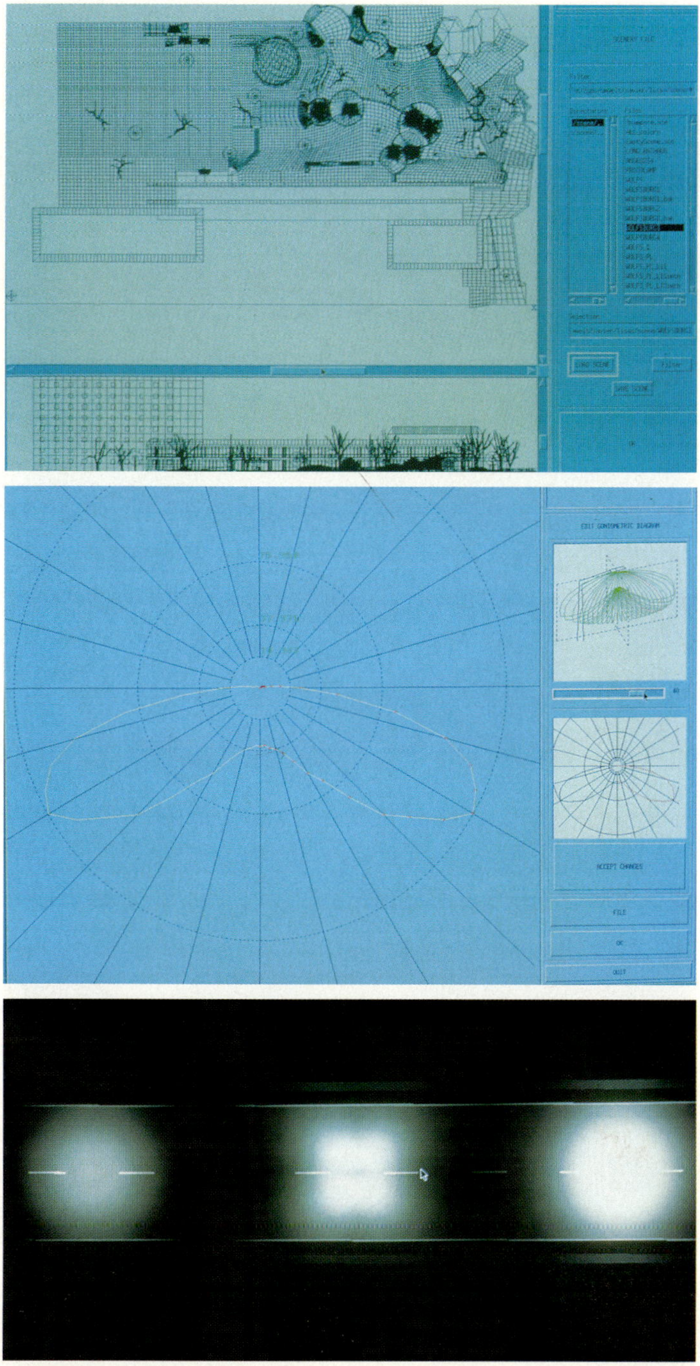

Figure 26:
a) Top and side view of the geometry with LISA
b) C-plane for one type of light source
c) Illuminating a plain diffuse road surface with three different light sources

Figure 27: Views of the scene for the three different light sources

Figure 28:
Different views of the scene

3. Sensitivity to Light and Color

3.1. Visual Perception of Achromatic Light and Shape

3.1.1. Adaptation

Local and Global Adaptation

Since human visual dynamics enclose a luminance range of about 130 dB it is not possible for the eye to modulate this range simultaneously. It has to provide several control mechanisms to manage the luminous dynamics. The visual system calculates a mean value for the illumination of the visual field (adaptation luminance) and controls its actual sensitivity according to that value. This mechanism is called *global adaptation*. When only parts of the retina are individually adjusted then it is called *local adaptation*. The adaptation is accomplished by several correlated features:

- *The change of the pupil's diameter*
- *The shared responsibility of cones for daytime ($> 20\ cd/m^2$) and rods for night-time ($< 1\ cd/m^2$) vision*
- *Chemical processes*
- *Clustering of rods*

If Y_A denotes the adaptation luminance then the diameter d of the pupil changes according to Eq. (20) [141].

Rapid changes of the luminance of up to ca. 20 dB in 100 ms can be managed. Larger ranges cause glare effects and adaptation must occur successively. Good visual conditions are provided when the dynamics is less than 3:1 in the central field of vision and less than 10:1 in the periphery.

$$d \approx 5.5 - \log\left(\frac{Y_A}{\frac{cd}{m^2}}\right) \qquad (20)$$

Y_A: *adaptation luminance*

The temporal adaptation is shown in Fig. 29. The threshold curve for the perception of a test stimulus depends on the time elapsed since the switching off of the adaptation stimulus, which for this example was approximately 100 cd/m^2.

Figure 29: Threshold curve for temporal adaptation [118]

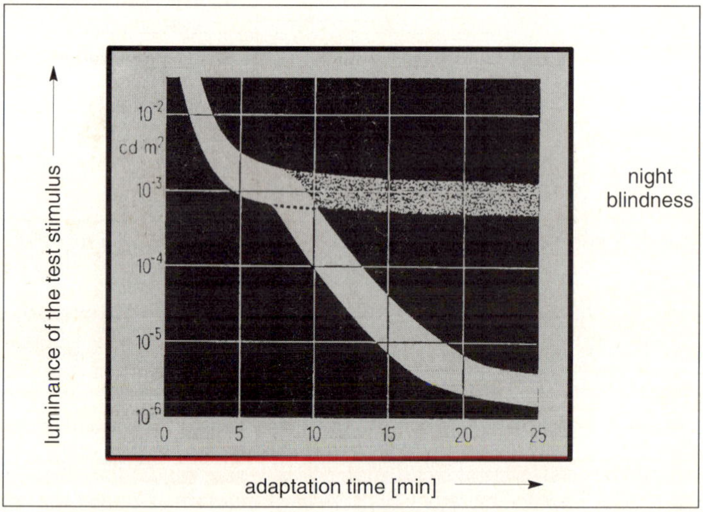

In cases where the adaptation from dark to light can be performed in less than 3 minutes, the inverse process requires up to 40 minutes.

The range of luminance > 20 cd/m^2 is also called photopic vision, between 1 cd/m^2 and 20 cd/m^2 mesopic vision, and beyond 1 cd/m^2 scotopic vision where only the rods are active and no color perception is available.

The Definition of Contrast

The perception of objects depends strongly on the difference of their luminance to the background, not only on their absolute amount of luminance. Thus a black ink line on a white paper sheet will be perceived more clearly than on grey paper. A measure for the relative difference of the luminances Y_1 and Y_2 of two adjacent patches is introduced by the definition of the contrast C according to Eq. (21):

$$C = \frac{(Y_1 - Y_2)}{Y_1} \qquad (21)$$

The threshold for the minimum contrast, when two patches may differ in perception under special conditions is also called contrast sensitivity C_{min} and depends on the actual level of adaptation as well as on the test patches. Often, the inverse of the contrast sensitivity is presented as in Fig. 30, which shows the relationship between this threshold and the adaptation luminance Y_A for several test conditions.

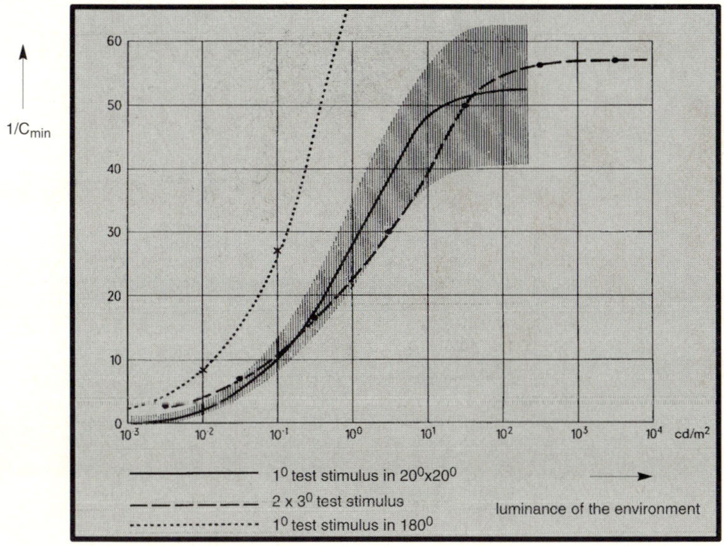

Figure 30: Relationship between the contrast sensitivity and the level of adaptation [118]

These curves are independent of the spectral distribution of the light for daylight vision.

Another function is shown in Fig. 31. The threshold contrast depends also on the size of the object to be presented to the test person. Standard values for the contrast sensitivity are often given with 0.02 for target recognition ([84, 85, 98, 55]).

These curves show that contrast sensitivity is by no means constant and that it may also have an influence on a smooth representation of images on graphics screens. For instance, if the dynamics of a screen is about 20 dB between 1 cd/m^2 and 100 cd/m^2 and 256 grey levels are available, the average difference of luminance is about 0.4 cd/m^2 supposing the screen shows linear behavior. Two adjacent patches at 100 cd/m^2 have a contrast of 0.004 and cannot be distinguished by the visual system. However at 1 cd/m^2 they have a contrast value of 0.4 and can thus be distinguished. Consequently, for many applications perceptual corrections have to be introduced, as proposed in [46] or [50] or [243].

Figure 31: Threshold contrast for several object sizes dependent on the level of adaptation [141]

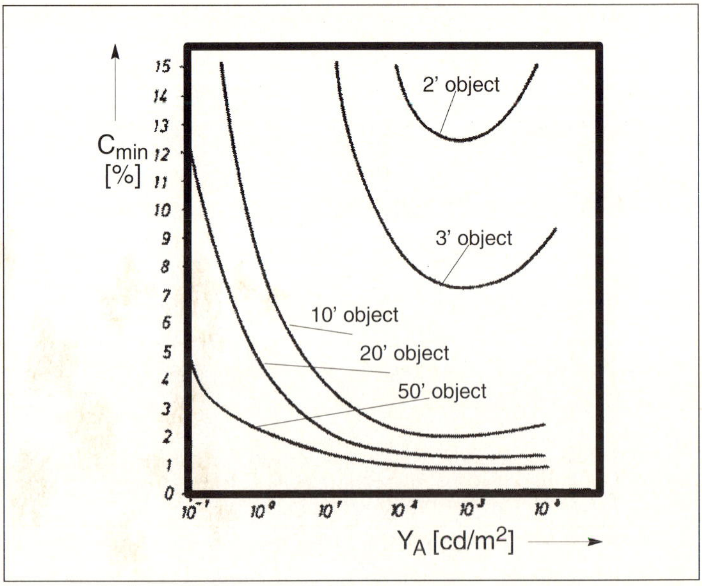

Simultaneous and Successive Contrast

Contrast sensitivity and adaptation may also cause some well known optical illusions. Figure 32 shows an example for simultaneous contrast – the grey disk on a black background seems to be brighter than on a white background. The observer should fix his eyes on the cross in the center of the image. On the respective retinal positions we have different local adaptations.

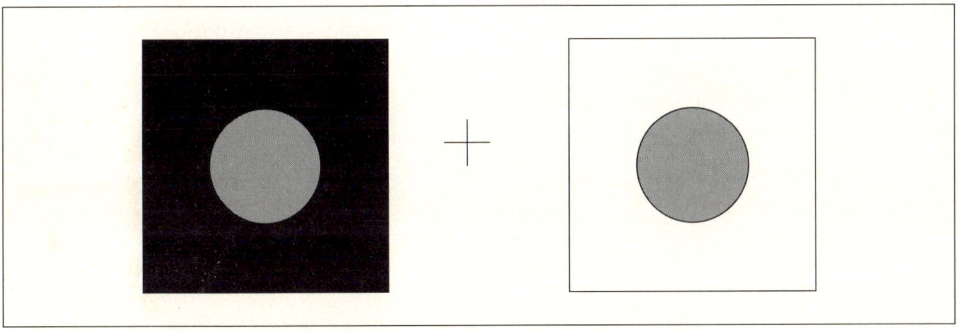

Figure 32:
Simultaneous contrast

Another example for successive contrast are after-images caused by highly contrasted objects which were observed for long periods of time. If we first regard the left object in Fig. 33 for ca. 30 seconds, and then the right one, we seem to perceive an after-image which disappears from time to time. The receptors of the retinal surface covered by the object are more sensitive and adapted to a lower light level. A uniformly illuminated surface projected onto the retina now seems to be brighter on such areas.

Figure 33:
After-images

Finally, the Mach band effect is presented in Fig. 37. Two adjacent patches with different luminances seem to be darker, i.e., brighter at their borders. The perceived brightness changes across the patch surface although the luminance is preserved. This effect is caused by the lateral inhibition of retinal neurons which perform a spatial high-pass operation and edge enhancement. This effect also appears for colors (see Sect. 3.2). Further optical illusions are given in [70].

Luminance–Brightness–Transforms

The introduced features show that the sensation of brightness of a particular object also depends on the level of adaptation and not only on its absolute amount of luminance. The relationship between the physiological measurement of brightness B, which is often given by relative values between 0.0 and 1.0, and the physical measure of luminance Y is nonlinear and has been investigated by many scientists in illumination engineering. To express this behavior by mathematical descriptions there are competing approaches. Its functional course is illustrated in Fig. 34 for different adaptation values according to [243].

One of the basic rules in psychophysics, the so-called law of Weber and Fechner, supposes a logarithmic relationship according to Eq. (22).

$$B \approx \log(1 + Y) \tag{22}$$

However, this transformation, which is often applied in the area of image processing for dynamic compression, is limited in its description of psychophysical aspects. Moreover, it is only able to describe the linear part of the curves in Fig. 34. In more advanced approaches sigmoidal functions are used.

Glare and High Intensity Points

The reduction of contrast by means of over-illumination in the visual field is called glare. The artefacts generated by glare are based on physical phenomena, such as diffraction and scattering. In most cases the light is diffracted either at the iris or at the eye lashes, but is sometimes scattered into the eye. This is illustrated in Fig. 35. The light source that causes glare produces scattered light at the cornea, the retina, the lens, etc. This process can be described as a superposition of the adaptation luminance Y_A with a luminance Y_S generated by the scattered light. This leads to a higher adaptation level at particular locations of the retina, and the discrimination thresholds decrease. However, objects that differ by a certain value ΔY against the background might not be able to be detected any longer. We can interpret these phenomena as a kind of inner-eye interreflection which leads to a contrast reduction and a milky appearance of the objects.

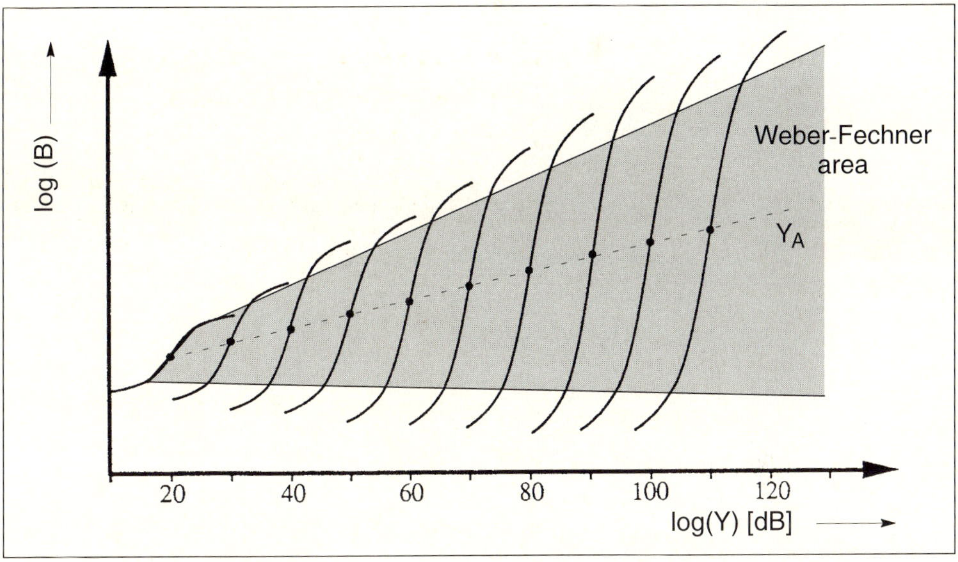

Figure 34:
General presentation of the luminance–brightness dependency for different adaptation levels (see [243])

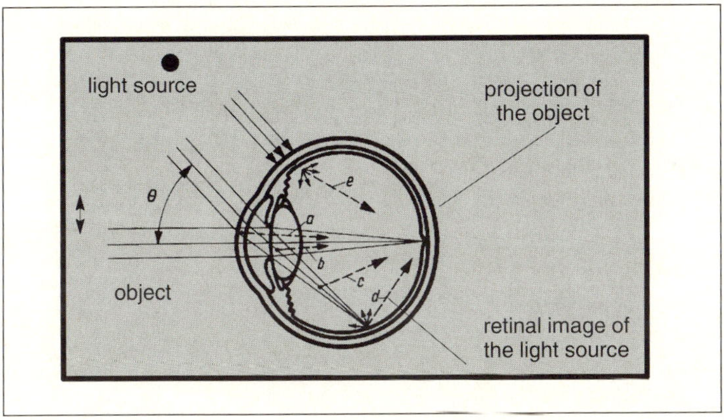

Figure 35:
The generation of glare by means of scattering [118]

There have been several attempts to render high intensity points for computer generated images. One of the most interesting approaches can be found in [184]. The blooming up of high intensity points and the streaks of light that appear in the image are caused by diffraction effects at the pupil as well as the eyelashes which can be modeled by a diaphragm or by simple gratings. These can be rotated in the image plane according to the required results. If a ray passes through a diffraction grating that consists of N slits according to Fig. 36, the intensity distribution of the diffracted light $I(\theta)$ depends on the diffraction angle θ thus:

$$I(\theta) = \frac{\sin^2 \alpha}{\alpha^2} \frac{\sin^2 (N\beta)}{\sin^2 \beta} \tag{23}$$

λ:	*wavelength*
θ:	*diffraction angle*
a:	*width of the slits of a grating*
b:	*length of one period of a grating*
θ:	*rotation angle of the grating*

where

$$\alpha = \frac{\pi}{\lambda} a \sin \theta \tag{24}$$

$$\beta = \frac{\pi}{\lambda} b \sin \theta \tag{25}$$

The diffraction angle θ is given by:

$$\theta = | a \cos \phi + b \sin \phi | \tag{26}$$

The streaks are affected by interference and only given with

$$\alpha \sin \phi - \beta \cos \phi = 0 \tag{27}$$

For all other directions we obtain

$$I(\theta) = 0 \tag{28}$$

In order to produce radial streaks the simple grating should be rotated by ϕ using some random numbers. It should be noted here, however, that these streaks of light are equal to the distribution of the electromagnetic field behind a diaphragm (see also Sect. 2.2.3, Fig. 16). From field theory we learn that this distribution is equal to a spatial Fourier transform of the initial intensity distribution. In our case the $\sin(x)/x$ functions that express the streaks are Fourier transforms of a spatial rectangle function describing the profile of the diaphragm. The implementation of this method uses a look-up table

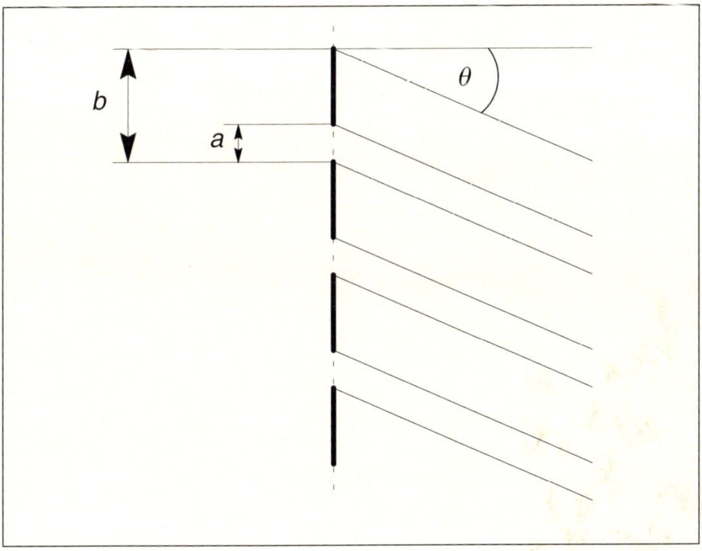

Figure 36:
Nakamae's grating model for the simulation of glare effects (from [184]).

to store the weight coefficients of $I(\theta)$, and a 2D convolution-based filtering method to apply this function on the image. Since the diffraction of light strongly depends on the wavelength, a correct treatment requires a spectral sampling method that is quite expensive. It is possible to label the high intensity points during rendering in R, G, B and to apply the filters for different spectral samples only at these points. In this case the whole procedure is a post–process to the rendering but could also be integrated in 3D. Figure 38 illustrates the results of these methods. Here a night scene was rendered showing a wet street and foggy weather (see also [184]). Another extension of these ideas would be to include the scattering effects described above as some kind of inner-eye radiosity.

3.1.2. Spatial Sensitivity

Visual Acuity and Resolving Capacity

The sensitivity of the human visual system for spatial shapes depends not only on physiological and physical constraints but also on cognitive processes. Generally speaking, it may depend on

- *Structure, size and contrast of the object*
- *Quality of the optical projection*
- *Physical effects (see also Chap. 1)*
- *Number of receptors per unit retina surface*
- *Level of adaptation*
- *Eye movements*
- *Cognitive processes*

Figure 37: Mach band effects

Figure 38: Effect of diffraction under foggy conditions (This picture was first published in [184]; courtesy of the Prefectural University of Hiroshima, Computer Graphics Lab, Prof. Dr. E. Nakamae)

The visual acuity V can be measured by the inverse of the minimum visual angle α_{min} (in arcmin) achievable when detecting a target.

$$V = \frac{1}{\alpha_{\min}} \tag{29}$$

V is measured via test persons using the so-called Landolt ring of Fig. 39.

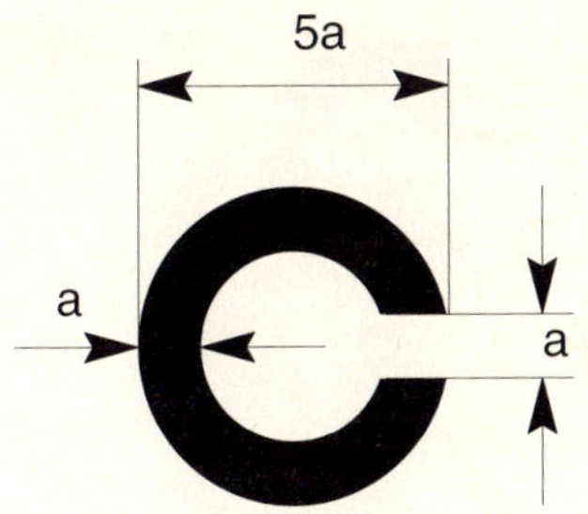

Figure 39: Landolt ring

Under daylight vision the visual acuity has its maximum in the fovea centralis and decreases towards the periphery. The dependence of visual acuity on the retinal position for daylight and night-time vision stimulated by Landolt rings is shown in Fig. 40.

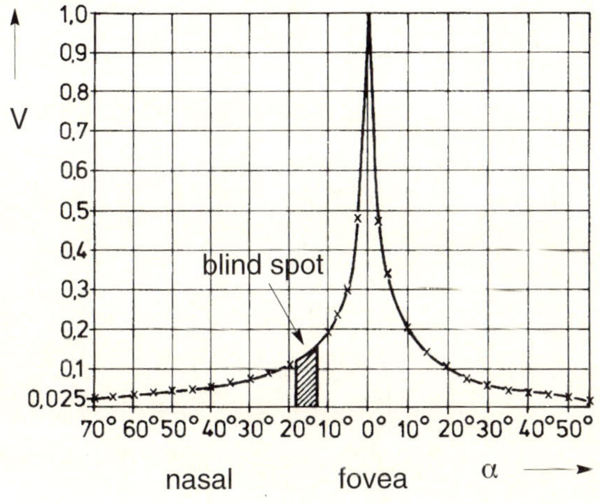

Figure 40: Relationship of the visual acuity and the retinal eccentricity [230]

The acuity also depends on the level of adaptation, and under ideal conditions it is possible to achieve values of about 2.0–3.0 corresponding to visual angles of 0.5′–0.33′. Thus the optical limitations introduced in Chap. 2 have to be improved by retinal image processing. Finally, Fig. 41 shows the minimum visual angle that can be achieved for several objects under ideal conditions.

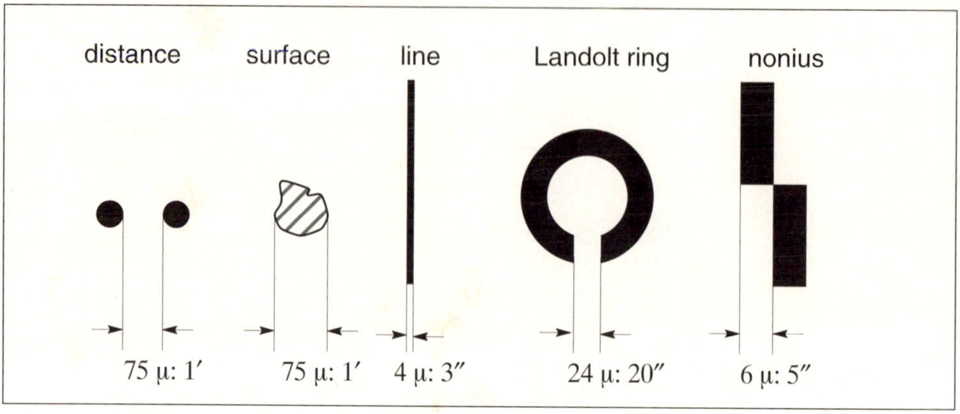

Figure 41: Visual acuity for several objects ([141])

Retinal Transmission Functions

The increase of visual acuity caused by retinal image processing can be explained by the structure of the receptive fields of retinal ganglion cells. Recapitulating from Chap. 2, the receptors connected to the center are excitatory, those which are connected to the periphery are inhibitory. This recalls a typical operator which is shown in Fig. 42.

Figure 42: Sensitivity of a retinal ganglion cell

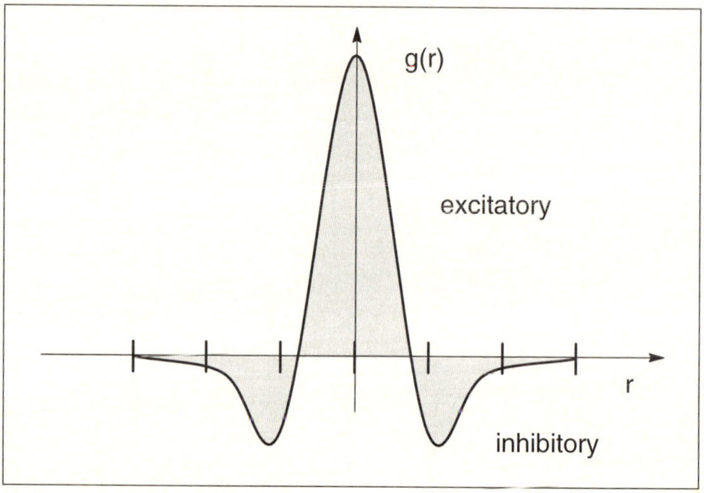

This rotationally symmetric curve $g(r)$ can be approximated according to [165] with a superposition of two Gaussian functions described by Eq. (30).

$$g(r) = E_0\, e^{-\frac{r^2}{R_1^2}} - I_0\, e^{-\frac{r^2}{R_2^2}} \qquad (30)$$

E_0, I_0, R_1, R_2 : *parameters*

The low-pass behavior of the lens and of the pupil is now post-processed by a high-pass operation and thus certain bandpass characteristics are achieved. This operator is derived from the Laplace of a Gaussian function and corresponds to the Marr–Hildreth–operator of Chap. 5. Its bandpass behavior can be proved by measurements (Fig. 43) according to [40]. This function is also called the *spatial sensitivity function.*

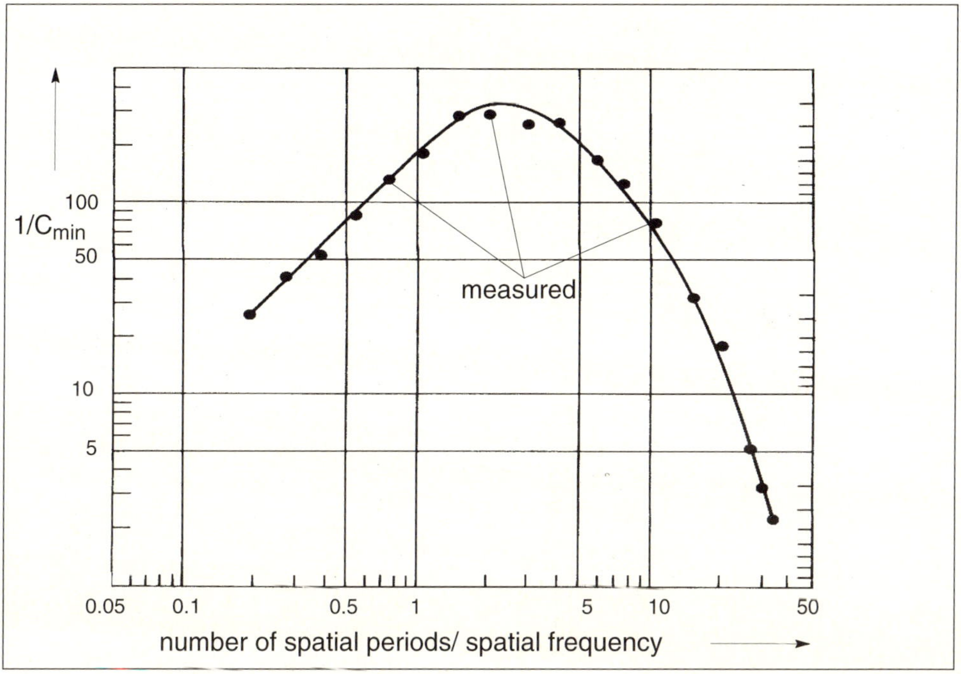

Figure 43: Contrast sensitivity as a function of the spatial frequency for sinusoidal stimuli [40]

3.1.3. Temporal Sensitivity

Threshold Frequency

Thresholds and sensitivities presented so far presuppose that the observer has infinite time to detect the target presented. If, however, the presentation time for images is reduced, the total stimulus of visual neurons also decreases and the performance of the visual system will be reduced. According to the laws of Bondel and Ray [118], the relationship between the threshold luminance for infinite presentation time $Y_{\min\infty}$ and the threshold luminance $Y_{\min}$ for a time interval t can be expressed according to Eq. (31).

$$\Delta t(Y_{\min} - Y_{\min\infty}) = const. \tag{31}$$

This is only valid for rectangular impulses. For arbitrary presentations, more complex functions have to be introduced. Both animation and television rely on quickly oscillating luminance impulses. Increasing the presentation frequency of the image will bring about a flickering and finally a fusion of the single frames into one image. This effect can be described by the threshold frequency for flickering f_v and depends strongly on the actual level of adaptation. In Fig. 44 f_v is shown against the mean luminance $\overline{Y}$ for the rotating disk pattern depicted.

Figure 44: Threshold frequency f_v depending on $\overline{Y}$ [228]

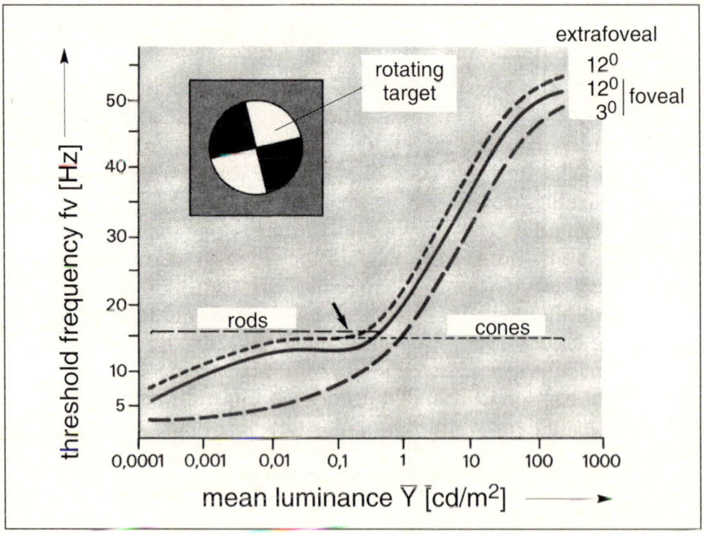

Saccades, Eye Movement and Eye Tracking

One of the most important anatomic capabilities of the human eyes and head is their rapid movement when tracking a moving target or when scanning scenes. If an observer looks around, his eyes move from one fixation to another. These rapid and dynamic changes of the fixation are called saccades and last between 10 ms and 80 ms. The times at rest are between 150 ms and 400 ms. Longer fixations are connected with so-called drifts of the line of sight. This microtremor has frequencies of 20–150 Hz and amplitudes of about 1–3 arcmin.

The measurement of the actual line of sight is required in a lot of computer graphics applications, for example user interfaces or flight simulators. There are several methods for eye tracking available. A sophisticated survey on these techniques is given in [127]. One technique is to project infrared spotlights onto the eye and measure the corneal reflectance by a camera. An additional camera recording the actual visual field produces an image that can be merged with the eye recorded information. Figure 45 shows the principle of the corneal reflection method.

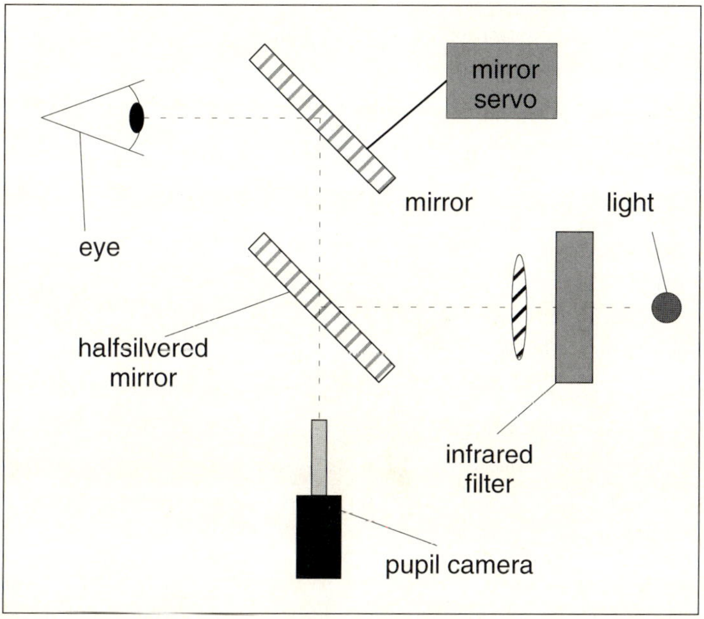

Figure 45: Principles of the corneal reflection method for eye tracking

The result of such a record is presented in Fig. 46, a German advertisement plate. The figure shows that the trajectory of the tracking depends on cognitive processes and cannot bc included in functional descriptions at all.

Figure 46: Eye track of an advertisement plate

Particulary in advertising the measurement of the fixation time and order for several image components is very important and gives, for instance, information about the efficiency of a new design. A lot of interdisciplinary research has been done with eye trackers to adapt the display acuity to the line of sight.

Temporal Discrimination of Shapes

Interesting studies also examine the mean reaction times to discriminate rotated or mirror-reversed 3D objects or to distinguish several pairs of them [67]. Figure 47 shows, for instance, the results obtained when rotating a 3D object in its picture plane (top) as well as into its depth (middle) or by a reflection (bottom). The mean time to verify that the two objects are identical in shape is plotted as a function of the angular disparity. The time required depends almost entirely on the angle and is independent of whether the image or the object is rotated. Thus the 3D object is imagined rotating, not its projection as a 2D picture. The 3D object first has to be recognized.

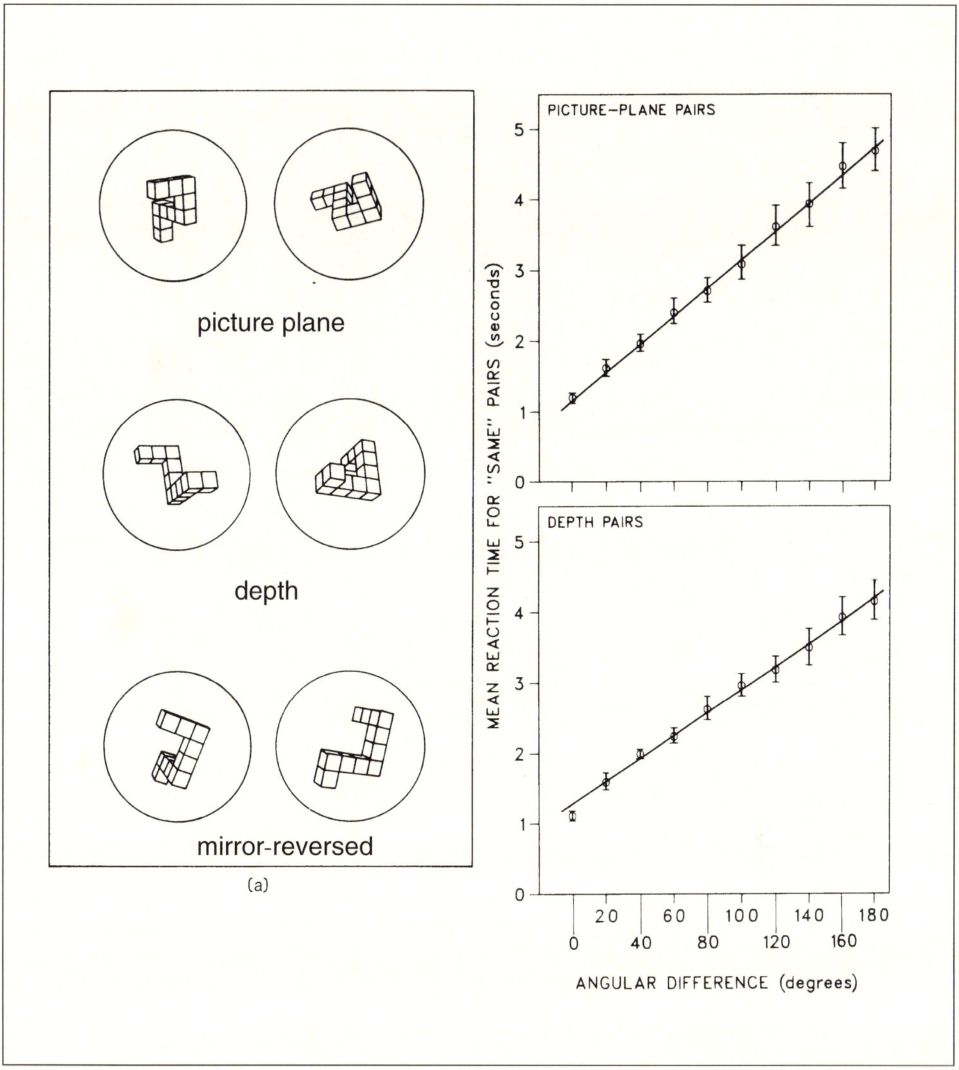

Figure 47: Discrimination times for angular rotations of 3D objects [67]

3.1.4. Binocular Vision

Horopter and Panum Area

The matching of the two images arriving onto the retinas of the eyes is called binocular fusion and it is one of the basic features for perceiving shape and 3-dimensionality. The reconstruction of depth performed by our visual system is accomplished by the referencing of images that are of different disparities. To express these effects mathematically it is necessary to consider the stereoscopic space. If we analyze Fig. 48 we see that all points on the circle are projected onto corresponding retinal areas. This circle determined by the fixation point and the eyes is called the Vieth–Müller circle or horopter circle for idealized conditions. Generally the horopter is defined by a complicated shape which describes corresponding retinal points.

Points in space that are not located on the horopter are said to have a disparity, i.e., they don't fall onto the same retinal positions. Figure 49 illustrates the disparity of two objects and their retinal projections. If the dark object is fixed, then it will be projected onto corresponding retinal points. The white object, which is closer to the observer, won't be projected onto the same retina points. Thus the difference between the projections onto the right and left eye retinas denoted by m and n is a measure for the disparity d. There are several mathematical descriptions, for example Eq. (32):

Figure 48: Horopter circle

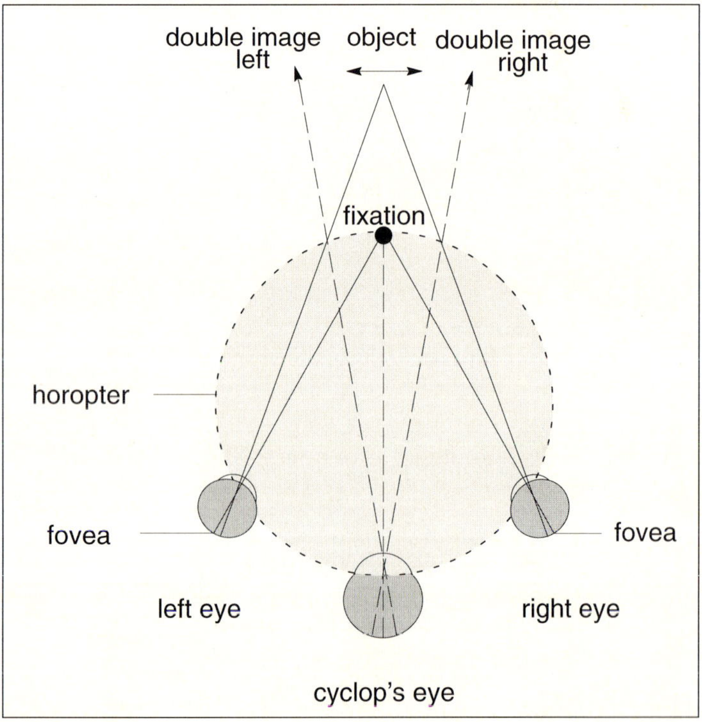

$$d = m - n \quad (32)$$

The sensitivity of the visual system for disparities is about 5 arcsec and refers to the acuity for nonius vision (see also Fig. 41).

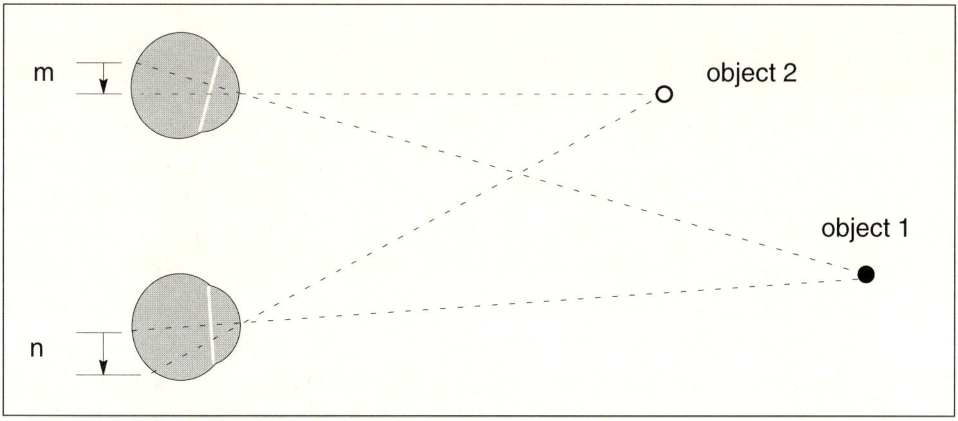

Figure 49:
Definition of the disparity

On the one hand, all objects on the horopter have no disparity and thus cannot be perceived in 3D. But on the other hand, disparate projections will give rise to different competitive images. These images can be fused by the visual system if their disparity is below a certain threshold. This can also be expressed by an area in space surrounding the horopter. This area is called the panum area and is illustrated in Fig. 50.

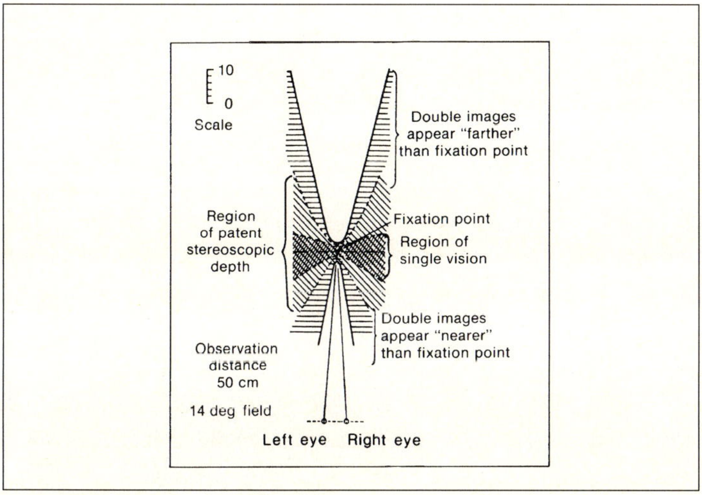

Figure 50:
Horopter line and panum area illustrated in a 2D top view [14]

Other experiments [14] have demonstrated the binocular advantage in the detection of contrast in grating stimuli and found that the ratio between binocular and monocular vision is about 1.4 or $\sqrt{2}$ for the same stimuli, as shown in Fig. 51.

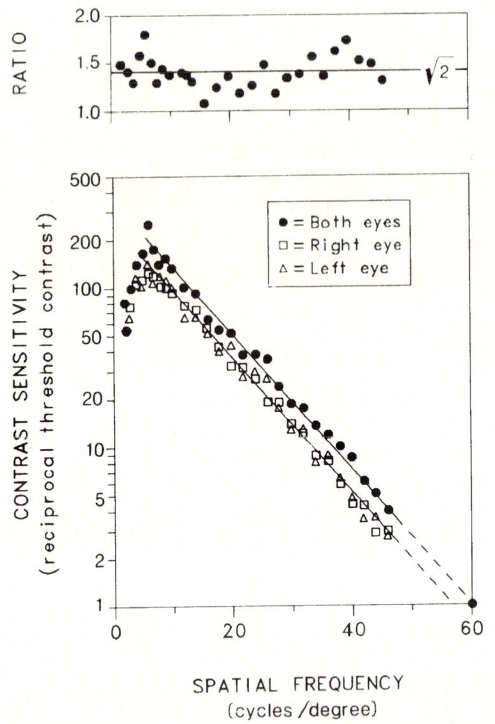

Figure 51: Relationship between binocular and monocular sensitivity for sinusoidal gratings [14]

Stereo Perception

The stereo vision process is of crucial importance for the perception of 3D shape for human beings. Many attempts have failed to model this feature of the human brain. The basic problem of stereo matching, which will be explained in detail in Chap. 5, is to find corresponding points in two stereo images and to calculate their disparity. Due to ambiguities in the images the computational formulation of this task is nontrivial. In order to learn from our visual system, psychologists have done interesting experiments with stereo vision. One of the most exciting investigations was made by Bela Julesz [129, 130] at Bell Labs, who invented *random dot stereograms.* These diagrams consist of pairs of patterns, where pixels are set to black or white according to some random process. The only difference in the two images is that a square patch of the pixels is moved a little bit to the left or right respectively. This is illustrated in Fig. 52. Thus a part of the image contains disparity information. Looking at just one of the images we cannot discover shape at all. The only information we receive is some white noise.

If, however, the two images are presented simultaneously to an observer through a stereoscope and the brain matches them, we perceive 3D shape in terms of a square in front of the image plane (see Fig. 53).

Figure 52: Random dot stereograms that contain only disparity information

The interpretation of this result is extremely interesting since, obviously, no monocular 2D hints have to be discovered for the matching process to work successfully. Moreover, a correspondence has to be found between simple picture elements (i.e., pixels) without prior recognition of larger coherent symbolic features. Although there are many ambiguities on a pixel level, the brain finds a fast and robust solution and recovers the square from just the initial displacements of the random dots. Random dots have been widely used to test automatic stereo matching algorithms (see also Chap. 5).

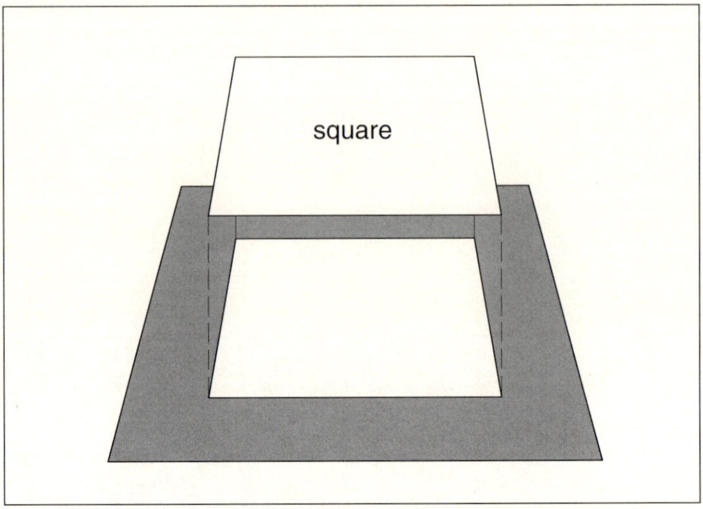

Figure 53: Shape perceived by an observer when matching the two random dot stereograms

Head-Mounted Stereo Displays

Various techniques have been introduced to generate stereo effects with a 2D display. Some of these systems are used with success in computer graphics, such as the stereo shutter which uses liquid crystal glasses with adjustable opacity. The transparencies of both eyes are changed mutually and are synchronized to the image frequency of the display. If two disparate images are then displayed successively, the right and left eye will each receive only one image. Other approaches use complementary color images and corresponding filters in front of the eyes (red–green) or try to adjust the adaptation of each eye to a different level and influence the speed of the visual signal. An alternative is the head-mounted display, which has its origin in flight simulation and is currently popular for virtual reality (Fig. 55).

Unfortunately, most low-cost versions of head-mounted displays that are available nowadays use only low-resolution and low-dynamics LCD displays. For advanced computer graphics applications, such as flight or driving simulators more sophisticated versions have to be introduced, as for instance in Fig. 54. Here, the video signal is projected into the eye via film optics. In order to take into account the distribution of visual acuity in the field of vision, a high-res inlet is usually combined with a low-res periphery.

Head-mounted displays are often combined with head-tracking systems or with eye trackers. An alternative display system is the "boomer", a two-cannon CRT display attached on a platform and used in scientific visualization.

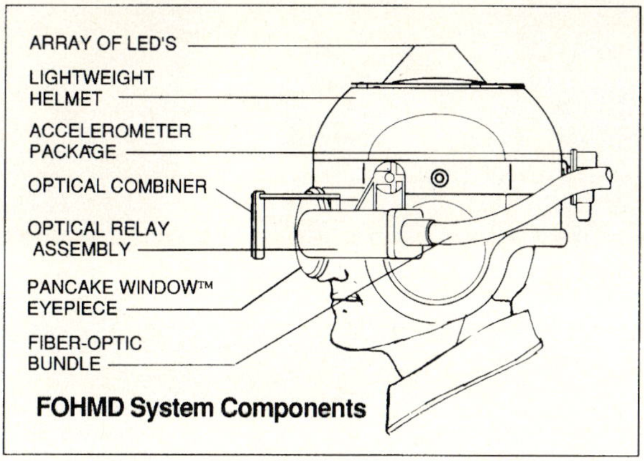

Figure 54: Advanced head-mounted display with fiber optics for flight simulation

The 3D input device currently used most is the data glove, which detects hand and finger movements and positions in space by means of fiber optics. It can be used to navigate and to interact in virtual worlds. Figure 56 shows a scene from the 3D interaction toolkit GIVEN [247] and the optical echo of the user's hand.

3.1.5. Visual Clustering, Grouping and Gestalt

The perception of the shape and gestalt of an object by our visual system is a very interesting phenomenon. In the past a lot of work has been done by experimental psychologists [242] and the impact on artificial intelligence and vision has been investigated [65]. One of the most exciting features is the ability to interpolate sparse data such as dots or points in order to detect higher-order objects. This is illustrated in Fig. 57, where several dots are clustered together representing objects like circles, squares, and lines. From this point of view it is not possible to explain the perception of shape only with the stimuli arriving on the retina.

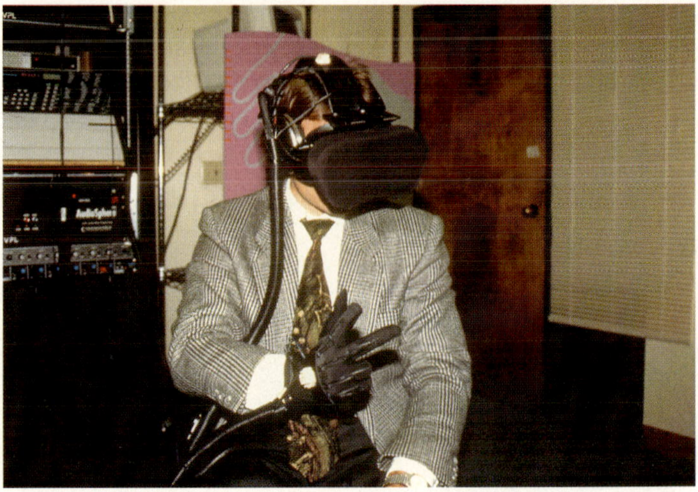

Figure 55: Virtual reality equipment with head mounted display and data glove (from [91])

Figure 56: 3D-interaction with a dataglove in GIVEN

Other types of optical illusion are also presented in Fig. 57. The black and white map of western Europe cannot be discriminated if we focus our attention on the dark areas that represent the sea.

The third classical optical illusion presented here is a variation of Kanzisa's triangle (Fig. 57f). In this case our visual system detects an ellipse that is not presented explicitly at all. Moreover, this ellipse seems to appear brighter than the white background. Edges are detected and interpolated from a simple arrangement of basic structures. These phenomena are also used by some famous painters such as Salvador Dali [161], who created numerous pictures where the observer discovers objects by grouping other objects depending on the way he looks at them. Aside from static situations, groupings arising from motion and optical flow are also interesting [211].

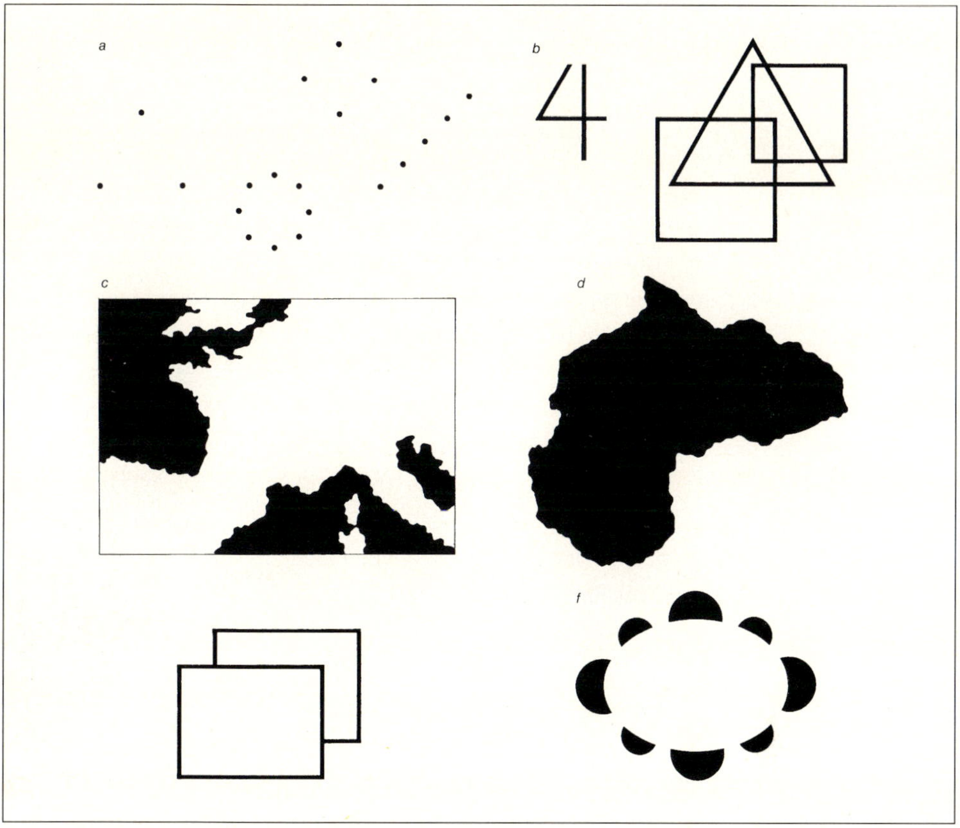

Not all the psychological results can be presented here in detail; however, they are of crucial importance for graphics and visualization. For instance, the perception of reconstructed surfaces affects the level of interpolation and approximation that has to be selected for visualizing data sets. The motion and animation that is often used to support the visualization process has to be considered from the point of view of psychology. Generally speaking, the visualization process is more deeply influenced by psychological phenomena like those sketched here than by purely mathematical procedures. Detailed views are given in [242].

Figure 57: Optical illusions that illustrate the grouping, clustering and interpolation feature of the visual system [217]

3.2. Color Vision

3.2.1. Physiological Basics

A Definition for Color

The sensations of real world objects are much richer than those caused by achromatic light considered in the previous chapters. Color vision plays an extraordinarily important role in the field of computer graphics, as well as in image processing. Thus a large number of related publications have dealt with the use and calculation of colors [261, 111]. This section gives an introduction to the psychophysical basics of color sensation and shows how much influence they have on our color systems.

The term color arises from either physics, physiology, or psychology and is not easily definable. The basics of color theory go back to Johann Wolfgang von Goethe. An often-used definition of [205] states that:

> *Color is that aspect of visual perception by which an observer may distinguish differences between two structure-free fields of view of the same spatial and temporal properties, such as may be caused by differences in the spectral composition of the radiant energy concerned in the observation.*

Chap. 2 has shown that each physical light source has a characteristic spectral energy distribution. Fig. 58 illustrates this for sunlight absorbed by the atmosphere. The maximum intensity is achieved around 500 nm [yellow], corresponding to black body emission at about 6000 K.

Spectral Sensitivity of Cone Cells

The tristimulus theory of Helmholtz presumes the retina to have three different types of cone cells with different spectral response functions. Estimates of these functions are given in Fig. 59 [205].

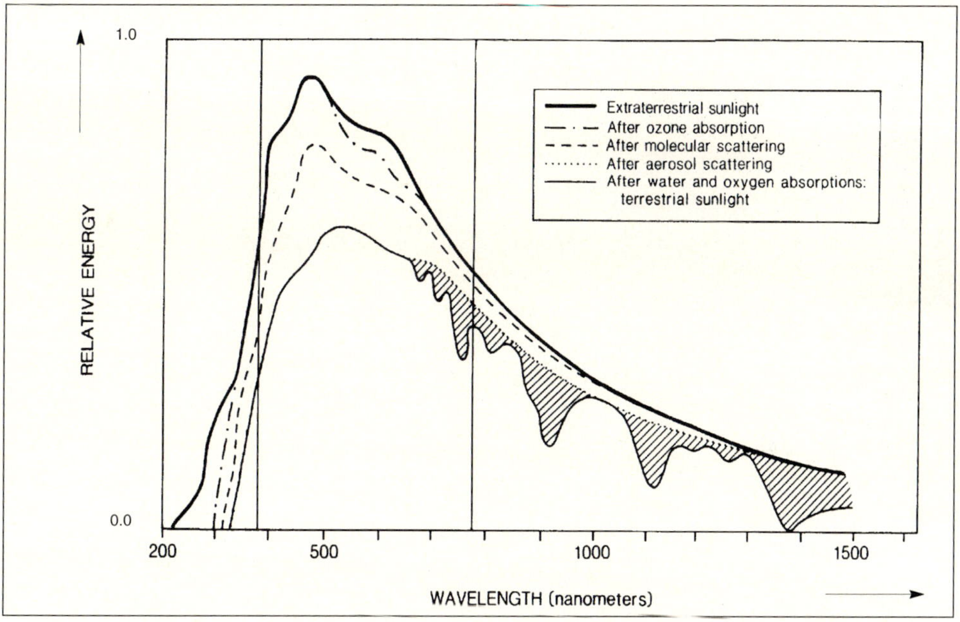

Figure 58: Spectral distribution of sunlight absorbed by the atmosphere [205]

The curves are normalized to their own maxima. The three cone types are maximally sensitive to quanta around 440, 540, and 565 nm. Further interesting measurements are given in Fig. 60, which shows the threshold for color discrimination as a function of the spectrum. These wavelength discrimination functions are correlated with the spectral response functions. They have a local minimum at about 550 nm where the spectral sensitivity for brightness has its maximum (see also Fig. 60).

Color Coding and Chromatic Response

We saw previously that the retinal cone cells have three characteristic response functions: however, we know that they are connected with ganglion cells whose receptive fields are antagonistically organized. Examining the retinal and CGL cells of primates, three different types of ganglion cells have been found which can also be interpreted as visual channels according to Fig. 61. One type is independent of the wavelength, yet the other two have a yellow-blue and a red-green behavior. Thus, a red (yellow) spotlight inhibits or

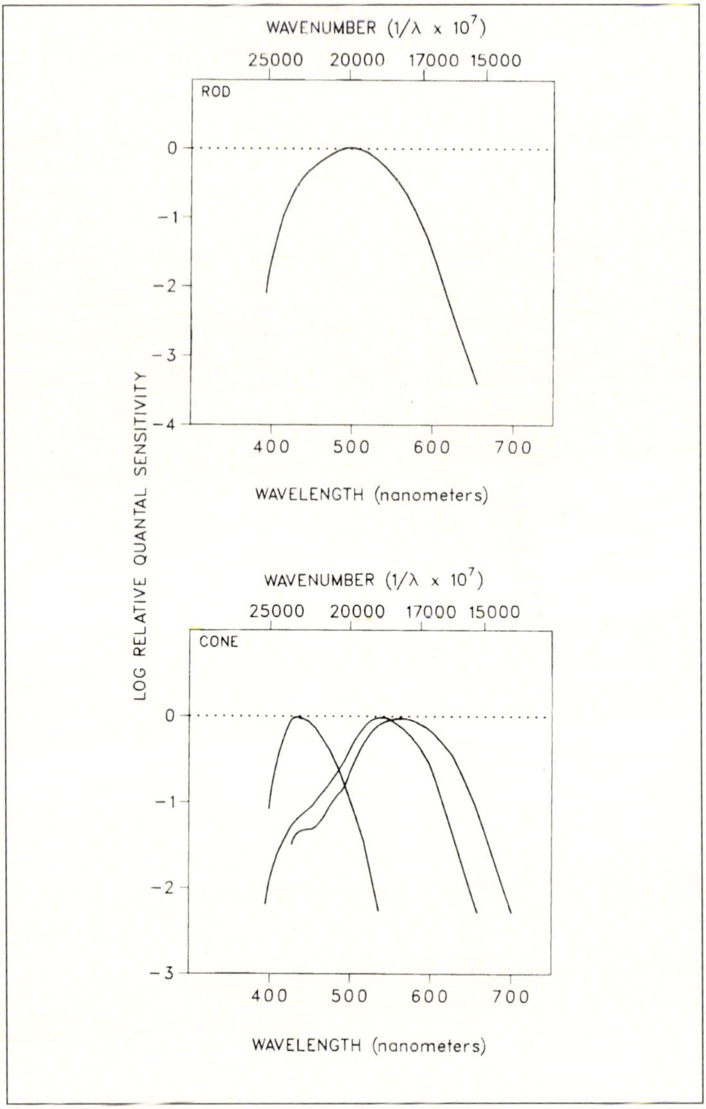

Figure 59: Estimates of the spectral response functions of retinal cones [205]

excites the cell depending on whether it is located at the center or on the periphery of the receptive field.

The resulting theory that takes this fact into account is the opponent color theory. Measurements, such as those shown in Fig. 62, demonstrate the response functions for opponent colors [205, 261].

One criterion for this theory is the fact that the phenomenon of successive contrast also works for opponent colors. This shows at least the presence of antagonistic receptive fields. Indeed, some re-

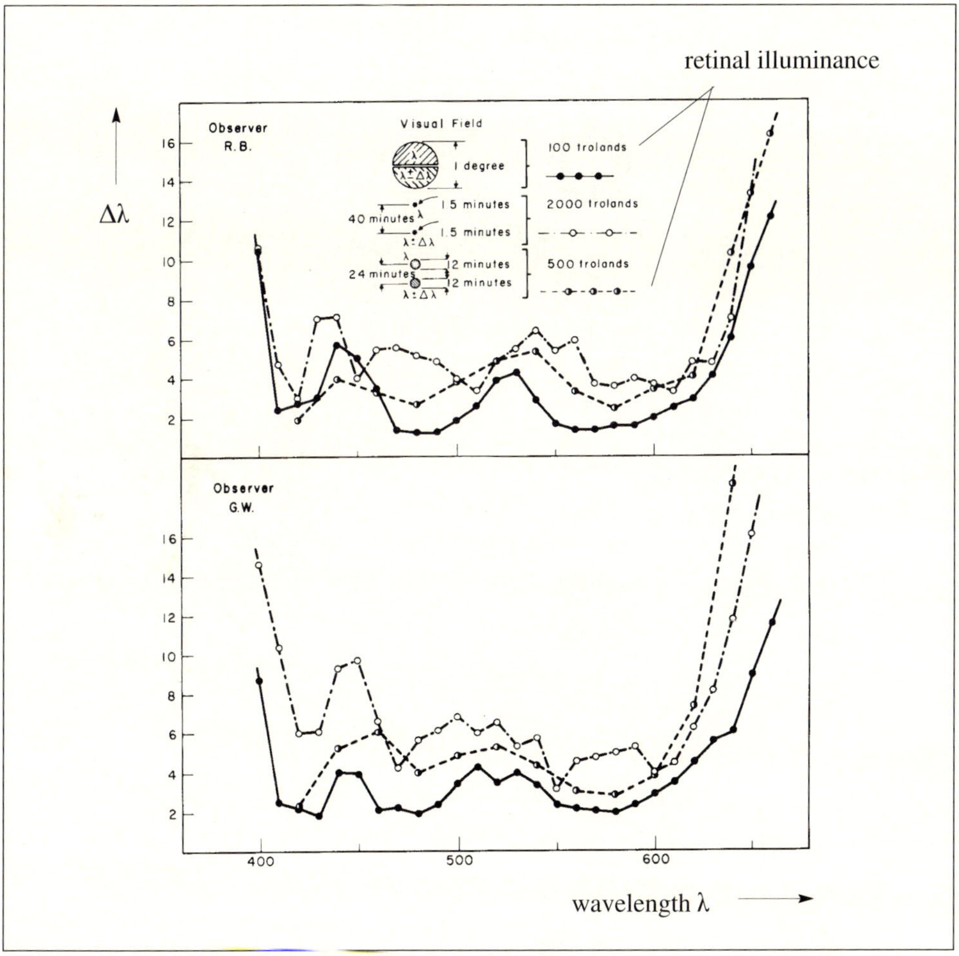

search results show that retinal amacrines and bipolars compute a differential signal of two different cone types. Other calculation schemes try to transform one theory into another. The current understanding supposes a hybrid scheme for color coding in human vision consisting of trichromatic sensors in the retina and antagonistic transmission in the color channels of Fig. 61. The visual system also provides features like color adaptation that can be found in Land's retinex theory of color vision [148].

Figure 60: Wavelength discrimination function for two different observers [261]

Figure 61: Different types of retinal ganglion cells [228]

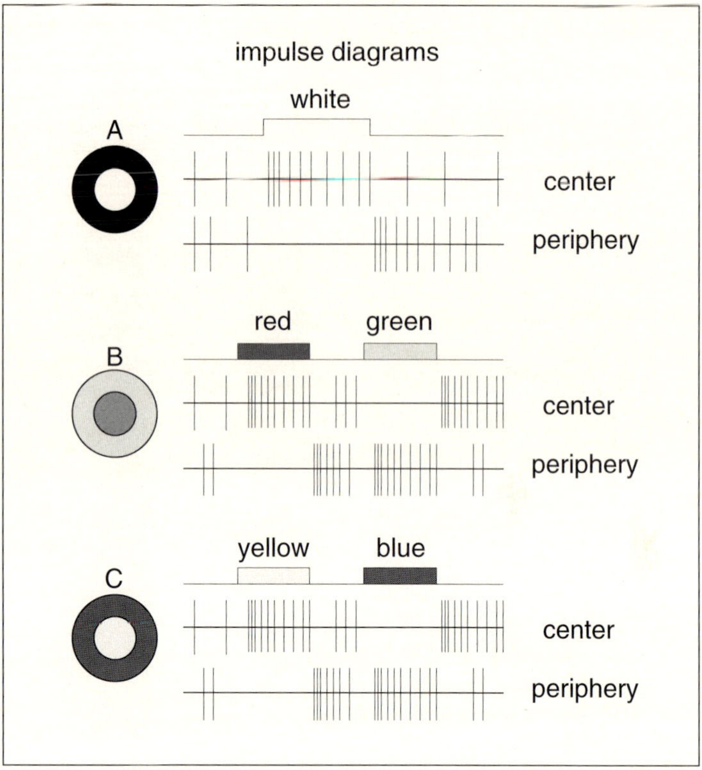

Figure 62: Chromatic response functions according to the opponent color theory

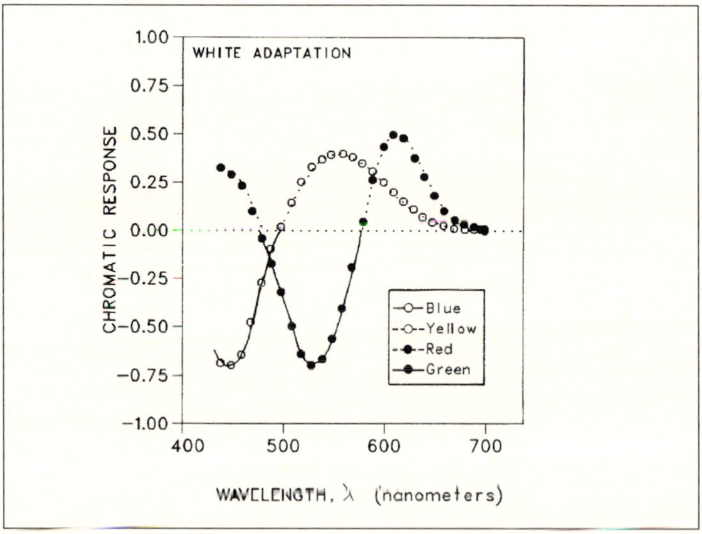

Linear Color Vision Models

This hybrid scheme can be expressed by a simple linear color vision model. If the response functions $R(\lambda)$, $G(\lambda)$ and $B(\lambda)$ are given for the cones, then we obtain the antagonistic processes $YE(\lambda) - B(\lambda)$ and $R(\lambda) - G(\lambda)$ according to Eq. (33):

$$
\begin{aligned}
YE - B &= (R(\lambda) + G(\lambda)) - B(\lambda) \\
R - G &= R(\lambda) - G(\lambda)
\end{aligned}
\tag{33}
$$

The color vision models considered according to these theories are two-pass linear models as in Fig. 63.

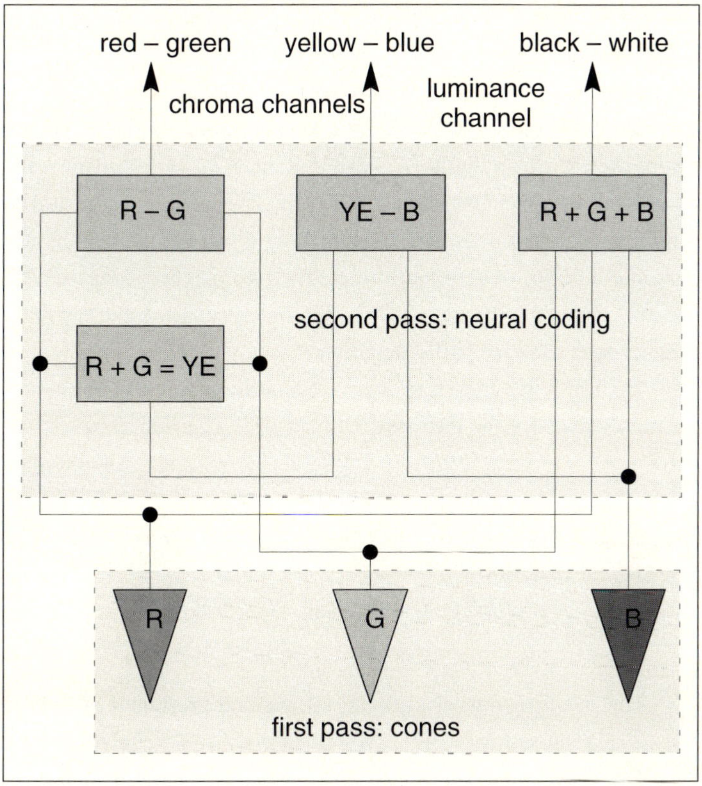

Figure 63: Diagram of a two pass color vision model according to [261]

The first pass models the cone mechanism, detecting the R, G, B values by characteristic filters, this by way of the spectral power distribution of the stimulus. The second pass calculates the differences between the perceived primaries and refers to the retinal ganglion cells. The result of this linear operation are three channels: one luminance channel and two chromatic channels.

3.2.2. Measuring Color

The CIE Primary System

The problem of measuring colors led to the definitions of the CIE (Commission Internationale de L'Eclairage 1931 and 1964) and to its diagrams based on psychophysical experiments. As illustrated in Fig. 64 a test person was confronted with two colored patches. The reference patch was illuminated with a monochromatic light of wavelength λ, the other one with a superposition of three spectral primaries of wavelengths λ_1 = 435.8 nm, λ_2 = 546.1 nm and λ_3 = 700.0 nm. The intensities of the primaries could be adjusted by dimmers. The task was now to dim these three lights until the test person could no longer discriminate the two patches. Since not all spectral colors can be matched by the three primaries, the resulting sensitivity curves are partly negative.

The following transformation, also defined by the CIE, ensures positive values for the three virtual primaries *X*, *Y* and *Z*.

$$
\begin{aligned}
X(\lambda) &= 2.36R(\lambda) - 0.515G(\lambda) + 0.005B(\lambda) \\
Y(\lambda) &= -0.89R(\lambda) + 1.426G(\lambda) + 0.014B(\lambda) \\
Z(\lambda) &= -0.46R(\lambda) + 0.088G(\lambda) + 1.009B(\lambda)
\end{aligned}
\qquad (34)
$$

The resulting curves are well known and presented in Fig. 65 for a 2° (1931) and for a 10° (1964) observer.

The curve $y(\lambda)$ exactly corresponds to the sensitivity function $V(\lambda)$. The CIE primaries of a color stimulus of the spectral energy distribution $P(\lambda)$ can now be calculated by integration over the visible spectrum weighted with the corresponding response functions according to Eq. (35):

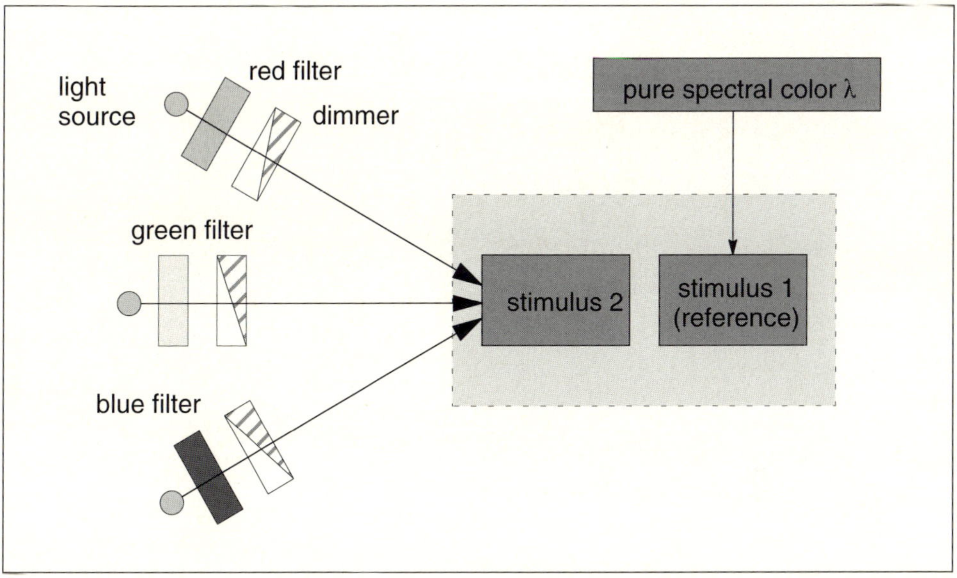

Figure 64: Psychophysical experiment for the evaluation of the spectral response functions of the CIE

$$X = \int_{380nm}^{780nm} P(\lambda)x(\lambda)d\lambda$$

$$Y = \int_{380nm}^{780nm} P(\lambda)y(\lambda)d\lambda \qquad (35)$$

$$Z = \int_{380nm}^{780nnm} P(\lambda)z(\lambda)d\lambda$$

The Y value corresponds to the luminous flux or to the luminance defined in Chap. 2. Other descriptions used in the CIE system are obtained when normalizing the X, Y, Z triplet on its sum.

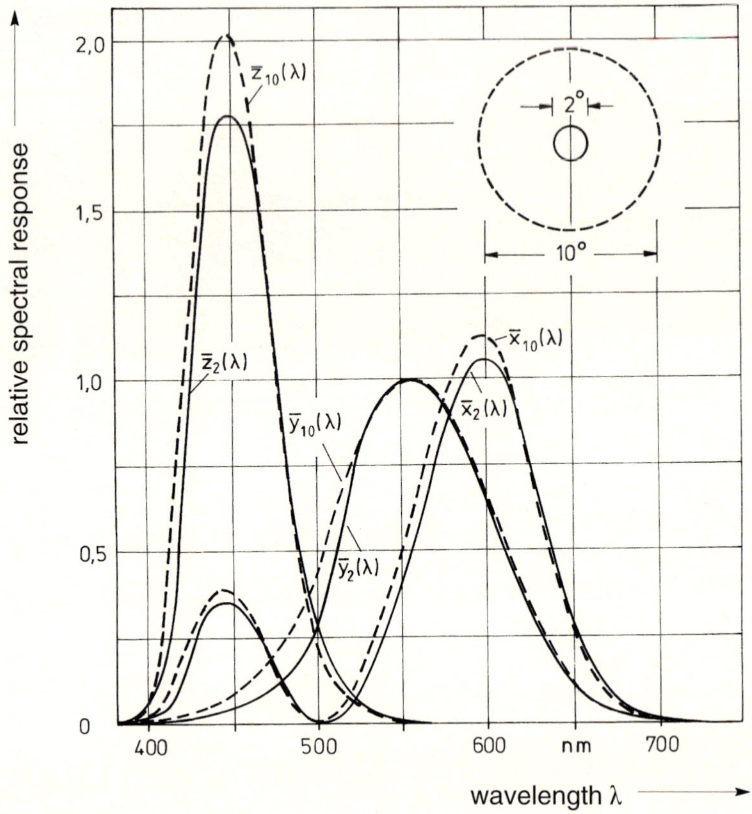

Figure 65:
CIE spectral response functions of 1931 and 1964 (see also [261])

$$x = \frac{X}{X + Y + Z}$$

$$y = \frac{Y}{X + Y + Z} \tag{36}$$

$$z = 1 - X - Y$$

Any color can now be characterized unique by the color coordinates x and y and by its luminance Y. The chart resulting from this transformation is the CIE chart limited by the pure spectral colors and often used in practical color science (Fig. 66).

The color white is obtained when all the three values x, y, z are the same and lie on (0.33,0.33) in the chart. The CIE values can be measured by special hardware, emulating the response functions with optical filters.

Examples

In Fig. 66 typical color coordinates of selected objects are included that have been adjusted with respect to the weather conditions in Germany [98]. Most natural colors are not highly saturated and are located around the white point of the chart. The triangle also presented in the chart is defined by the three primaries of the phosphors of a CRT display. Since the display is only able to synthesize color coordinates surrounded by the triangle, we cannot generate all possible colors with a three-primary system.

Higher-Order Colorimetry

So far our task was to find a system for the description of colors. In many applications, however, it is very important to know how well two colors can be distinguished with regard to the perceived stimulus. A first attempt may be to plot them into the CIE chart and to calculate the Euclidian difference. But the work of McAdams [261] proves that the perceived differences in color are not equal over the chart. Using a test environment he measured the discrimination thresholds for several colors located in the chart. The results were the ellipsoids presented in Fig. 67. They differ in size and orientation and can be described mathematically using Eq. (37):

$$1 = g_{11}(\Delta x)^2 + 2g_{12}(\Delta x \Delta y) + g_{22}(\Delta y)^2 \tag{37}$$

g_{11}, g_{12}, g_{22}: *parameters that depend on the locus in the CIE chart.*

The goal of higher-order colorimetry is to find perceptual color spaces. From the great variety of spaces defined in the past, the following ones are illustrated.

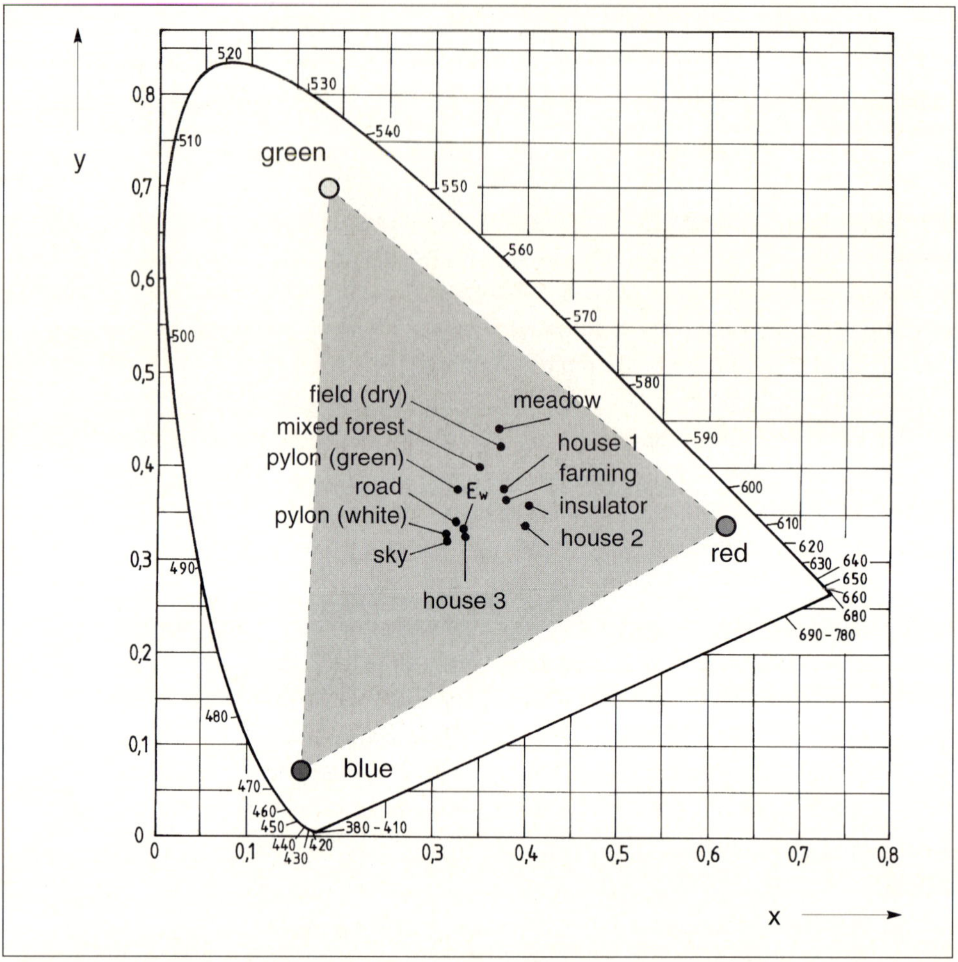

Figure 66: Samples for the color coordinates of selected objects, adjusted according to weather conditions in Germany [98]. The display primaries of a Hitachi monitor are also included

Color Spaces

Figure 66 shows that all color coordinates in the CIE chart surrounded by the R, G, B triangle of a monitor can be matched using the three primaries. CRT displays usually have three different electron guns, each one of which produces a spectral primary when exciting the phosphors of the screen. Thus in graphics we use the RGB color model supposing that the required color is matched by the superposition of R, G and B values. If the primaries are plotted on the axes of a cartesian space then we obtain the color cube presented in Fig. 68a.

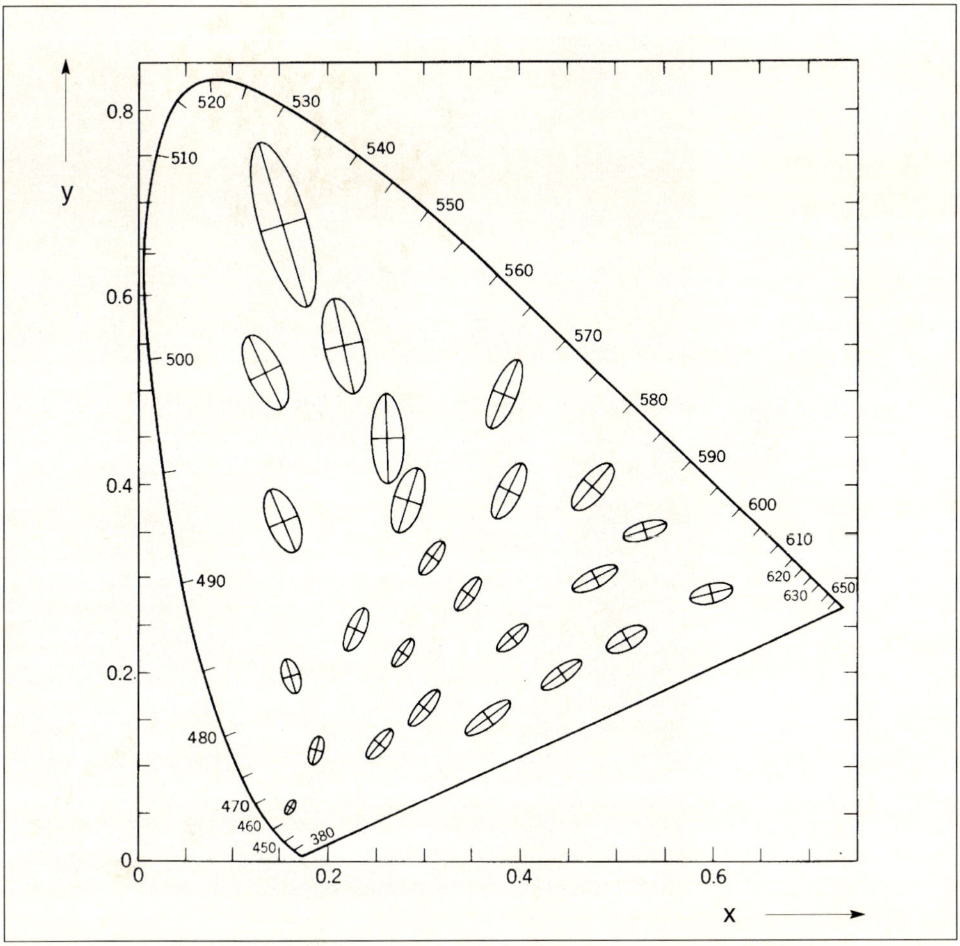

Figurc 67: McAdams ellipsoids 10 times scaled for a luminance of 50 cd/m² according to [213]

If the CIE primaries of the phosphors of a calibrated display are measured, then the transformation matrix [$\mathbf{X}_{RGB}$] is given and each CIE triplet may be transformed into an R, G, B triplet according to Eq. (38):

$$
\begin{aligned}
R &= X_R X + Y_R Y + Z_R Z \\
G &= X_G X + Y_G Y + Z_G Z \\
B &= X_B X + Y_B Y + Z_B Z
\end{aligned}
\qquad (38)
$$

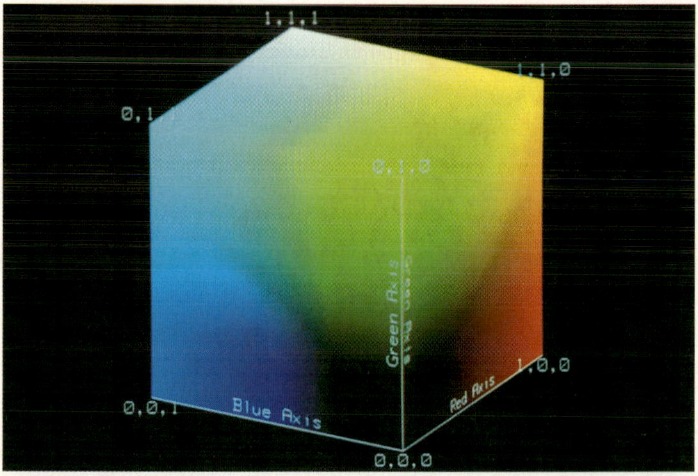

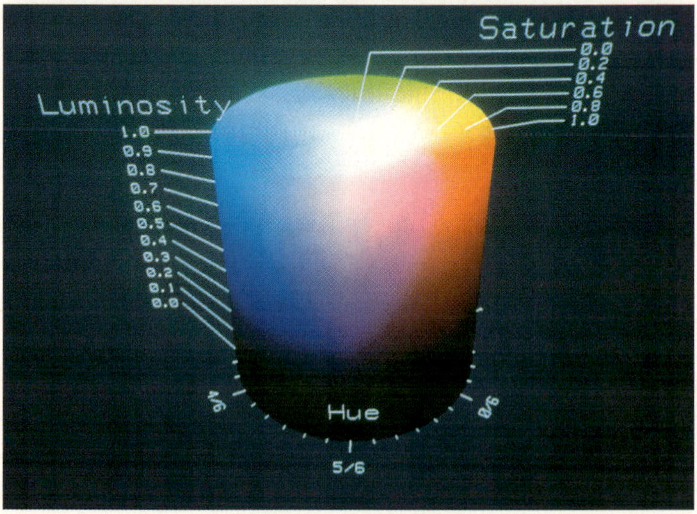

Figure 68:
a) RGB color space
b) HLS color space

Since not every CIE color can be presented on a display, negative R, G, B values can occur. In such cases a next neighbor has to be found.

A problem arises for the user when trying to define a certain color in R, G, B because this color space is not defined in a perceptual way. Another description of color is possible using the three psychophysical expressions *hue*, *lightness*, and *saturation*. Hue may be defined by an angle between 0 and 360 degrees, saturation and lightness by numbers between 0.0 and 1.0. The result is the cylindrical space shown in Fig. 68b.

Detailed descriptions of the corresponding transformations are presented in the standard literature, e.g., [68, 60]. There are also various other competing color spaces.

The R, G, B, H, L, S or X, Y, Z color spaces are perceptually nonlinear. X, Y, Z is very useful for color reproduction but not for evaluating relative changes in color. However, there have been other attempts to give a perceptually linear presentation of color. From the large variety of these so-called uniform color spaces the L^*,a^*,b^* and L^*,u^*,v^* of the CIE might be introduced. We obtain the transformation from X, Y, Z to L^*,a^*,b^* according to

$$L^* = 25\left[\frac{100Y}{Y_w}\right]^{1/3} - 16 \tag{39}$$

$$a^* = 500\left[\left(\frac{X}{X_w}\right)^{1/3} - \left(\frac{Y}{Y_w}\right)^{1/3}\right] \tag{40}$$

$$b^* = 200\left[\left(\frac{Y}{Y_w}\right)^{1/3} - \left(\frac{Z}{Z_w}\right)^{1/3}\right] \tag{41}$$

(X_W, Y_W, Z_W): *coordinates of the nominally white color*

This nonlinear warping of the X, Y, Z coordinates by the uniform color spaces of the CIE is illustrated in Fig. 69 that shows the projection of the R, G, B cube into L^*,a^*,b^* and L^*,u^*,v^* according to [111].

According to Eq. (42) we obtain the two coordinates u and v by

$$u = \frac{4X}{X + 15Y + 3Z} \qquad v = \frac{9Y}{X + 15Y + 3Z} \tag{42}$$

and the triplet L^*,u^*,v^* by

Figure 69:
RGB color cube mapped into L* a* b* and L* u* v*

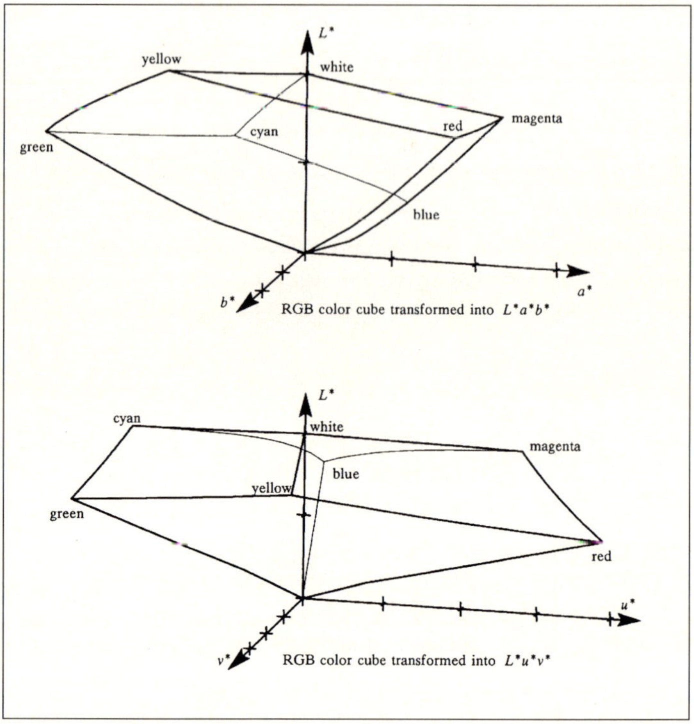

$$
\begin{aligned}
L^* &= 25 \sqrt[3]{\frac{100Y}{Y_W}} - 16 \\
u^* &= 13\,L^*(u - u_W) \\
v^* &= 13\,L^*(v - v_W)
\end{aligned}
\tag{43}
$$

Y_W, u_W, v_W: *coordinates of the nominally white color.*

Thus a Euclidian color difference ΔE can be defined according to Eq. (44):

$$
\Delta E = \sqrt{(\Delta L^*)^2 + (\Delta u^*)^2 + (\Delta v^*)^2} \tag{44}
$$

ΔE is a measure for the perceived difference of two colors, but it should be noted that none of the color difference formulas introduced so far is able to provide a valid description under all conditions [261].

For advanced rendering, computations based on spectral curves are recommended, as for instance in Hall [110]. In these cases each spectral curve is first low-pass filtered and then sampled to get a set of values for computation. After calculating the illumination model for each sample, the values are transformed into the CIE-X, Y, Z scheme or into R, G, B for the display. The initial method Hall proposed [110] used an interactive search for the appropriate sample locations until an error measure was minimized. The error measure is based on a calculation of the difference between the original curve and the sampled and reconstructed one in the L^*,u^*,v^* space. The need for such time consuming methods was proved by rendering two optical filters that did not have overlapping nonzero values. This was the first straightforward approach to this problem. Another simple idea for deriving a spectrum from R, G, B was proposed by Glassner in [77]. Meyer [176] proposed an improved technique based on an examination of the human visual system and derived a set of color axes that correspond most closely to the tristimulus values. This can be performed by an eigenvector transformation. The resulting coordinate system is called A, C_1, C_2 space and is related to X, Y, Z by Eq. (45). The corresponding sampling curves are shown in Fig. 70. The basic idea behind this approach was the observation that most spectral curves can be approximated by low-order polynomials when using an appropriate color space and Gaussian quadrature methods to determine the sampling. Once the corresponding color space has been found according to Eq. (45), the Gaussian quadrature numerically integrates the low order polynomials, provides the color coordinates of the reconstructed spectral curve and gives the sampling points. After carefully examining several numbers of samples and different integration orders from 1 to 10 he found that approaches with 4 samples already yield good results. The study was also subjectively evaluated by test persons.

$$\begin{aligned} A &= -0.017\ X + 1.0090\ Y + 0.0073\ Z \\ C_1 &= -1.537\ X + 1.0821\ Y + 0.3209\ Z \\ C_2 &= 0.1946\ X + -0.204\ Y + 0.5264\ Z \end{aligned} \qquad (45)$$

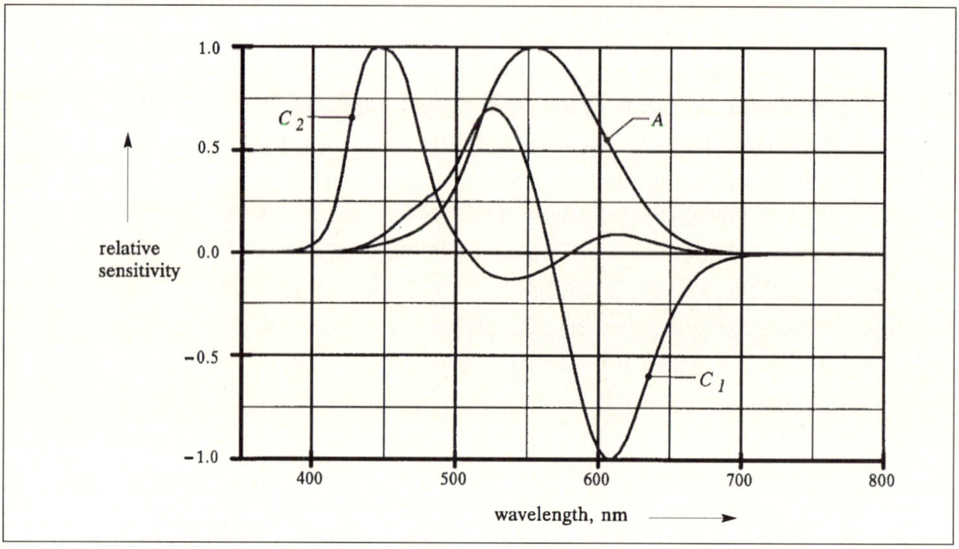

Figure 70: Sampling curves for Meyer's A, C_1, C_2 color space

3.3. Imaging Transforms

As we saw in the previous section, a correct physically based rendering process has to provide spectral sampling methods. Spectral sampling however, is a very expensive method compared to the common rendering techniques using the three primaries R, G, and B. The correct presentation of such images on a color screen requires a post-processing as shown in Fig. 71 according to [106]. We receive the CIE primaries X, Y, Z of each pixel from its spectral distribution (see also Fig. 25) by using the basic transforms introduced above. In order to present the calculated values in a correct way it is necessary to adapt the luminous dynamics of the scenery on the capacities of the screen. Thus a dynamic transform must be performed on the luminance before converting it into R, G, B. Due to the nonlinear behavior of the screen guns we have to correct these effects by means of a so-called γ-correction. A γ-correction according to Eq. (46) provides linear display behavior when the display is previously calibrated.

$$(R_\gamma, G_\gamma, B_\gamma) = \left[\frac{R^{\frac{1}{\gamma_R}}}{C_R}, \frac{G^{\frac{1}{\gamma_G}}}{C_G}, \frac{B^{\frac{1}{\gamma_B}}}{C_B}\right] \tag{46}$$

$\gamma_R, \gamma_G, \gamma_B$: *γ–values for the primaries of the display*
C_R, C_G, C_B : *constants*

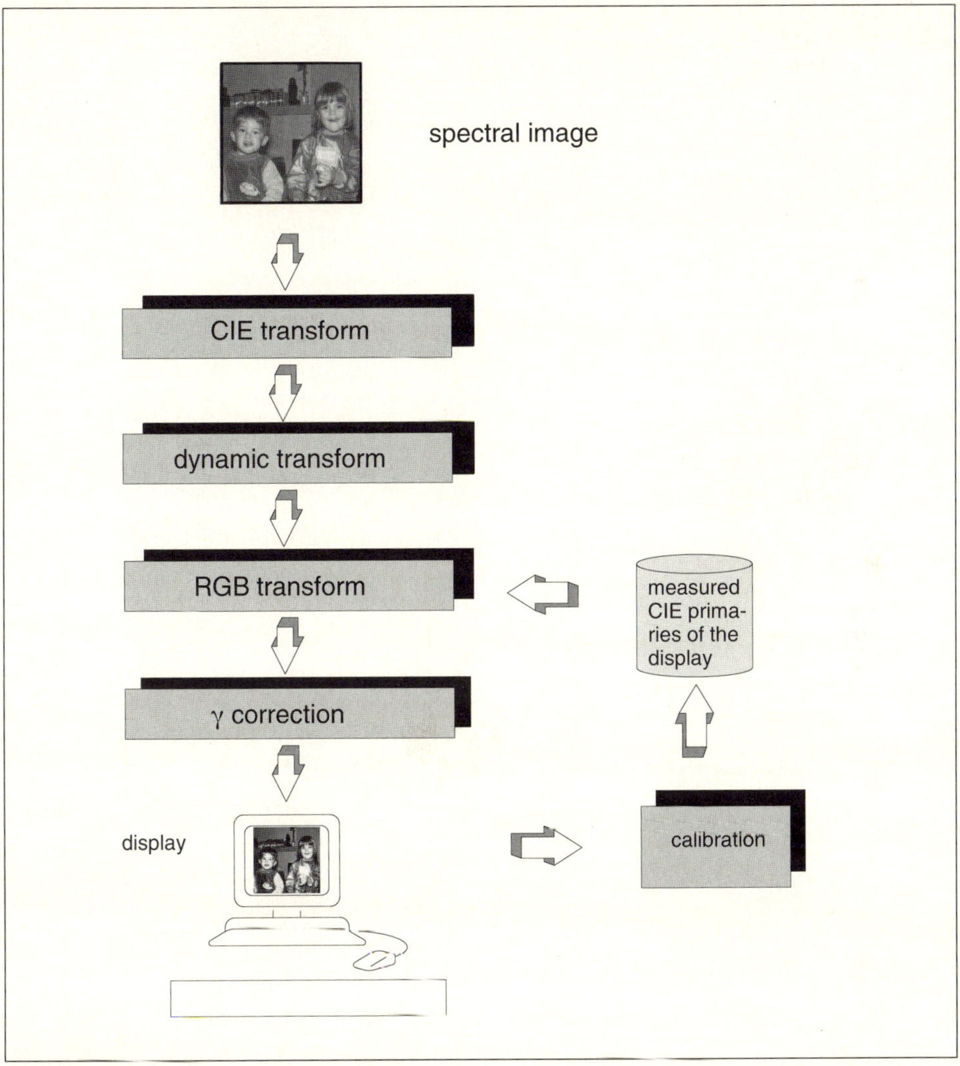

Figure 71:
Imaging transforms for the spectral treatment of light and color

4. Visualization and Visibility Analysis

4.1. Introduction

This chapter illustrates how to make use of specific perceptual features and how to integrate them into graphics and imaging methods. For this purpose, two examples from the field of environmental analysis are explained in detail, both of which have been developed and successfully used in the past. They are visual analysis of objects and integrated modeling, and visualization of air pollution. The goal of both applications has been to develop and to provide efficient and easy-to-use methods that can be integrated into industrial systems.

The first example treats the problem of the assessment of the optical impact of technical systems in the landscape. To that effect, overhead power lines were analyzed based on a recently developed algorithm for the quantification of the visibility of objects. The proposed method is based itself on a geometric model of the scenery that is combined with physical attributes. The visibility analysis is then performed by an image analysis method affected by perceptual features of human vision. Thus, *both graphics and imaging techniques* had to be combined to solve the task. The efficiency of the method is documented by an evaluation of a real planning example.

The second application deals with interactive numeric modeling and visualization of air pollution. We will see in particular that when focusing on advanced interactive visualization, we have to design the appropriate mapping carefully. First, the underlying ideas of the visualization and interaction pipeline are explained and the basic principles of the modeling tasks are illuminated. Furthermore, results from a simulation of a chemical industry plant are documented and the concept of an integrated system is proposed. These results undoubtedly use *advanced imaging methods* that accomplish automatic modeling and classification and give motivation for the further chapters of this book.

4.2. Visibility Analysis Using Graphics and Imaging

4.2.1. Introductory Remarks

The optical conspicuousness of objects is of great importance for many civilian [84, 85] and military applications. It has always been, and still remains, the object of computer aided image processing and image analysis procedures in these fields to obtain a quantitative statement of the identifiability or camouflage of objects as a function of their shape, color, texture, and environment. Classical methods of identification generally work with statistical operations [129] on images.

Most existing methods for image analysis only give general statements because they lack similarity with the human visual system and therefore cannot be used for a differentiated analysis. In the classical experimental psychology of advertising, examinations are thus carried out by means of eye trackers and test persons [221], which are then analyzed and interpreted and consequently lead to a statement on the conspicuousness of the depicted object on the basis of the glimpse length or other criteria.

On the other hand, during the last few years, promising attempts have been made to model the human visual system [32, 8]. Apart from the classical procedures of computer vision such as shape from shading [122], aiming at the extraction of 3D shapes from images or sequences of images, particular emphasis should be laid on algorithmic transformations of the cortical cell activities ascertained by Nobel prize winners Wiesel and Hubel [124]. Basic work in this field was done by David Marr [165] (see next chapter). However, as biological details of the human visual system are as yet insufficiently known, all models either orient themselves through examined facts or through generally known performance characteristics of human vision.

The method presented here was stimulated by the following facts: During the planning process of new industrial constructions or power plants as well as in many other fields there is a growing demand for the optical integration of objects into their environment [253, 183, 191]. Terms such as visibility or camouflage are often used in discussions regarding locations or rights of way. Due to the absence of objective engineering techniques that determine those quantities [191], the decisions are currently taken on the basis of subjective and intuitive criteria. Thus we face the problem of developing an easy-to-use method for the evaluation of the visual impact of objects on the landscape [89]. Both *computer graphics and imaging techniques* have to be combined with *psychophysical laws* to satisfy these requirements.

4.2.2. Factors Influencing the Visibility

The wish to build a simple, robust, and straightforward method lead us first to classify psychophysical and physical factors that have an influence on visibility. Higher-order psychological and knowledge based factors are extremely difficult to quantify and therefore cannot be included in such a method. To a certain extent the following method quantifies the stimulus of the object that is transmitted from the retina into the cortex. The method was tested with an environmental application, namely the planning of overhead power lines.

Image Projection on the Retina

Figure 72 illustrates the path of the rays in the projection of an object – in this case an overhead line pylon – onto the retina surface, seen at a distance r. The area of the retina surface which is thus covered can be represented by the solid angle Ω. At a greater distance r from the observer, we can approximate Ω with:

$$\Omega \sim \frac{1}{r^2} \tag{47}$$

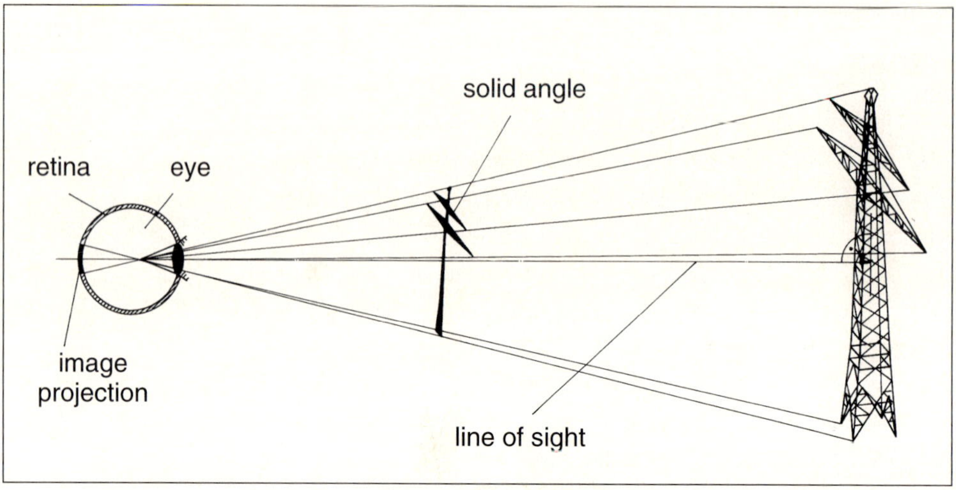

Figure 72: Projection of an image onto the retina surface

Modelling Visual Acuity

Another important aspect is the fact that the visual acuity V is not equal on all parts of the retina. Its maximum lies in the center of the retina and decreases towards the periphery. This was explained in detail in Chap. 3 and the corresponding curves can be found in Fig. 40. Figure 73 shows a simplified model of the acuity V dependent on the visual angle α for a static scenery. We can assume this curve to be rotation-symmetric according to Eq. (48):

$$V(\alpha) \approx c_1 + \frac{c_2}{\alpha + c_3} \tag{48}$$

c_1, c_2, c_3: *parameters*

It is shown in [98] that the optimal parameters can be obtained using Gaussian mean-square optimization. We obtain:

$$\begin{aligned} c_1 &= -0.0323 \\ c_2 &= 0.0524 \\ c_3 &= 0.0507 \end{aligned} \tag{49}$$

This implies that each solid angle area $\Delta\Omega$ covered on the retina has to be weighted with the corresponding value of the visual acuity V. Nevertheless, this is only applicable if the observer fixes his eyes on the object. However, if the observer analyzes details with saccadian jumps, then we have to find more complex descriptions (see Chap. 3).

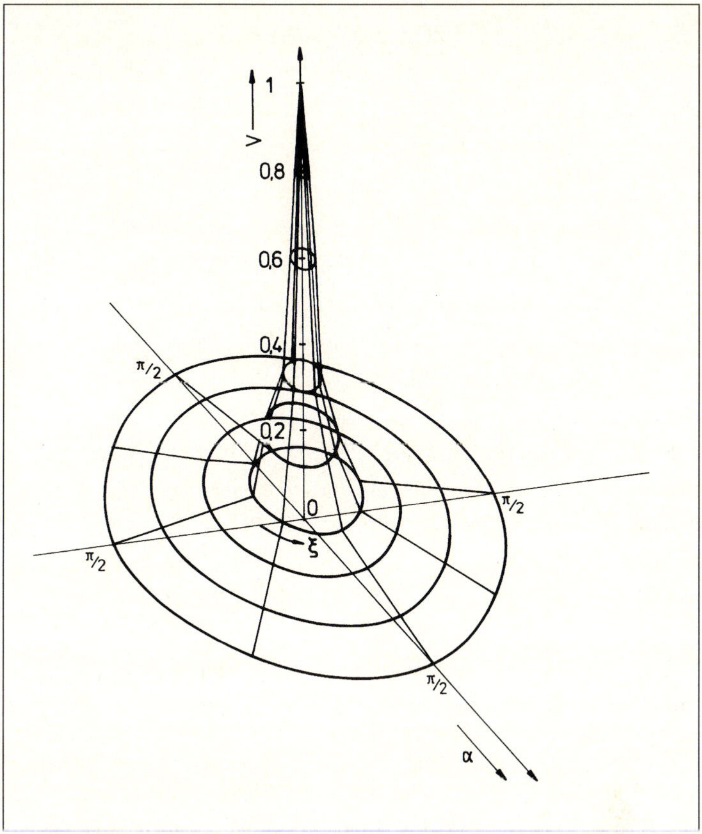

Figure 73: Simplified, rotation symmetric model of the visual acuity V as a function of the visual angle α

Color Distance and Atmospheric Attenuation

According to Chap. 3 the difference in colors is expressed by so-called color difference formulas. The difficulty is to select a uniform color space that is appropriate. As a compromise regarding computational complexity [98] proposes a modified distance measure in the Y, x, y color space of the CIE.

With the introduction of a system of polar coordinates (r, ϕ) (see Fig. 74) which expresses the distance between the observer and an object, the contrast $C(r)$ can be calculated for monochrome conditions as follows:

$$C(r) = \frac{|Y_{H0}\ e^{-Z(r+r_H)} - Y_{O0}\ e^{-Zr} - Y_{Hi}\ (e^{-Z(r+r_H)} - e^{-Zr}\ )|}{Y_{H0}\ e^{-Z(r+r_H)} + Y_{Hi}(1 - e^{-Z(r+r_H)})} \quad (50)$$

Y_{O0}, x_{O0}, y_{O0}	*: color coordinates of the object*
Y_{H0}, x_{H0}, y_{H0}	*: color coordinates of the background*
Y_{Hi}, x_{Hi}, y_{Hi}	*: color coordinates of the sky*
r_H	*: distance between the object and the background*
Z	*: atmospheric extinction coefficient*

The fact that the contrast is degraded exponentially by the atmosphere is taken into consideration [55] and a mean value of $Z = 0.3$/km for Germany [135] may be assumed. A lot of basic work has been done on the optics of the atmosphere and both contrast and color shifting can be described mathematically. In this approach the two color coordinates x and y are shifted easily with increasing distance r in accordance with Eq. (51) and (52) to those of the sky:

$$\Delta x(r) = x_{H0}\ e^{-Z(r+r_H)} - x_{O0}\ e^{-Zr} - x_{Hi}\ (e^{-Z(r+r_H)} - e^{-Zr}\ ) \quad (51)$$

$$\Delta y(r) = y_{H0}\ e^{-Z(r+r_H)} - y_{O0}\ e^{-Zr} - y_{Hi}\ (e^{-Z(r+r_H)} - e^{-Zr}\ ) \quad (52)$$

This was verified by measurements illustrated in Fig. 75. The color locations of a test object were measured in fog with high extinction values Z from various distances r. The values for $x(r)$ and $y(r)$ are compared with those calculated in Eqs. (51) and (52). The small inaccuracies are, on the one hand, due to the fact that Z could only be determined approximately, and on the other to inhomogeneities in the atmosphere. A sophisticated investigation of atmospheric simulation with a special regard to computer graphics is also given in [256].

From the great variety of color difference formulas stated in the past, the following one was selected according to its correlation with perceived differences in color [86, 90] and contrast [55] for a bichrome case:

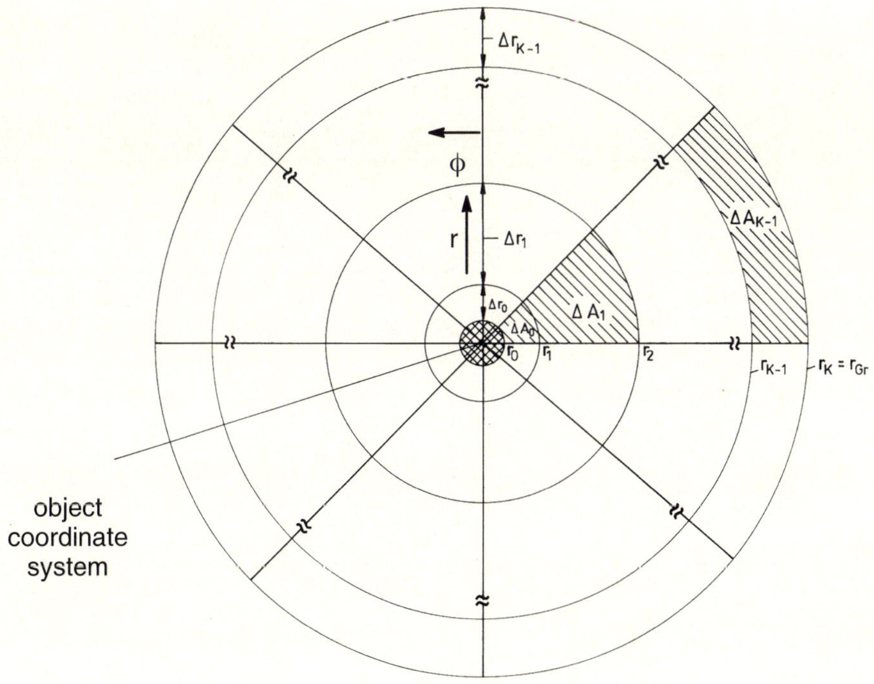

Figure 74:
Polar coordinates to describe the position of observer and object (see [98])

$$\Delta E(r) = \sqrt{C(r)^2 + (\Delta x(r))^2 + (\Delta y(r))^2} \qquad (53)$$

The Treatment of Steel Constructions

The statements made up to now are valid for solid, monochrome objects. With an overhead line pylon, however, the steel struts cause many contrast transitions which could become a "number crunching" problem with the method which will later be explained. In this case, texture becomes more and more important. For our easy-to-use method, however, another possibility arises. One solution is to adapt the pylon's color location. Here the pylon is taken as a solid object and its color location is adapted against the background, in accordance with the ratio b_A of the area of the retina actually cov-

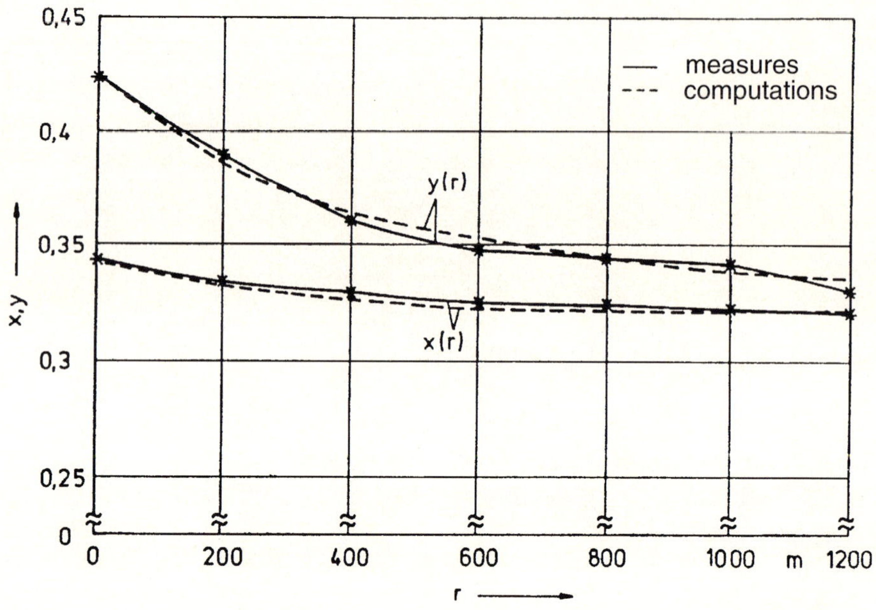

Figure 75: Measured and calculated values for the color locations x(r) and y(r) of a test object (meadow) from various distances (Z = 2.6/km)

ered by the image Ω_{Re} to the area of the retina which is inside the contour of the pylon Ω_{Co} as in Eq. (54). This is especially plausible for greater distances, when the individual struts are no longer distinguished due to the eye's resolving capacity and the pylon appears as a seemingly solid grey area.

$$b_A = \frac{\Omega_{\text{Re}}}{\Omega_{Ko}} \qquad (54)$$

For a 110 kV pylon $b_A \approx 35$ % [98].

4.2.3. Mathematical Description of the Visibility

The following section presents a mathematical framework for the definition of the visibility of objects according to [89]. It is founded on the factors described above and will be taken as a basis for the formulation of discrete image analysis methods. For reasons of simplicity, the following definitions are based on the situation of a monochrome object in front of a monochrome background.

Specific Visibility

The ***specific visibility*** $S''(r,\phi)$ (unit: sr/m^2) is a measure for the optical impression made by an object at a given observer point in line with the factors stated above. It is computed as an integral over the solid angle area of the retina Ω taken up by the object, evaluated with visual acuity V and color difference against background ΔE, normalized to the observer's surface area dA (unit: m^2):

$$S''(r,\phi) = \frac{1}{dA}\int_{\Omega} V(a)\Delta E(r,\phi)d\Omega \qquad (55)$$

Visibility

Visibility S (unit: sr) describes a global measure for the optical impression of an object. For this an integration has to be made above all possible observer points, weighted with the elements of surface allocated to them, $dA = r\,dr\,d\phi$. It can be taken as a surface integral over S''.

$$S = \int_{A} S''(r,\phi)dA \qquad (56)$$

It has been proved that the integral converges under atmospheric conditions.

Further interesting measures are obtained when the given specific visibility S'' is extended to the maximum specific visibility S''_{max}, which is defined for the same object that is analyzed from the same observer point, but in front of a clear sky and with no obstacles in between (worst case).

Now it is possible to state an ***efficiency of camouflage*** η'', which indicates the reduction of the specific visibility due to the actual location and surface shape of the landscape. It is defined as follows:

$$\eta'' = \frac{S''_{max} - S''}{S''_{max}} \tag{57}$$

The analogous definition of η expresses the global ratio of camouflage:

$$\eta = \frac{S_{max} - S}{S_{max}} \tag{58}$$

4.2.4. Image Generation and Image Analysis

Generation of Terrain and Object Models

The basic modeling task is to create a geometric model of the scenery to be analyzed. Therefore, a digital terrain model (DTM) is used and the corresponding objects are given by CAD data sets. The color coordinates of all objects in the scene are stored in Y, x, y as an attribute of the geometry.

Figure 76: Rendered CAD-model of a 110-kV overhead line pylon

Figure 76 shows a 110 kV overhead line pylon. It was modeled using approximately 200 000 polygons. A procedure for the generation of pylon models can be found in [133].

Table 3 gives some examples of color coordinates that have been measured and adjusted with respect to the weather conditions in Germany.

Table 3: Test readings for the color coordinates of selected objects (from [89])

Object	*Y*	*x*	*y*
Sky	5881	0.315	0.322
Mixed forest	254	0.352	0.400
Grey pylon	457	0.316	0.325
Green pylon	570	0.327	0.376
Meadow	415	0.370	0.442
Field (dry)	1213	0.373	0.422
House 1	2968	0.363	0.381
House 2	394	0.402	0.337
Road	1216	0.335	0.339

DTMs are applied to several purposes with great success [86, 191, 90] and a large number of DTM algorithms have been so far introduced. The most common techniques used for digital terrain modeling are interpolation and triangulation methods for given digitized contour lines, for instance Delaunay tessellation [207, 179], which are derived from computational geometry. Detailed descriptions of these techniques are also given in [268] and [16].

Basically, digital terrain modeling can also be taken as a scattered data problem [69, 187]. From the large variety of algorithms, a Shepard-like formulation and a first-order interpolation technique are often applied. It is illustrated in Fig. 77 and follows the notations of Eq. (59). The result is an equidistant mesh.

$$z_P = \frac{\sum_{i=1}^{4} \frac{z_{Pi}}{d_i}}{\sum_{i=1}^{4} \frac{1}{d_i}} \tag{59}$$

z_P : *altitude of a mesh node P to be determined*

z_{Pi} : *altitudes of neighboring contour lines*

d_i : *horizontal and vertical distances to neighboring contour lines.*

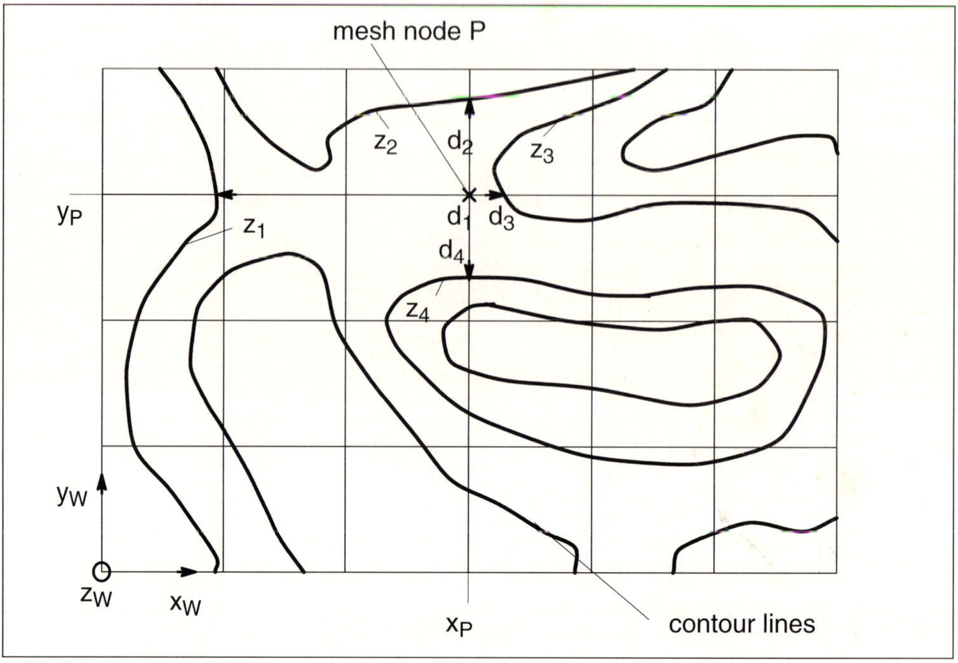

Figure 77: Illustration of a fast DTM interpolation method

[101] proposes further quadtree optimization of the model to reduce the number of polygons. Some of the latest approaches also use higher-order splines, as described in [64] or [30]. An efficient generic surface approximation method is provided in [258].

In order to reference objects in the DTM, the external models must be transformed from their local coordinate systems into the terrain coordinate system that is related to the lower left mesh vertex. If the elevation data is given for each vertex of the mesh, the following bilinear interpolation method calculates the altitude of an arbitrary location onto the terrain surface using the four vertices of the corresponding patch (see Fig. 78).

Let z_P be the altitude of an arbitrary point (x_P, y_P) onto the terrain surface that has to be determined. The following equation defines the bilinear function:

$$z_P = z_G + \frac{z_H - z_G}{y_2 - y_1} \cdot (y_P - y_1) \qquad (60)$$

z_G *: linear interpolation from* z_1 *and* z_4

z_H *: linear interpolation from* z_2 *and* z_3

Thus, the reference of an object in the terrain is accomplished by the translation vector (x_P, y_P, z_P). Due to its first-order properties this method is very fast, especially when object motions or terrain-following flight simulations have to be achieved in real time.

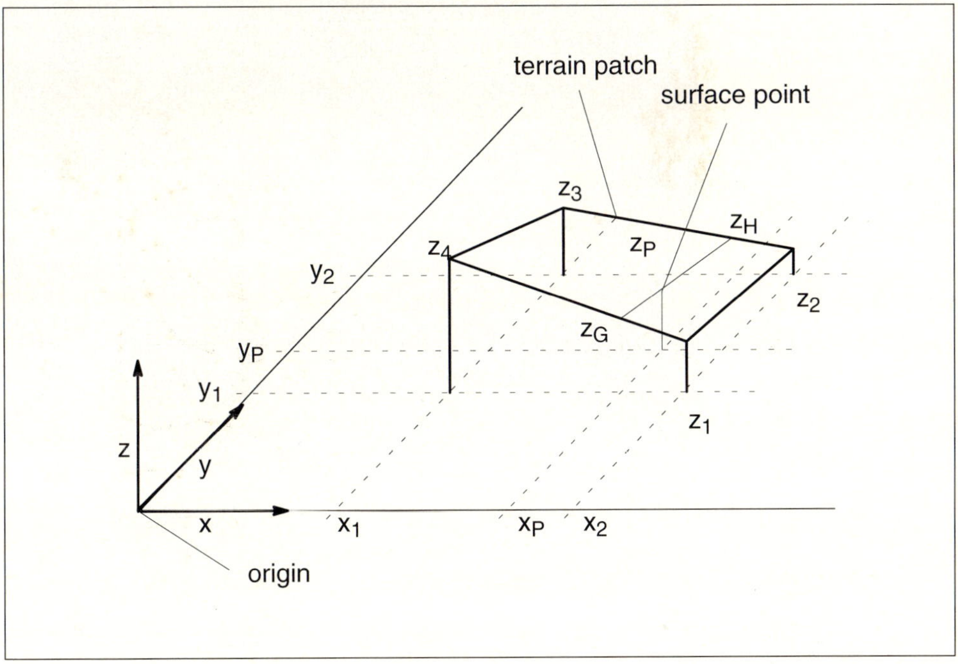

Figure 78: Bilinear interpolation of arbitrary surface points

Rendering of Outside Scenes

The rendering of terrain and object data is very difficult because of the large amount of data to be dealt with [133, 184]. Thus, an accurate representation of each detail in the scenery is not possible and also not necessary. The level of detail should be high in the local zone. Far away from the observer, however, it is sufficient to present the scenery at a low level of detail using hierarchical data sets [9] in order to limit the corresponding data. This aspect is very important during real-time applications such as in flight simulation [262].

Generally, photorealistic rendering is provided with great success by texture mapping of remote sensing data on the digital terrain model. This method, presented in [192], is particularly useful for large distances from the observer. Former approaches used 2½D-methods, scanning a photograph of the scenery and presenting it as a background pixmap [191]. An example of texture mapping is given in Fig. 79.

Figure 79: Terrain model, mapped with a photographic texture from a landsat–TM image

It should be noted here that the various texture mapping techniques introduced so far (see for instance [116]) give rise to aliasing effects depending on the frequency characteristics of the texture. For this reason, careful prefiltering techniques have to be employed before mapping.

Ray Tracing Methods for Scene Analysis

This section provides a discrete formulation of the computation of the assessment terms, as the visibility based on ray tracing methods for image generation.

The surface integral of Eq. (56) for the visibility S can be computed from a Monte Carlo integration of S'' over all observer positions in a polar coordinate system, where the observers are distributed with an exponentially decaying density around the object. For this purpose a network is constructed surrounding the object under analysis as in Fig. 74. It is generated in accordance with Eq. (61):

$$(r_n + \Delta r_n/2)\Delta\phi = \Delta r_n \qquad (61)$$

$n = 0, \ldots, K-1.$

The exponential increase has the advantage of high precision in the local zone with moderate computation costs. An observer point (i) is determined randomly within each element of surface ΔA_i in order to prevent a correlation of single observers.

The object is viewed from each of the observer points as shown in Fig. 80, where the line of sight is fixed at the center of the object. To obtain the specific visibility, the selected object and its surroundings are analyzed by means of a ray tracer, taking into account the influencing factors stated above. The ray that is projected into the scene creates a discrete image by scanning the object and its immediate surroundings.

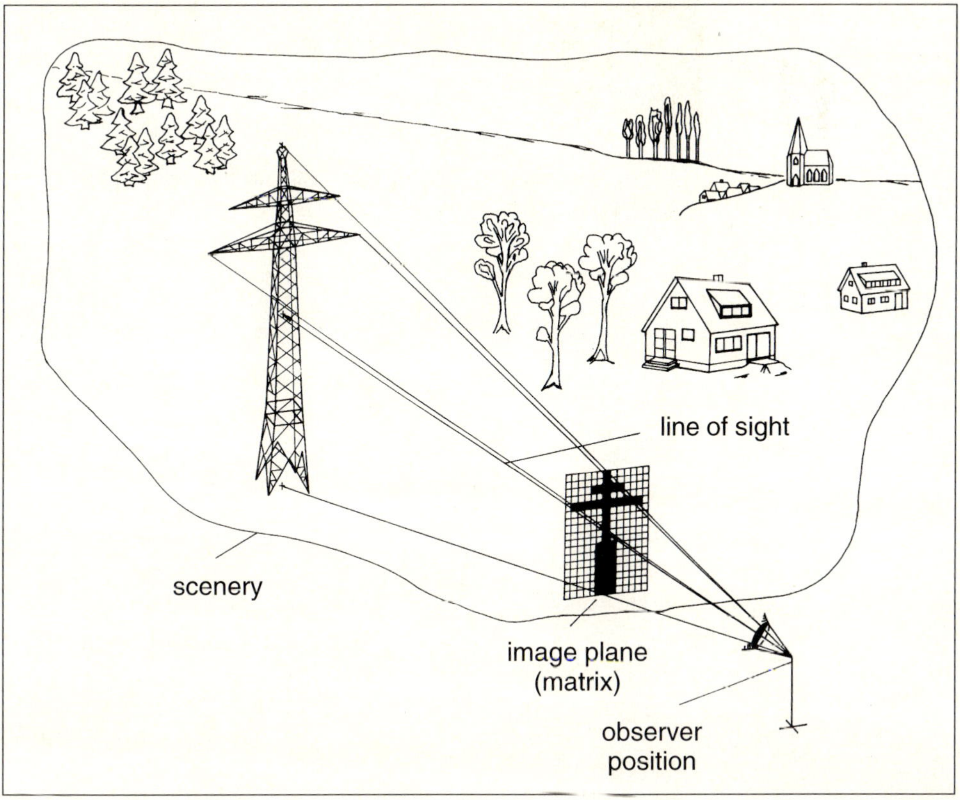

Figure 80:
Ray tracing for image generation and analysis

The analysis of this image, and therefore, also the computation of the optical impression made by the object in the landscape, is carried out by analyzing every scan line of the image matrix taking into account the stated influencing factors. This image matrix addressed by the indexes j and k can be interpreted as the retina of the observer modeled. Each image pixel has a characteristic color location corresponding to the object to be represented or to the background, and is taken from real measurements (see also Table 3).

To compute the specific visibility, the image is scanned line by line. If an object pixel occurs in a scanline, then the color difference $\Delta E_l(j,m)$ from the previous pixel is calculated. Each pixel is evaluated with its own particular visual acuity $V(j,k)$ and with the corresponding solid angle $\Omega(j,k)$. With each transition from an object pixel to a background pixel, the color difference $\Delta E_r(j,m)$ is calculated. The overall color difference $\Delta E(j,m)$ defined for the part m of the scan line where one transition is enclosed is the arithmetic mean in accordance with Eq. (62):

$$\Delta E(j,m) = \frac{\Delta E_l(j,m) + \Delta E_r(j,m)}{2} \qquad (62)$$

The specific visibility S_i'' from a selected observer position (i) is obtained using Eq. (63):

$$S_i'' = \sum_{j=1}^{N} \sum_{m=1}^{O(j)} \Delta E(j,m) \sum_{k=k_1(j,m)}^{k_2(j,m)} V(j,k)\ \Omega(j,k) \qquad (63)$$

where $O(j)$ represents the number of transitions in each scan line (j) and N the vertical resolution of the image. This scheme also provides a simple method for analyzing transitions in the texture; however, alternative approaches based on multichannel analysis [31] have been proposed.

The visibility S is obtained by summing up all specific visibilities S_i'', weighted with the area ΔA_i in accordance with Eq. (64):

$$S = \sum_i S_i'' \Delta A_i \qquad (64)$$

The results of the process described above are diagrams that quantify the optical impression of any object in question. A more detailed investigation on the reliability and performance of this algorithm can be found in [98].

Applications

This section describes the application of the above algorithm in the field of overhead line design. An existing 30 kV overhead line should be replaced by a 110 kV overhead line and several variants had to be examined in terms of their visibility. Conductors and insulators are not considered in the following investigation.

Figure 81 shows the contour map of the terrain in the Schwäbische Alb, in Germany. Arrow 3 marks the observer position and the line of sight for the 3D reconstruction that is illustrated in Fig. 82. The vertical dashes in Fig. 81 indicate the position of the overhead line pylons.

Subject of the following investigation was the calculation of the visibility of different variants within a sensitive right of way area that is marked by a rectangle in Fig. 81.

The following variants were analyzed:

Variant 1: *existing 30 kV line*
Variant 2: *planned 110 kV line at the same locations (Figs. 83 and 84)*
Variant 3: *possible pybass of the village in short span (Figs. 85 and 86)*
Variant 4: *possible bypass of the village in large span*

Table 4 shows the calculated visibilities and the efficiencies of camouflage. The results for all pylons of a single variant were added.

	Var. 1 30 kV	**Var. 2 110 kV**	**Var. 3 110 kV**	**Var. 4 110 kV**
S [sr]	1566	2247	1974	1585
η [%]	36	34	44	44

Table 4: Visibilities of the analyzed variants

The best result of the analyzed 110 kV overhead lines is provided by variant 4.

Another interesting insight into the results of the described simulation process is shown in Figs. 83–86. The specific visibilities and the efficiencies of camouflage were calculated by observers distributed uniformly over the surface area. The result of this process is a distribution of these parameters over the landscape in question.

The pseudocolor mappings of Figs. 83–86 show that they depend on the location and distance of the observer, the structure of the landscape, obstacles, and the background.

This example has shown how to combine methods from *computer graphics, imaging, and visual perception* to develop algorithms for approximating the visibility of objects. Although the presented method is straightforward and neglects higher-order features of human vision, such as grouping and gestalt, it is easy to implement and can be used for any kind of object. In particular, it is obvious how a physically based geometric model can be used to approach real world problems.

In general, physically based modeling has become increasingly important during the last few years, thus demanding that computer graphics provide concepts for the interactive integration of both visualization and numeric modeling for any kind of natural phenomenon. The following section gives an insight into these concepts taking environmental simulation [101, 100, 103] as an example.

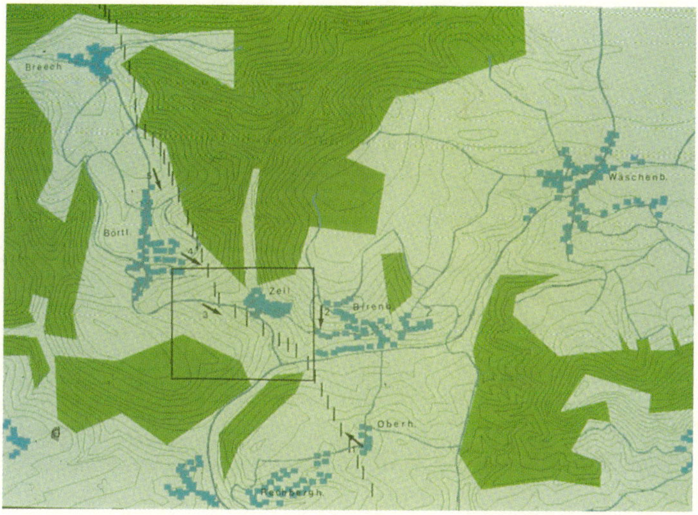

Figure 81:
Topographic map of the terrain (Schwäbische Alb, Germany)

Figure 82:
3D reconstruction of the landscape according to arrow 3 (variant 2)

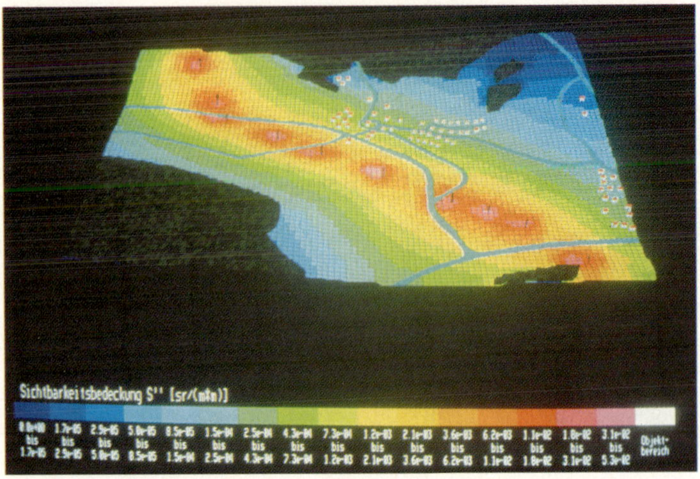

Figure 83:
Distribution of the specific visibility for variant 2

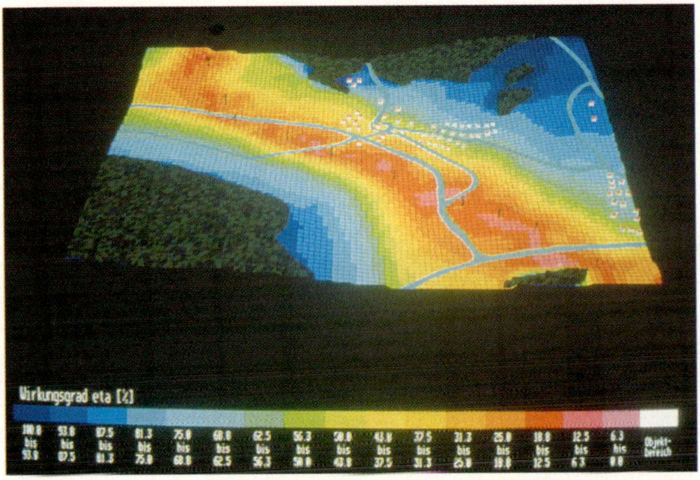

Figure 84:
Distribution of the efficiency of camouflage for variant 2

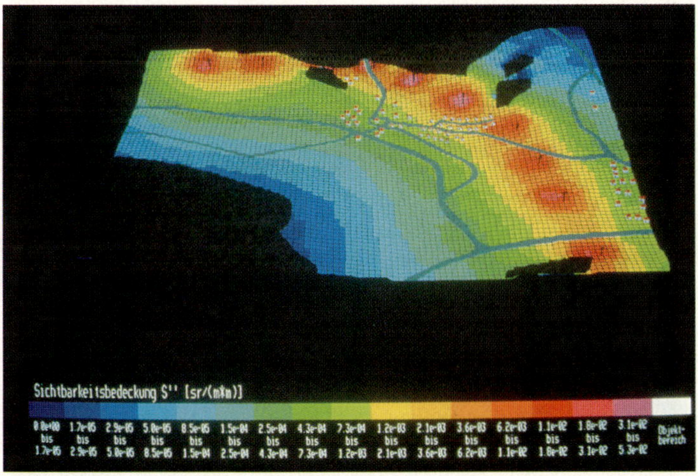

Figure 85:
Distribution of the specific visibility for variant 3

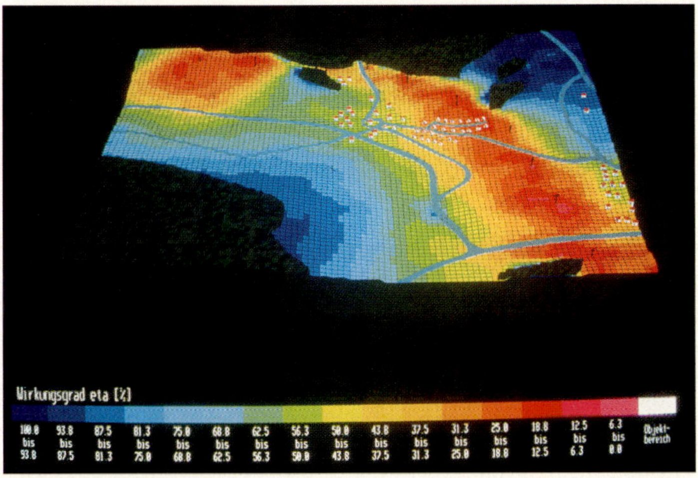

Figure 86:
Distribution of the efficiency of camouflage for variant 3

4.3. Interactive Visualization and Simulation

4.3.1. Introductory Remarks

During the last decade, scientific visualization has emerged as an increasingly important subfield of computer graphics. It can be described using the classical definition of [171]:

> Visualization is a method of computing. It transforms the symbolic into the geometric, enabling researchers to observe their simulations and computations. Visualization offers a method for seeing the unseen. It enriches the process of scientific discovery and fosters profound and unexpected insights. In many fields it is already revolutionizing the way scientists do science.

In order to fulfill this task, so-called visualization pipelines have been proposed and general purpose toolkits such as the AVS [59] have been developed. This global concept is presented in Fig. 87. The application usually generates data in terms of measurements or numeric simulations. These thematic data sets first have to be filtered in order to be visualized. These filtering algorithms can be subsampling, interpolation, scaling, dimensionality reduction, or any other kind of processing that brings the data into an appropriate form. The visualization tools map these data onto attributed primitives such as polygons. These code the data by means of shape, color, transparency, etc. The primitives are then rendered, where shading and illumination or volume-rendering is computed. The result is displayed as a discrete image on a graphics screen and can be post processed with low-level imaging techniques (such as anti-aliasing).

With the upcoming low-cost computing and graphics power, however, research has moved away from batch-oriented processing and towards an integration of physically based modeling and visualization under real-time conditions.

It thus became necessary for the interaction cue to find a way back. The user has to have the possibility of retrieving the original data from a pixel of the displayed image. Thus, a so-called interaction pipeline has been defined, which allows the user to communicate with the image and to modify the parameters of a simulation

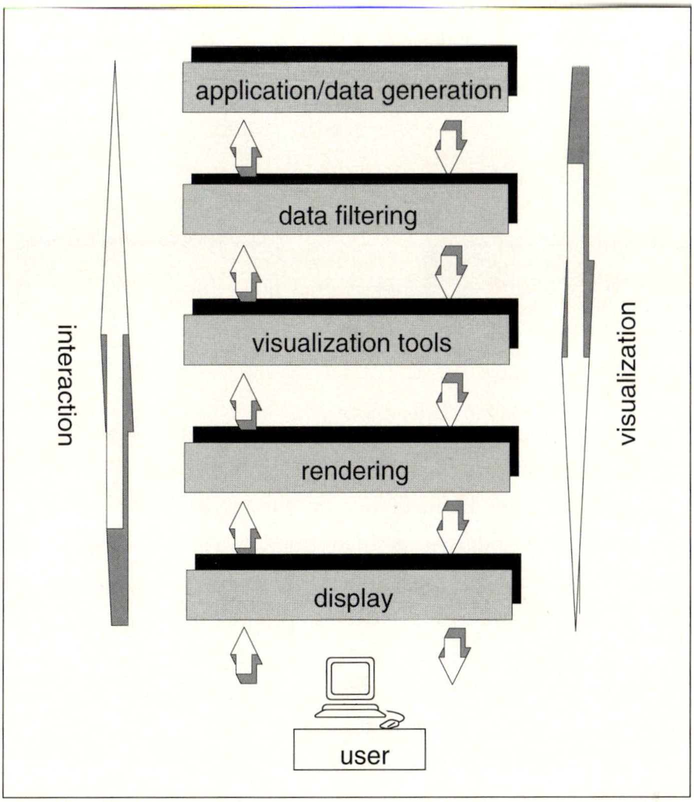

Figure 87: Visualization and interaction pipelines

process in real time, depending on the current results. This is also illustrated in the concept of Fig. 87. We can easily see that it is straightforward in relation to the ideas pointed out at the beginning of this chapter. It has to integrate *both graphics and imaging techniques* for closing the cycle and for getting images from data and backwards.

Furthermore, scientific visualization has a canonical relationship to visual perception [242]. Since data has to be presented for visual interpretation of human beings, appropriate, natural attributes have to be discovered for it. For this, perceptual aspects form one of the mainstream research lines in visualization [93].

In order to build an integrated system for environmental applications, as explained below, we had to set up a concept according to Fig. 88. The three principle components are geometric modeling, simulation, and visualization.

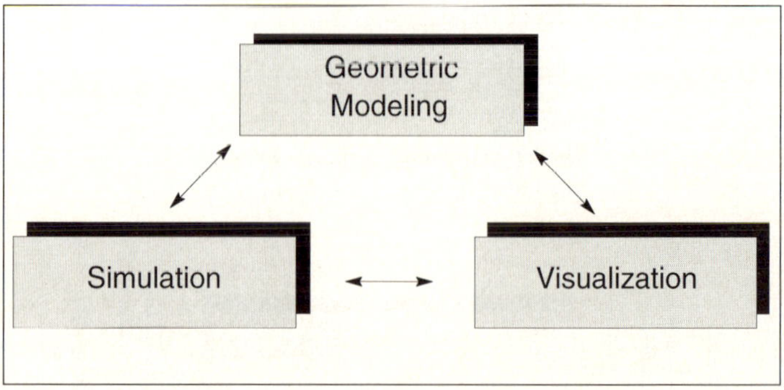

Figure 88: The three components of an advanced integrated system

The following section gives an example for this integration using one of the most striking problems we face today, namely the protection of our environment. For this purpose [92] built an interactive system for the numeric simulation and visualization of pollutant matter in the air. The basic problems and models we faced when building this system, called TERRA, are illuminated below. Moreover, it will be shown that advanced environmental information systems require *both computer graphics and imaging techniques* to increase efficiency and reliability.

First of all, the geometric modeling task had to be solved. Depending on the model employed, we have to use a digital terrain model (mesoscale) or even single buildings (microscale). These geometric models have to be attributed with the respective physical parameters for the numeric modeling, which creates the thematic data to be visualized as a 3D distribution of velocity and concentration. Thus the visualization pipeline has to be fed with both the geometric model and with results of the simulation. To achieve interactivity these channels have to be open in both directions.

4.3.2. Modeling of Wind and Air Pollution

Meteorological models of the atmosphere have a long tradition [26, 219, 169, 39]. Basically, numeric models that describe the temporal and spatial distribution of pollutant matter in the air have been introduced in different realizations in computational fluid dynamics [216]. Due to the complexity and nonlinearity of this task, most of them are linearized simplifications or represent nonlinear vortices by particular velocity distributions derived from measures in wind tunnels [218]. The computation is a two-pass process as illustrated in Fig. 89.

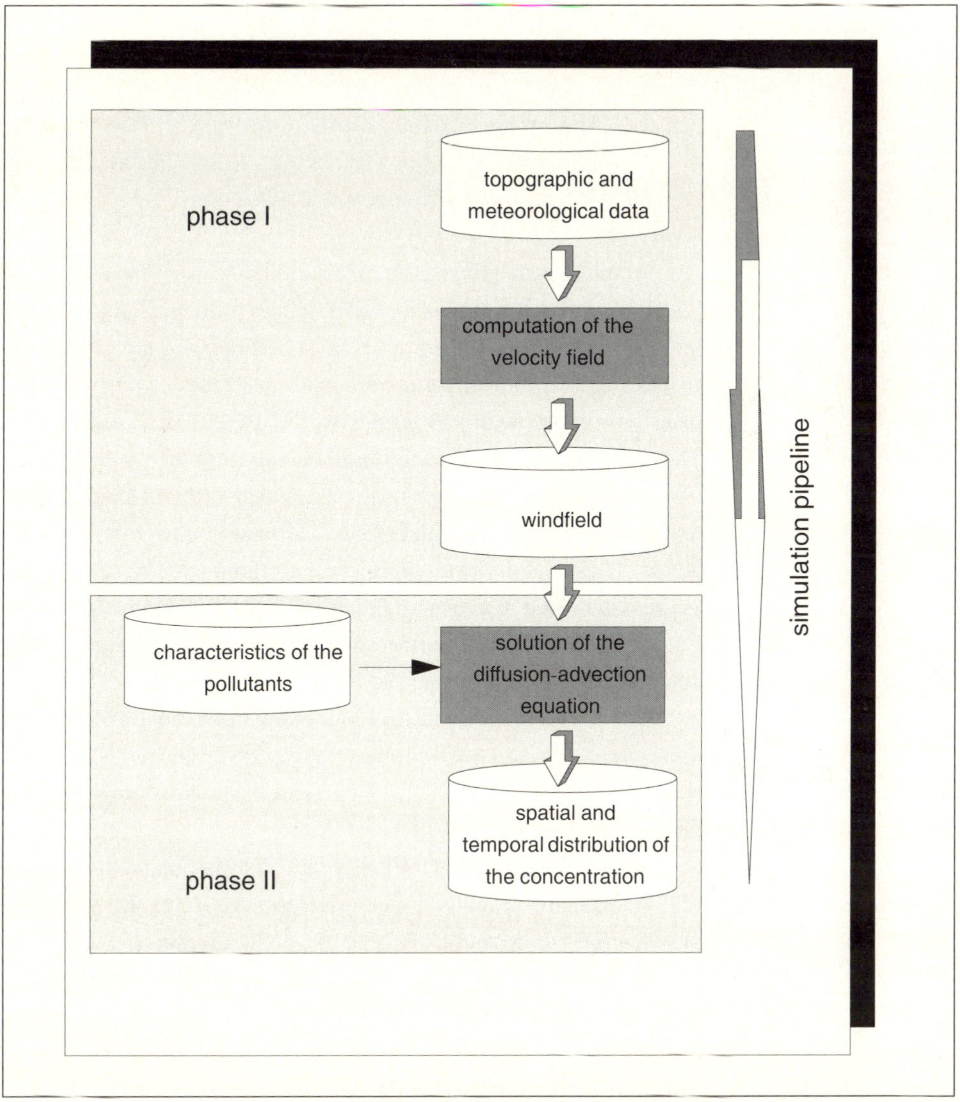

Figure 89:
Two-pass process for the simulation of air pollution

Based on geometric and meteorological input data, the velocity distribution of the wind field has to be computed. This can be accomplished using an appropriate fluid dynamics model [216] that depends strongly on the constraints of the problem to be solved. In general, one can distinguish between

I. Prognostic models, maintain impulse, energy and mass
II. Diagnostic models, maintain the mass only

With regard to the scale in which they operate, it is possible to divide them into:

I. Microscale (<2 km, gridsize 5–100 m, T<1h)
II. Mesocale (<1000 km, gridsize 2–20 km, T<1d)
III. Macroscale (>200 km, gridsize >10 km, T>1d)

A microscale diagnostic wind model is also introduced in [218]. It computes a stationary wind field as follows: First of all, the initial 3D wind field is computed by superimposing the global mesoscale meteorological parameters with distributions derived from measures of simple object primitives (boxes, etc.) in wind tunnels. These distributions take particularly into account the nonlinear vortices generated by sharp obstacles in a linear velocity field. Due to this superposition, the initial wind field is no longer free of divergence. Thus a variational approach that minimizes the divergence of the initial field in a relaxation process has to be set up. Following Eq. (65) the integral describes both the variances of the velocity components u, v and w and the local velocity gradient. These two terms are antagonistic and a local minimum has to be found. A common technique for solving these type of problems is Succession-Over-Relaxtion (SOR), which is well known from computational fluid dynamics [216].

Figure 91 shows a 3D velocity field distribution on the campus of a large chemical industry plant in Germany. In this case we suppose the field to be stationary over the simulation time.

Once the underlying wind field has been computed, and in accordance with the pipeline in Fig. 89, the distribution of the concentration of air pollutant has to be computed. Since it has proved to be extremely difficult to develop reliable methods [143], most common techniques are still rough simplifications with a limited reliability. In particular, chemical processes, instabilities, and complex geometries of the pollutant source give rise to unsolved problems. The numeric solution of the concentration distribution $C(x,y,z,t)$ consists of finding an approximation of the diffusion-advection equation (66).

$$F(u, v, w, u_x, v_y, w_z, \lambda) =$$

$$\iiint \left\{ \alpha_h^2(u-u^0)^2 + \alpha_h^2(v-v^0)^2 + \alpha_v^2(w-w^0)^2 + \lambda\left(\frac{\partial u}{\partial x} + \frac{\partial v}{\partial y} + \frac{\partial w}{\partial z}\right)\right\} dx\, dy\, dz \quad (65)$$

x, y, z:	*spatial coordinates*
u, v, w:	*velocity vector*
u^0, v^0, w^0:	*initial velocity*
a_h, a_v:	*control parameters*
λ:	*variation parameter*
u_x, v_y, w_z:	*characterizes the constraint* div $\mathbf{v} = 0$!

$$\frac{\partial C}{\partial t} = P - DC + \underbrace{\frac{\partial}{\partial x}(uC) + \frac{\partial}{\partial y}(vC) + \frac{\partial}{\partial z}(wC)}_{\text{advection term}} + \underbrace{\frac{\partial}{\partial x}(K_x\frac{\partial C}{\partial x}) + \frac{\partial}{\partial y}(K_y\frac{\partial C}{\partial y}) + \frac{\partial}{\partial z}(K_z\frac{\partial C}{\partial z})}_{\text{diffusion term}} \quad (66)$$

P, D:	*parameters*
K_x, K_y, K_z:	*diffusion parameters*

These approximations can be divided into basically 3 categories:

I. *Gaussian models are the simplest ones, supposing a Gaussian density distribution of the concentration. They can be analytically solved at low cost. For this reason, they are often recommended [117].*

II. *Euler models are expensive in computation time, since they provide numeric solutions on a spatially fixed grid.*

III. *Lagrange models employ spatially varying grids in terms of particles. In these approaches the particles are taken as representatives for the pollutant matter and are distributed according to the underlying velocity field and to their associated physical laws. In this way they provide a somewhat natural approximation of the equation.*

It should be stated that the implementation of particle systems is by no means trivial and the computation of particle interactions is an NP-complete problem in the general case. For these reasons, advanced implementations [144] use an octree or other data structures for efficiency. The results of a particle simulation are shown in Figs. 91–95. For animation purposes, however, simplified models can be employed, using fractal methods for cloud simulation [226].

4.3.3. Shape and Color for Visualization

For the visualization of air pollution we have to sketch both the underlying geometry and the thematic data in terms of attributes associated with it. The efficiency of sophisticated visualization techniques for environmental and atmospheric data has been shown in [119, 101, 92, 91]. The algorithms applied derive either from computational fluid dynamics or from volume rendering [170]. They can be summarized as follows:

I. *Arrows or hedge dogs representing the velocity distributions*
II. *Particle trajectories and rubber bands to trace their motion*
III. *3D-isosurface reconstructions in clouds usually based on marching cubes*
IV. *Volume ray tracing of clouds including 3D texture*
V. *Texture mappings of satellite images onto DTMS*
VI. *Pseudocolor mappings for scalar surface parameters*
VII. *Particle visualizations and animations*

Particle animations and tracings are the most important tools related to air pollution applications. The Lagrange approach determines spatial and temporal distributions of pollutant particles representing a cloud. Each particle is usually specified with four-dimensional coordinates.

For real time applications fast and efficient methods are necessary and preferable to photorealistic and expensive rendering techniques for volume data. Modern hardware rendering systems that allow the definition of such geometric primitives as 3D points or globes can support these requirements. The simulation process, however, generates the irregular spatial particle distribution that must be transformed into a regular 3D grid of concentration values.

The following simple method from [101] exemplifies the determination of a regular 3D mesh of concentration values based on the particle positions for each time step. First, a bounding box encapsulates the particle cloud. A small cube according to the required resolution represents a marching counting volume of size V_A and is shifted through the cloud according to Fig. 90.

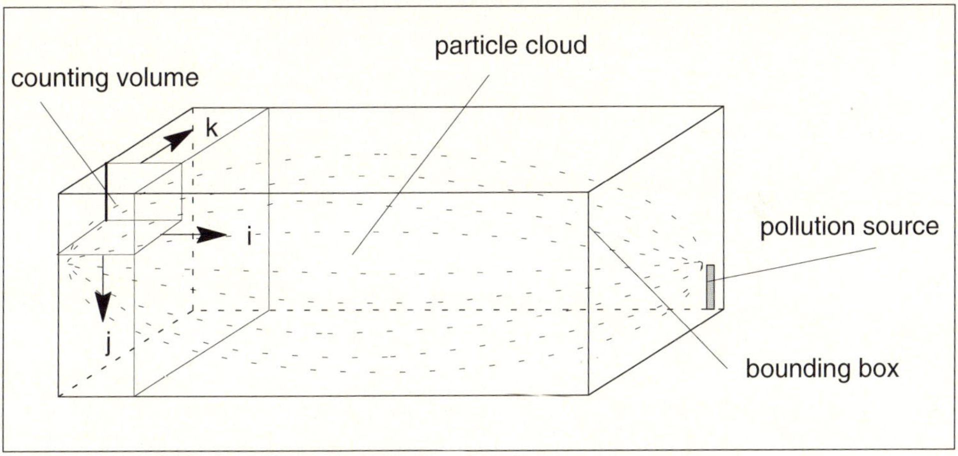

Figure 90: Scheme for the computation of the spatial concentration in a particle cloud [101]

The counting volume determines the concentration $C(x_i, y_j, z_k)$ at the spatial position (x_i, y_j, z_k) in a regular grid by adding up every enclosed particle. The mesh size is given by a bounding box and from the volume V_A. The concentration is obtained according to Eq. (67):

$$C(x_i, y_j, z_k) = \frac{N(x_i, y_j, z_k)}{V_A} \qquad (67)$$

$N(x_i,y_j,z_k)$: *number of enclosed particles*
V_A: *counting volume*

The method provides a regular 3D distribution of the concentration values that can be used as an input set for further visualization techniques. It should be noted that the above method is only an approximation of the volume density. More complex algorithms might integrate the time for each particle to remain in the counting box.

4.3.4. Examples

The following figures show the results of the application of the microscale wind model in [218] on a simulated accident in a large chemical industry plant. In this case study, a 100 kg of a poisonous gas was spontaneously emitted from a pipeline and observed for 10 minutes. The computation grid size was 5 m x 5 m at a total campus length of 360 m x 550 m, and the vertical resolution was shifted exponentially. The buildings were simplified and associated with their velocity distributions derived from a wind tunnel. The goal was to discover how the safety of the employees could be ensured and how the nonlinearities influenced the distribution.

Figure 91 shows one slice of the velocity field presented by colored arrows. The color indicates the absolute value of the velocity. In particular the vortices behind large buildings can be realized. Figs. 92, 93, and 94 illustrate the concentration of the gas close to the ground after 20 sec, 5 min, and 10 min respectively. For this reason, the 3D distribution calculated with this method was sliced horizontally and mapped as a pseudocolor on the ground. It is easy to recognize the local maxima in the concentration where the gas is captured in local vortices and may lead to dangerous situations for employees.

Finally, Fig. 95 illustrates the particle cloud after 10 min, where the color of each particle stands for the local concentration in the cloud.

4.3.5. The Need for Advanced Imaging Methods

In the previous section we have seen how advanced physically based models can help to solve complex problems in industrial applica tions. Aside from the request for interactive simulation, there still remains the modeling problem, which cannot be neglected when aiming at efficient and ergonomic systems. For this reason, we had to find an elegant way to recover 3D digital terrain models and 3D object geometrics without employing complex CAD systems. Furthermore, mesoscale wind field models require a detailed landcover classification. This can be accomplished by using satellite images and corresponding classification methods. Figure 97 shows the concept of a prototype system called TERRA that has been developed by [99] and [101] in order to give a vision of the next generation of integrated environmental information systems.

The goal was to *integrate computer graphics, imaging, and numeric modeling methods* for a highly interactively and user-friendly environmental simulation system. The input data, such as DTM, satellite images, external CAD models, and meteorological data, are derived from an external data base. An interactive scene editor allows a composition of the scene based on a Gauss–Krüger coordinate system. The model for image classification provides numerous mathematical methods for the automatic segmentation of different ground types in the remotely sensed images. By means of computer vision methods we achieve a recovery of 3D geometry from stereoscopic images as far as it was not presented in the data base. This is particularly interesting for DTM reconstructions and was also proposed by several other authors (see Chap. 5).

Once the geometry of the scene to be analyzed is composed and all physical attributes are set, the described two-pass modeling process can be performed and the results can be fed into the visualization pipeline. The whole system runs under an X/MOTIF user interface (Fig. 96). In particular, extensions have been implemented that allow 3D selection and manipulation of the visualized results. With these features it is possible to interact with the simulation and to modify the respective input parameters depending on the current results of the model. The time-consuming simulation process can be run on a supercomputer and connected via inter-process communication (TCP/IP) to the system.

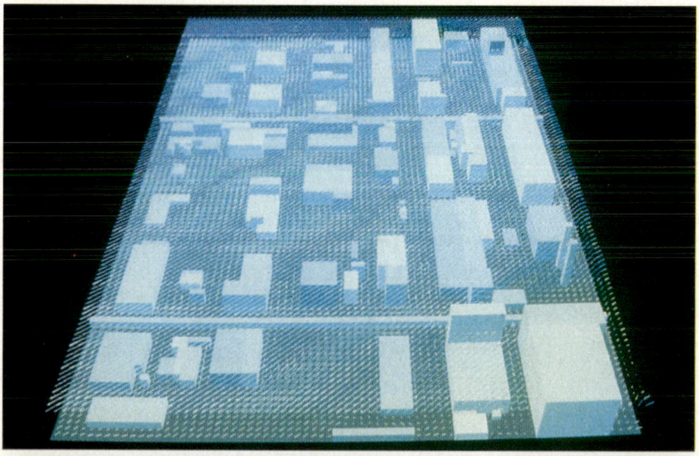

Figure 91: One horizontal slice of a 3D velocity field in a chemical industry campus

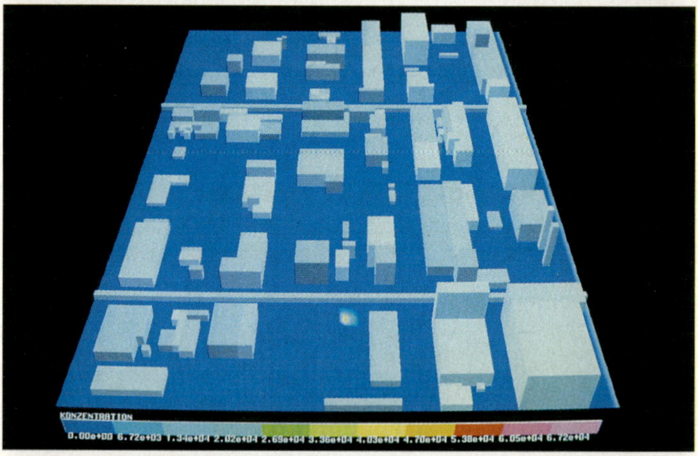

Figure 92: Distribution of the gas concentration 20 sec after the explosion of a pipeline

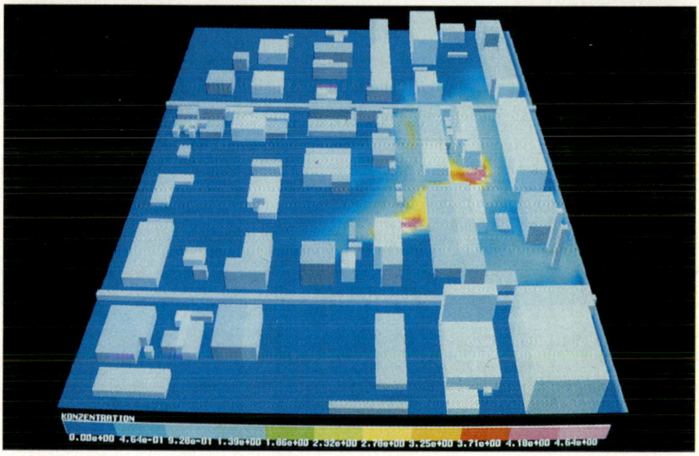

Figure 93: Distribution of the gas concentration 5 min after the explosion of a pipeline

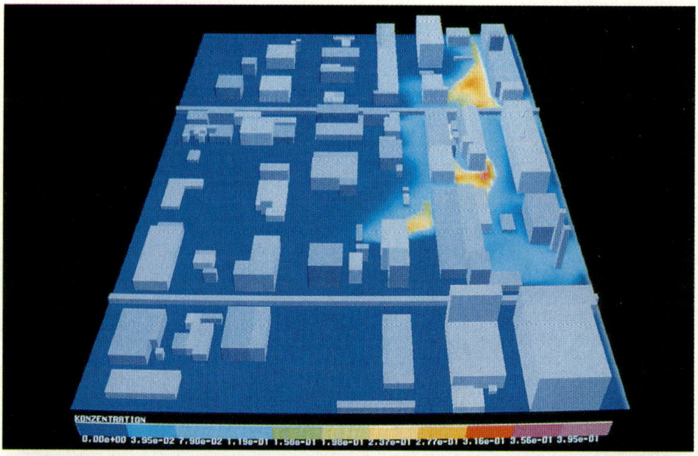

Figure 94: Distribution of the gas concentration 10 min after the explosion of a pipeline

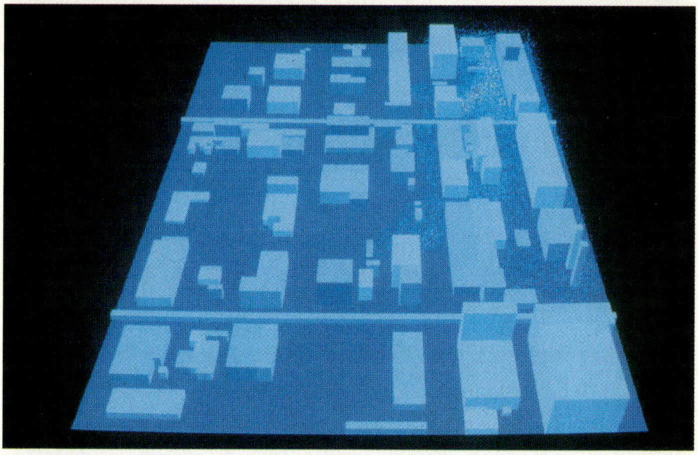

Figure 95: Particle cloud after 10 min

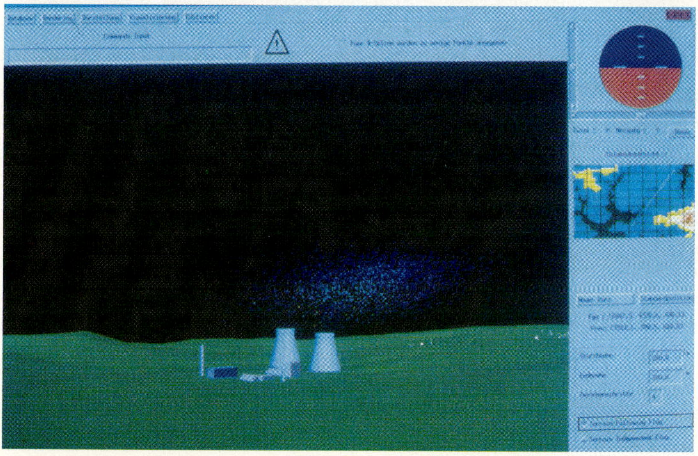

Figure 96: X/Motif user interface of the TERRA prototype

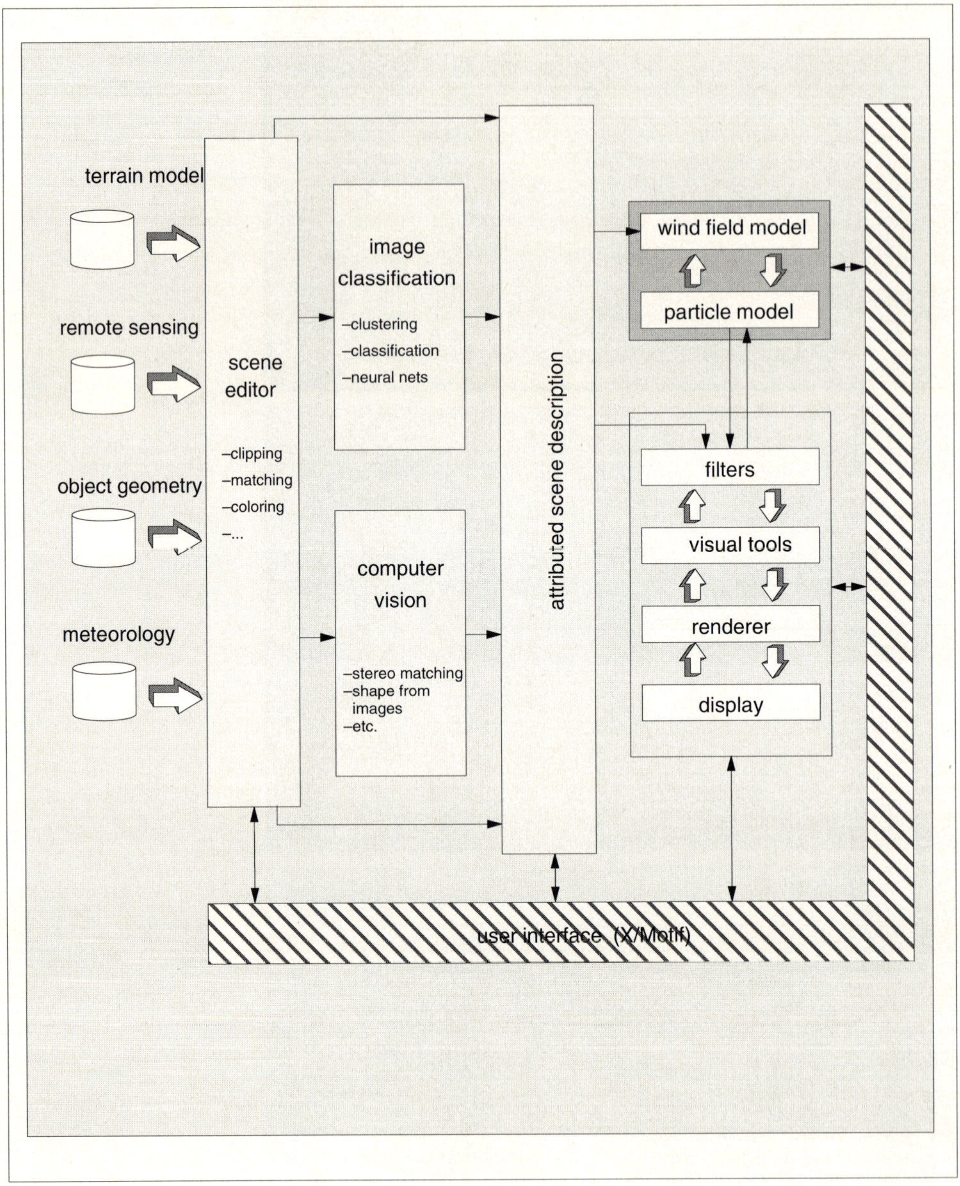

Figure 97:
Concept of an advanced environmental information system (from [99])

This application has shown that we have to employ *both computer graphics and imaging* methods to build advanced systems for the solution of complex problems. In particular, efficiency and interactivity can be achieved or increased leading to a reduction of the operating costs.

We have seen in particular that TERRA requires two categories of imaging methods, namely:

I. *classification methods*
II. *computer vision methods*

For this reason, the following chapters give a detailed algorithmic insight into these topics using some popular examples. Aside from the natural relationship of human vision and visualization [242], there is also a deep connection between computational vision and classification, and human perceptual features. Since we know that these tasks are done so perfectly by the brain, most computerized techniques try to benefit from human vision.

In this spirit TERRA exemplifies the thoughts and models explained in Chap. 1, namely, *it integrates graphics, imaging and human vision for an advanced industrial application.*

5. Computational Vision

5.1. Introduction: The Marr Paradigm

In the previous chapter we have seen that the automatic recovery of 3D objects and shapes from images can be used as a sophisticated way to solve modeling problems in computer graphics. The associated subfield of imaging dealing with this topic is called *computer vision*. During the last two decades many efforts have been made in this area and plenty of surveys have been published [8, 122, 165]. Aside from the classical approaches that derive from photogrammetry [152], most techniques try to model one of the human visual channels, namely

- *Stereo matching*
- *Shape from shading*
- *Shape from texture*
- *Shape from motion*
- *Shape from focus*
- *etc.*

The late David Marr from MIT [165] did basic work in this area. He was the first to present a unified model for human vision, in which he tried to integrate different visual modules, each representing one particular feature. He proposed what is now called the ***Marr paradigm*** based on a 3-pass imaging pipeline as illustrated in Fig. 98.

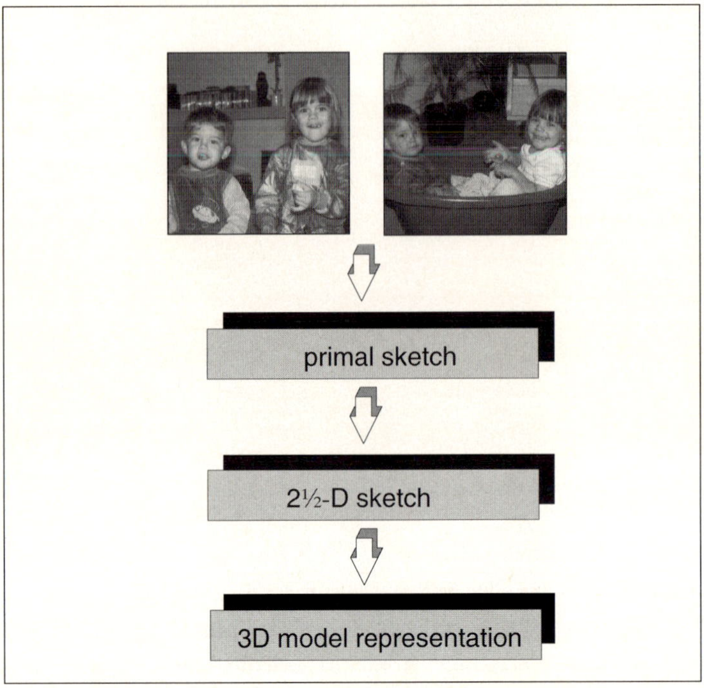

Figure 98: Illustration of the Marr paradigm

This framework divides the derivation of shape information from images into three representational steps:

I. *The* ***primal sketch*** *makes explicit basic properties of the 2D geometry and its organization. This can be accomplished by means of zero-crossings, edge segments, groups, boundaries, etc.*

II. *The* ***2½ D-sketch*** *renders a representation of properties of visible surfaces of objects in a viewer-centered coordinate system, such as depth and surface orientation, distance from the viewer, discontinuities, surface reflection, etc. The associated primitives are given with surface orientation, depth, discontinuity, and others.*

III. *Finally, the* ***3D model representation*** *gives an object-oriented view of the 3D structure as well as the organization of the viewed shape using a hierarchical representation that includes both surface and volume primitives. All information is then presented in an object-centered coordinate system.*

Thus the recognition path of Fig. 98 successively transforms observer-dependent intensity information into an independent symbolic hierarchy that describes the scene. Recent attempts [8] tried to extend this early paradigm to achieve a more homogenous model and to take into account the developments of the last decade.

The goal of this chapter is to give an insight into the field of computer vision in terms of selected methods which exemplify the problems to be faced. Fundamental techniques are presented, such as edge detection and early visual modeling or stereo matching, and also emphasis is given to recently exploited methods as wavelet transforms and laser rangefinding. On account of its novelty and the promising results so far, special emphasis will be placed on the wavelet transform, which will be illuminated in detail. In particular, we have to keep in mind that all these approaches aim at modeling basic properties of human vision and that they support the proposed integration.

5.2. Early Visual Processing

5.2.1. Basics

The primal sketch that gives a first rough representation of significant image features is often modeled by edge detection [166]. In imaging, edge detection itself plays an important role [80] and the development of robust edge detectors can prove to be extremely difficult [41]. Although there have been more advanced versions, the Marr–Hildreth approach described below is still of fundamental importance and often employed to describe early visual processing.

A common type of basic linear model that can be used on top of it is presented in Fig. 99.

This linear system is based on the ideas of [102] and models the response of retinal ganglion cells by Laplace–Gaussians and the anisotropic simple cells of the visual cortex using Fourier transforms. Operating on a discrete R, G, B image, the concept consists of three components:

I. Retinal processing
II. Cortical processing
III. Specific image analysis

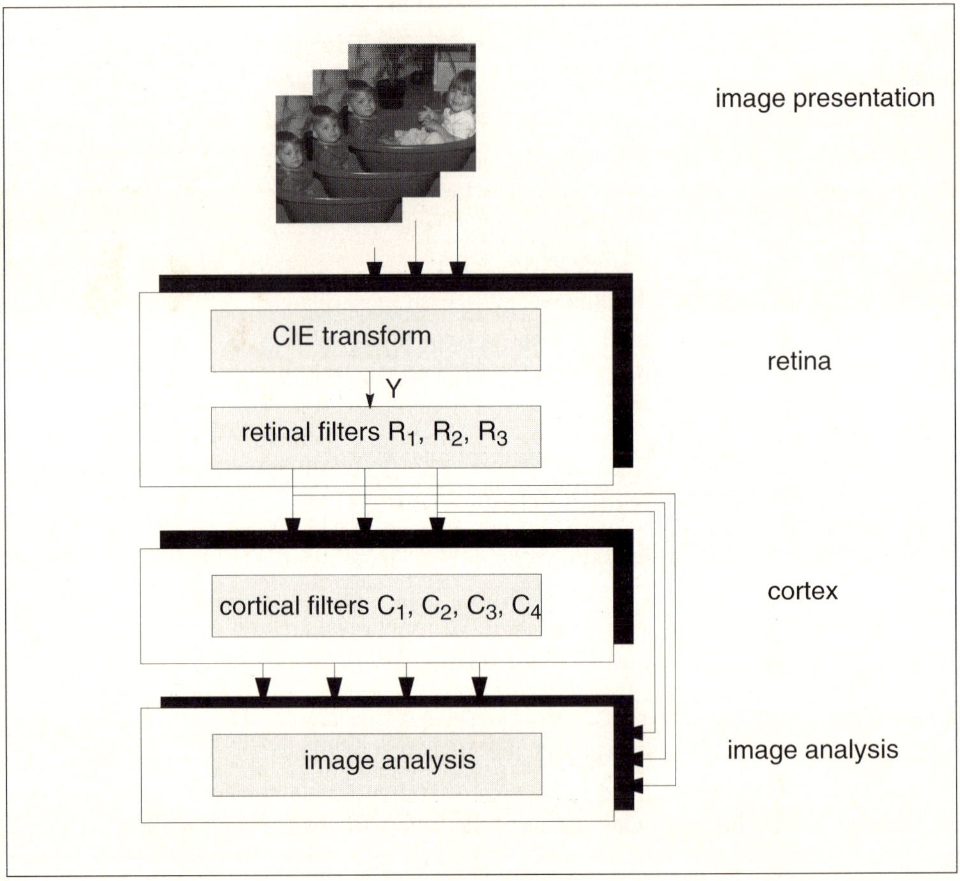

Figure 99: A model for early visual processing using linear filters [102]

How color information is processed in the cortex is still largely unknown, as opposed to the case for the retina (see also Chap. 3). Thus the model presented here is limited to grey-level descriptions of the initial image which then is evaluated.

Usually the image is presented in terms of a spatially discrete set of color values R, G, B that have first to be transformed into the CIE primary system. After extracting the luminances, the isotropic receptive fields of retinal ganglion cells are modeled by a set of K different Laplace–Gaussian functions. The resulting image description is given by $\{R_k(i,j)\}_{k=1..K}$.

As described in Chap. 3, the simple cells of the visual cortex carry out an anisotropic filtering to select edges of different orientations in the image. This can be achieved by simple linear filters in the Fourier domain and results in the descriptions $\{C_l(i,j)\}_{l=1..L}$ for each orientation and spatial frequency range in the image. In the past various filter types were proposed but the Gabor function and Morlet wavelets have been confirmed as the most appropriate ones [107] (see also Sect. 5.3).

[102] proposed an application of the explained model in the field of visibility analysis in the sense of an extension of the methods illustrated in Chap. 4.

5.2.2. Modeling Retinal Image Processing

We recall from Chap. 3 that the receptive fields of retinal ganglion cells are isotropic. A stimulation of the center of a neuron inhibits the periphery. The lateral inhibition increases the resolution of the stimulus. This behavior is again illustrated in Fig. 100.

Figure 100: Receptive field of a retinal ganglion cell and the activity profile

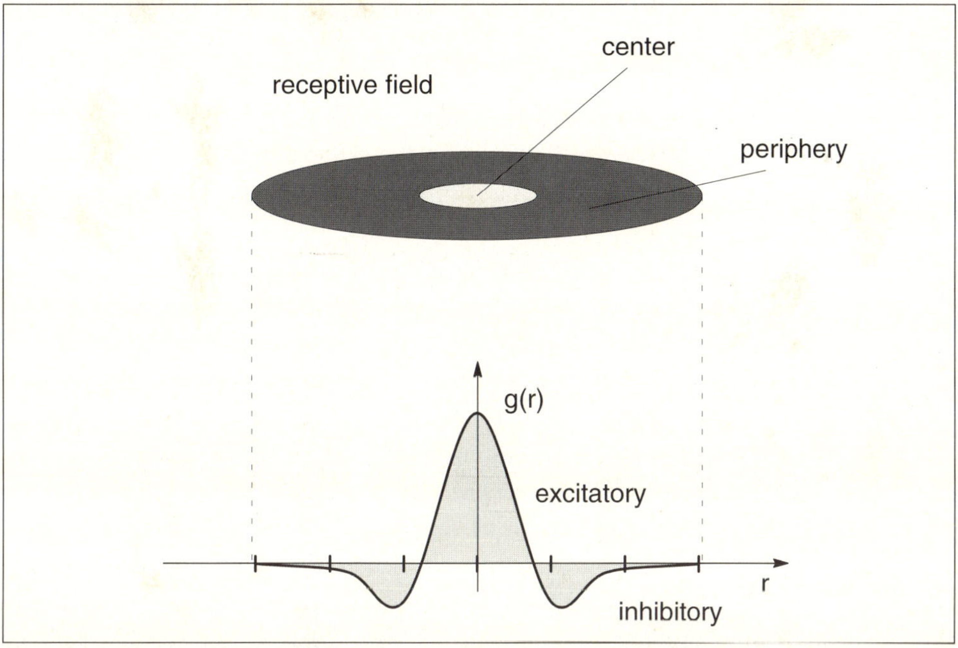

The procedure can be interpreted as a band-pass-filtering of the image that finally leads to edge detection, where among the countless strategies the most popular ones are the Marr–Hildreth [165] operator and the Canny edge detector [41]. Due to the low complexity of the first one and due to its close relation to the biological model above, the following section describes the Marr–Hildreth or LOG primal sketch operator.

Investigating stereo vision (see Sect. 5.2) Marr and Poggio [167] found that the constraints to be introduced to solve the stereo correspondence problem are the *uniqueness constraint* and the *continuity constraint.* The first one says that each image pixel can only have one corresponding point in 3D at a time. The second one expresses that real world objects are usually opaque and continuous in their shape, and that the depth function describing the object is continuous in between the boundaries of the object. Due to this, the continuous approximation is reliable for most problems. But the image intensity itself is not a reliable basis for the matching process. Along these lines, they had to find a more abstract coded description, a primal sketch of the scene (see Fig. 98) where all necessary information, such as position or size, is encoded. Instead of immediately using the intensities the idea was to apply some linear operations and to use the first and second order derivatives from the image intensity function.

Figure 101 illustrates this principle for a one-dimensional example. A change in an intensity function can be detected by the first order derivative. In order to locate the corresponding edge, the maximum of the first derivative has to be found. This maximum corresponds to a zero-crossing of the second order derivative. Thus the zero-crossing of the second order derivative is a measure for a local maximum change of the intensity, i.e., an edge of an object. But unfortunately, due to distortions arising from noise or others, the intensity changes are by no means as smooth as shown in Fig. 101a,b,c.

In a way, the high-pass characteristics of the derivatives ripple the function as illustrated in Fig. 101d,e,f. We now obtain a large number of zero-crossings that no longer deliver reliable estimations of the edge. This is the reason why it is necessary to smooth the intensity function before calculating the second derivative. Smoothing itself can be achieved in many ways, but the easiest method is to apply a low-pass filter. The resulting combination of low-pass and high-pass filters results in a band-pass filtering operation on the image. Such a filter only extracts a certain frequency range depend-

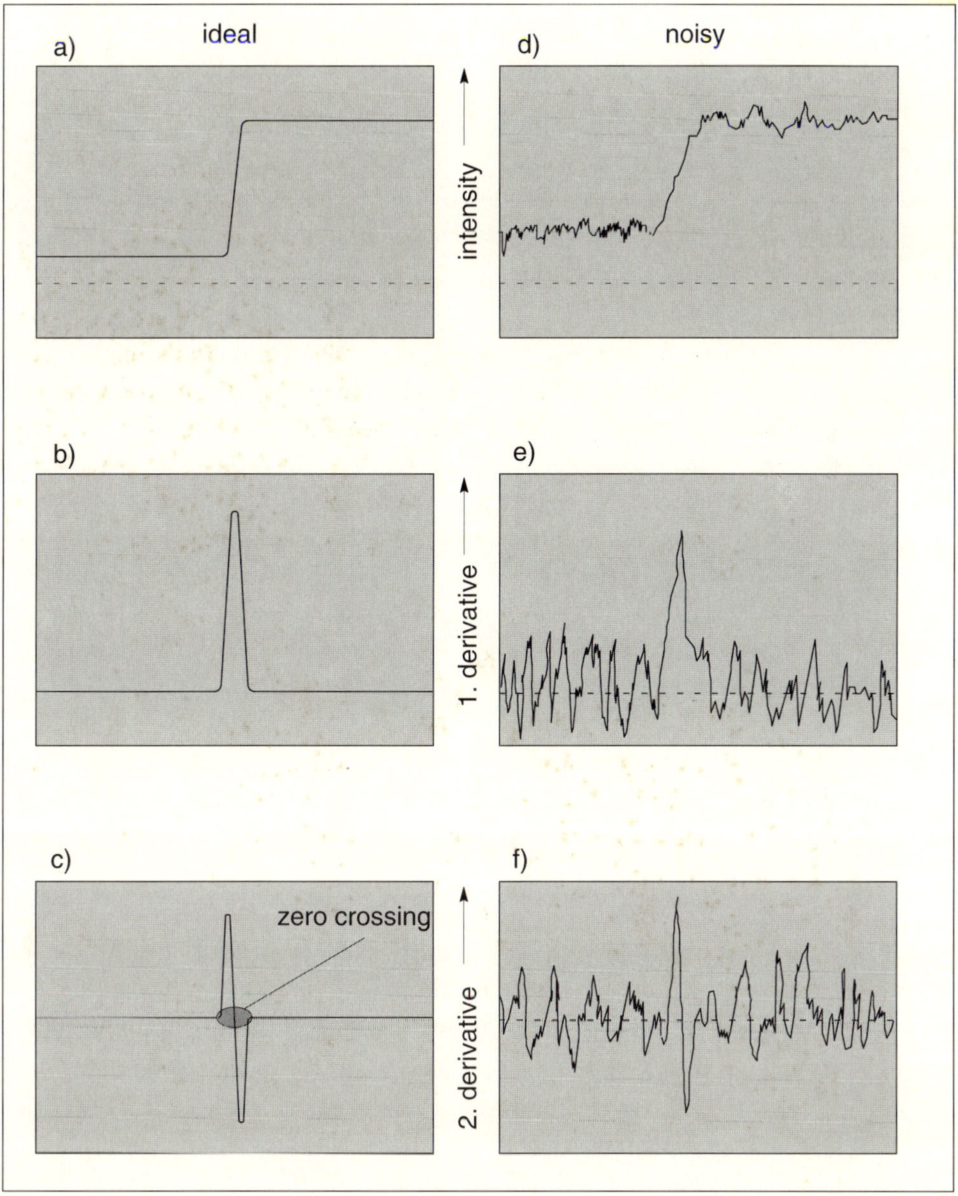

Figure 101:

a),b),c) Detection of an edge by means of a second order derivative of the image intensity function

d),e),f) Effect of noise and distortions for the edge detection using a second order derivative ing on the parameters of the low- and high-pass filters (see also Figs. 102–106).

Marr and Hildreth proposed the operator below which can be determined by taking a 2D Gaussian as in Eq. (68)

$$g(r) = \sigma^2 e^{-\frac{r^2}{2\sigma^2}} \tag{68}$$

σ: *variance of the Gaussian*

and defining the central panel width ω_{2D} as

$$\omega_{2D} = 2\sqrt{2}\sigma \tag{69}$$

The second derivative of the Gaussian can be accomplished by the Laplace operator ∇^2:

$$\nabla^2 = \frac{\partial^2}{\partial x^2} + \frac{\partial^2}{\partial y^2} \tag{70}$$

x, y: *spatial coordinates*

and we obtain the so-called Marr–Hildreth operator as

$$\nabla^2 g(r) = \frac{(x^2 + y^2) - 2\sigma^2}{\sigma^4} e^{-\frac{x^2+y^2}{2\sigma^2}} \tag{71}$$

$$r = \sqrt{x^2 + y^2} \tag{72}$$

The impulse response function of the filter of Eq. (71) recall a *Mexican hat* with a positive center and a negative surrounding (see Fig. 108). This corresponds well to the activation profile of the receptive field of retinal ganglion cells, as in Fig. 100.

On carefully analyzing the operator, we find that it can be decomposed mainly into a difference of two Gaussian functions. This closes the cycle to Chap. 3 and to Eq. (30). The bandwidth and mean frequency of the filter are controlled by means of the parameter σ. In order to obtain several descriptions on edges resulting from intensity changes of different gradients, we are able to define several versions of the operator each extracting a certain frequency range. The implementation of the operator, can be accomplished either by a convolution of the image intensity function $i(x,y)$ with the impulse function $\nabla^2 g(x,y)$ or via Fourier transforms. Boundary problems are handled by assuming the image to be symmetrical with respect to the x- and y-axes.

As we see in Fig. 101, edge detection is a two-pass process, where we have to find the zero-crossings of the second derivative of the image. In the linear model of Fig. 99 only the first pass, namely the filtering, is used to describe the size of the receptive field by the width σ of the Gaussian. According to the theory of linear systems we obtain

$$\int_{-\infty}^{\infty}\int_{-\infty}^{\infty} i(\alpha,\beta)g(x-\alpha, y-\beta)d\alpha d\beta \qquad (73)$$

or, in discrete signals I and G:

$$\sum_{\alpha=0}^{M-1}\sum_{\beta=0}^{N-1} I(\alpha,\beta)G(i-\alpha)(j-\beta) \qquad (74)$$

with $i: 0..M-1,\ j: 0..N-1$

The ganglion cells then transmit the different image descriptions to the cortex.

The second pass of the edge detection, namely the extraction of the zero-crossings, is essential for higher-order methods such as stereo matching, and will be illuminated later.

It should be noted that there have been several attempts to implement retinal image processing with special-purpose VLSI CCD sensors.

5.2.3. Modeling Cortical Image Processing

With a view to the achieved anisotropic filter effect, the modeling of simple cells of the visual cortex can be carried out by a convolution using compass operators [128] in the spatial domain or in the frequency domain by way of Fourier transforms. The advantage of the Fourier transform is the simple application of different oriented filters via masks which improves computation time for complex operators.

The filtering in the frequency domain bases on the two-dimensional FT and can be sketched as follows:

Using the Fourier integral

$$i^F(u,v) = \int_{-\infty}^{+\infty}\int_{-\infty}^{+\infty} i(x,y)\ e^{-j(ux+vy)}dxdy \qquad (75)$$

Figure 102:
a) Input color image
b) Grey–level image

u, v: spatial frequencies

or its discrete version

Figure 103:
Results of two different Marr–Hildreth operators for edge detection and overlays with the input image

$$I^F(m,n) = \sum_{i=0}^{M-1}\sum_{j=0}^{N-1} I(i,j)\ e^{-2j\pi\left(\frac{mi}{M}+\frac{nj}{N}\right)} \qquad (76)$$

Several FFT algorithms are available for fast processing of a discrete FT which are sufficiently described in [194].

Figure 104:
Fourier transform of the image:
a) Amplitude spectrum
b) Phase spectrum

If $I^F(m,n)$ and $H^F(m,n)$ are the Fourier descriptions of an real image $I(i,j)$ and of an impulse response $H(i,j)$ of a filter then the resulting signal $C(i,j)$ is the inverse Fourier transform of the product

$$C(i,j) = FFT^{-1}\left[I^F(m,n)H^F(m,n)\right] \qquad (77)$$

Figure 105:
a) Low-pass operation in the Fourier domain
b) Resulting image

Orientation-specific edge detectors in the Fourier range can now be constructed by transforming their convolution kernels into the Fourier domain and by multiplying them with the image spectrum. Figures 102–107 illustrate the effects of Fourier-transforms, edge detectors, and different Gaussian frequency filters.

Figure 106:
a) Band-pass operation in the Fourier domain
b) Resulting image

It should be noted that a lot of effort has been spent in using oriented filters for image processing. There are numerous implementations that construct filters using more constraints than introduced here. A very promising approach for applications like compact coding or feature extraction are wavelet filters [53]. These will be described in detail later.

Another important anatomic feature of the human brain has been so far neglected: the nonlinear topological mapping of the visual information from the retina into area 17 of the cortex (see Fig. 5, Chap. 2). We remember that a large area covered by visual information is located around the fovea centralis. [76] proposes non-

Figure 102

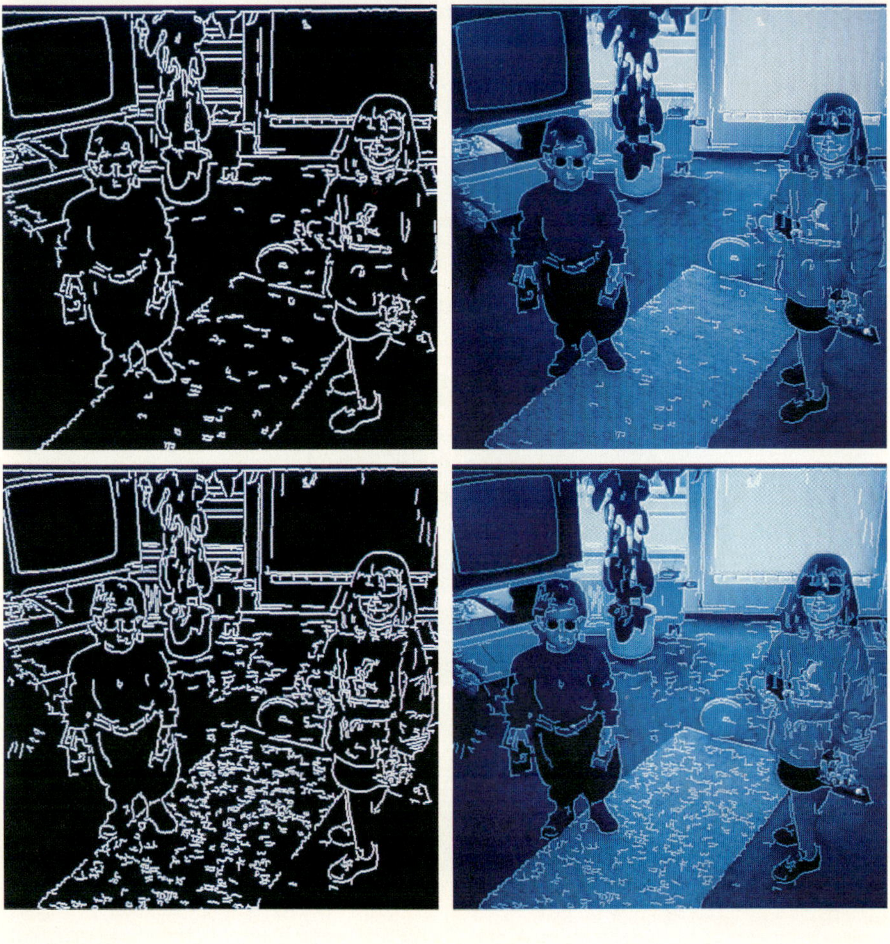

Figure 103

Figure 104

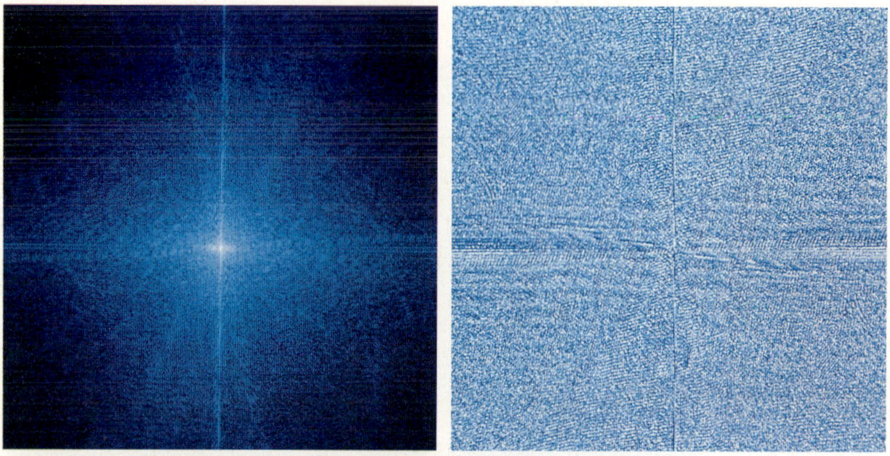

Figure 105

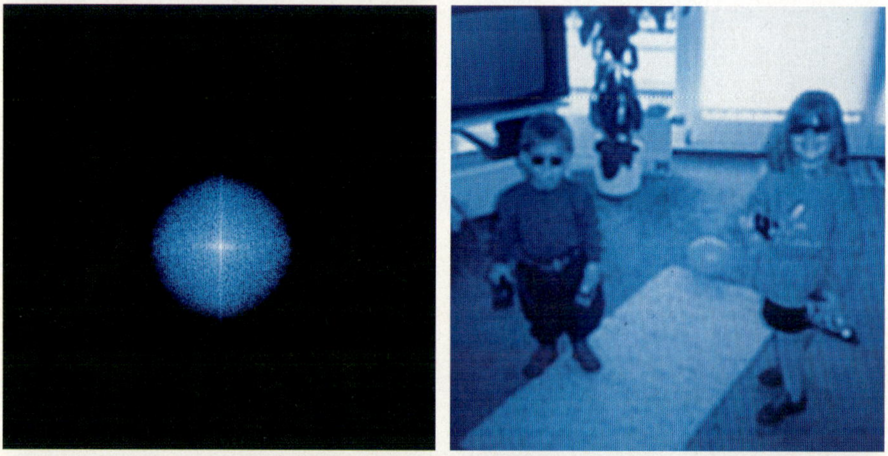

Figure 106

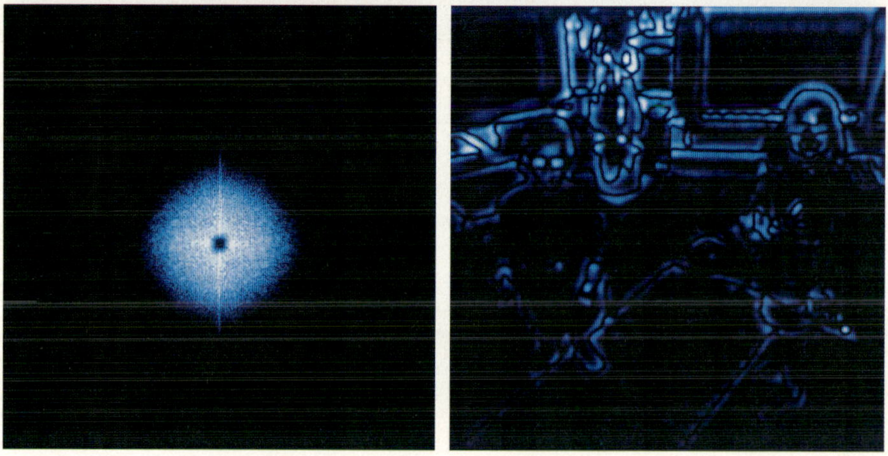

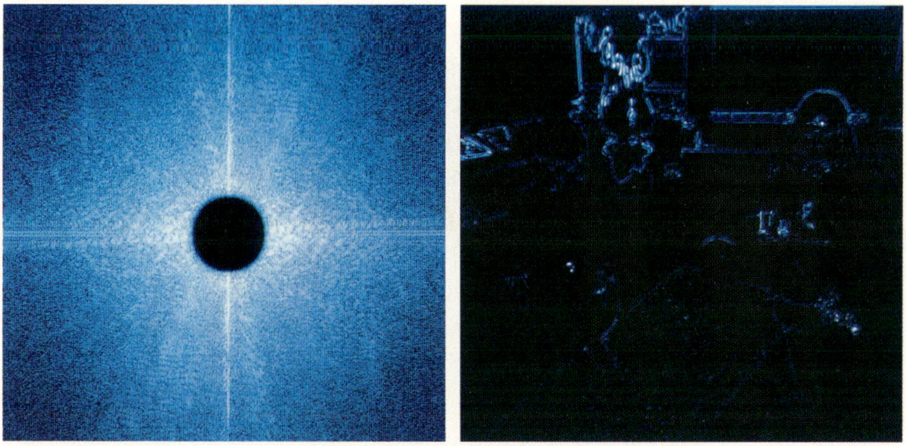

Figure 107:
a) High–pass operation in the Fourier domain
b) Resulting image

Figure 108:
Pulse-response function of the Marr–Hildreth operator

linear transforms that approximate this mapping mathematically. Other approaches use Kohonen maps as neural network implementations of this feature [76].

But apart from different ways to accomplish this, linear visual models are usually based on two types of filter banks, an isotropic one for the retina and a nonisotropic one for the cortex. The resulting descriptions can serve as a basis for further analyses, as illustrated in the following application.

5.3. Advanced Visibility Analysis for Advertising

In Chap. 4 we introduced a simple straightforward approach for the visibility analysis of objects in the landscape. This method is strictly based on psychophysical criteria combined in a heuristic approach that proved able to render robust and reliable results. For detailed investigations of optical attractiveness, for instance when analyzing advertisement plates, it is necessary to extend this method taking into account the early visual models explained above. In this sense the following application introduced by [102] illustrates how to make use of linear visual models. The method explained for visibility analysis neglects color, on the one hand, yet extends Chap. 4 in terms of texture, on the other.

The procedure presented here aims at using well known model components of the human visual system as a basis for the development of an image analysis procedure, therefore permitting the computation of optical conspicuousness in advertising. The basic idea of this procedure is to supply a geometric model of the scenery to be examined and of the target object on which the image generation is properly based. By choice of position as a second step, an image of the object and of the environment is generated by ray casting which is then further processed through filter operations. The resulting image descriptions form the basis for the analysis calculus. This presupposes a basic description of components of the human visual system and a presentation of procedures from the psychology of advertising. The image analysis procedure evaluates the image presentations appearing in the various components of the model and supplies a measure for the optical conspicuousness. However, the procedure is oriented only with physiologically proven facts. Individual interpretations and aesthetics belonging to higher mechanisms cannot be shown, of course. The described procedure is to be understood as an extension of the algorithm for the computation of the visibility of overhead lines formulated by the author [89]. It also exemplifies the spirit of this book since it integrates *graphics, imaging, and perceptual modules.*

5.3.1. The Psychology of Advertising

This section will first give a brief introduction to the background of the application, namely to perceptual aspects of advertising.

By advertising we generally mean the systematic influence of a group of people in order to induce them to behave in a certain way. The psychology of advertising is the part of applied psychology which analyzes the communication process triggered off by advertising, concentrating on experience and behavior [221]. Advertising itself is the manifestation of the phenomenon that, on the one hand, the market does not work to perfection, and on the other hand the western industrialized nations have not renounce a market economy merely because of weaknesses in the market. With the rise of advertising, price lost its central function in the regulation of market operations.

Classical rules for the design of advertising boards were thus influenced by the considerations of early theories of perception and design. One example is the AIDA–rule (**A**ttention–**I**nterest–**D**esire–**A**ction) shown in Fig. 109.

I. ***Attention*** *is created by the big fly*
II. ***Interest*** *is aroused by the headline*
III. ***Desire*** *to buy the product is brought about by statements in the text*
IV. ***Action*** *is generated by the voucher*

The process of perception [67], a central feature in the psychology of advertising, emerges from principles of design which can be divided into formal and semantic ones. Among the formal principles of design we find the separation of figure and background which has been the object of many investigations. The optical conspicuousness of an object is determined not only by its own appearance but also by the environment in which the object is placed. This formal principle of design is the subject of the following investigations.

Different processes have been developed to find out about the probabilities of perception. Aside from the methods based on quantitative examination and on gestalt theory (see also Chap. 3), tracking the eyes of test persons is used as the most reliable method.

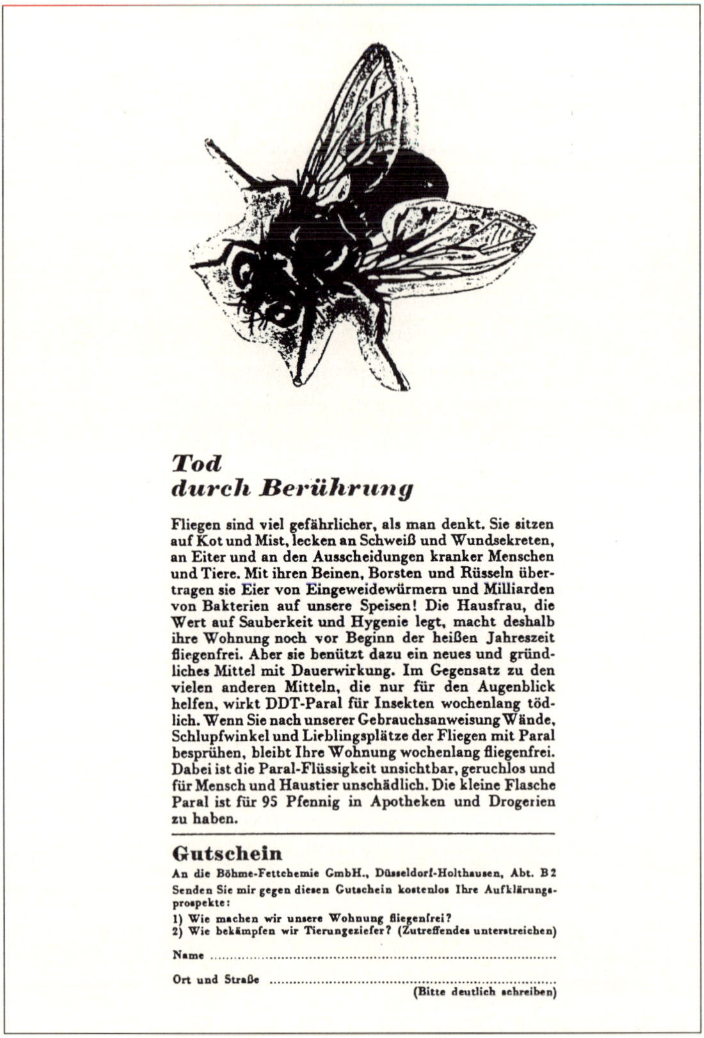

Figure 109: Example for the AIDA-rule [221]

In cyc-tracking we differentiate between fixations (0.2–0.4 sec, see Chap. 3) and saccades, i.e., fast movements of the eye between 0.03 and 0.09 sec. However, information is taken in exclusively during fixations.

In the eye-tracking method actual fixations in the image are recorded by video. Therefore, by analyzing the video tape, statements can be made on the frequency, duration, and sequence of fixations which in turn indicate the character and extent of information intake. Figure 46 shows the track of the eye while looking at an advertisement.

It must be mentioned that although the intake of information can be measured by eye-tracking, no direct conclusions can be drawn as to its processing. Yet this method is exact and reliable.

5.3.2. Analyzing Retinal and Cortical Images

On the estimation of optical attractiveness and visibility a lot of basic work has been done [129]. In particular, Julesz et al. found that statistical moments yield good descriptions for the visual perception of texture. Texture types that do not distinguish in their second order statistical moments can usually not be discriminated by human beings. Based on this work, texture analysis developed into its own separate and important field of imaging and computer graphics.

Optical conspicousness O is here defined in addition to visibility S in Chap. 4

To evaluate the optical conspicuousness of an object [102] proposes a computational object-environment analysis for individual retinal and cortical image descriptions based on the model of Fig. 111. This method also takes into account local texture properties of the object presupposing a segmentation of object and background. Following the simple model of Fig. 99 and using 3 LOGs for retinal, and 4 oriented filters for cortical processing we can formulate a scheme for the quantification of visibility. For this purpose the pixel intensities of the object and the environment are added up to I_O and I_U for each image description $R_k(i,j)$ and $C_l(i,j)$. Let the total number of pixels in the object be given P_O and of those in the environment as P_U. The optical conspicuousness O_{C_l} in the cortical channel C_l is then:

$$O_{C_l} = |I_{OC_l} - I_{UC_l}\, P_O/P_U| \qquad (78)$$

and the total optical conspicuousness O_{R_k} of retinal channels R_k is:

$$O_{R_k} = |I_{OR_k} - I_{UR_k} P_O/P_U| \qquad (79)$$

The final optical conspicuousness O is now obtained by the summation of all retinal and cortical channels:

$$O = \sum_{l=1}^{L} O_{C_l} + \sum_{k=1}^{K} O_{R_k} \qquad (80)$$

The part of the retinal image descriptions in the definition of conspicuousness is to be seen as an early stage of the image interpretation. The evaluation method is illustrated by a simple example using different texture types which assuming a disposition as shown in Fig. 111, where the structural elements of Fig. 110 are admitted for the object and the background:

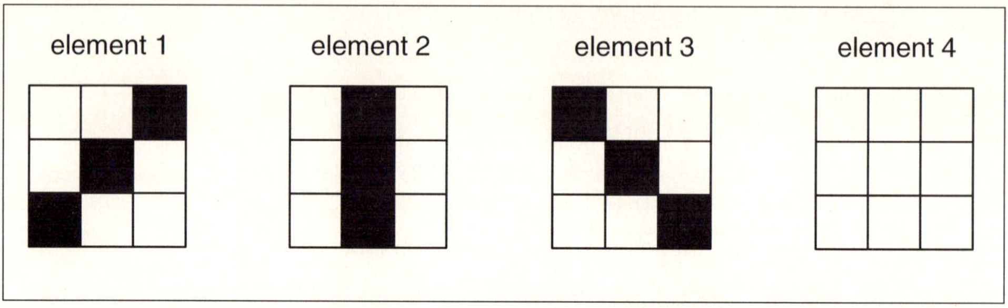

Figure 110: Structural elements to build the objects of Fig. 111

The objects shown in Fig. 111 are quadratic and consist of the 16 inner structural elements that were combined to build a specific texture type. The environment is represented by the 20 outer elements.

A simplified isotropic retinal filter can be thought as allocating the value 1 to the structural elements 1 ,..., 3 and the value 0 to the element 4. We assume, furthermore, that the three anisotropic cortical filters C_1, C_2, C_3 each have an optimal reaction to the structural elements 1, 2, 3 respectively, according to Table 5:

Table 5: Assumed output of the simplified cortical filters

cortical filter	structure element	output
C_1	1	1.0
C_1	2	0.6
C_1	3	0.3
C_2	1	0.5
C_2	2	1.0
C_2	3	0.5
C_3	1	0.3
C_3	2	0.6
C_3	3	1.0

Assuming $P_0 = 144$ pixels and $P_U = 180$ pixels the optical conspicuousness O results as indicated in Fig. 111 using the individual examples following Eq. (80).

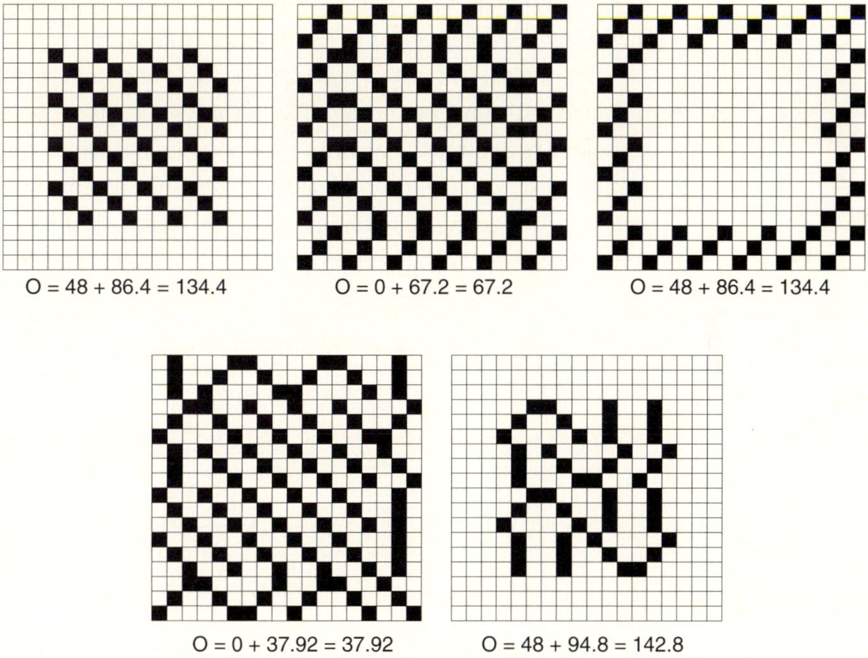

Figure 111: Simple examples of objects against various backgrounds

This simple example quantitatively confirms statements each of us may verify intuitively:

I. *The conspicuousness of a textured object against a monochrome background is greater than in a textured environment and depends on the texture parameters.*

II. *The conspicuousness remains constant if the textures of the object and of the environment are exchanged.*

III. *If one of the textures loses its characteristic orientation, changing over into a random distribution, the optical conspicuousness decreases.*

Although the proposed reaction of the simplified filters has no physical basis, the results correspond with the perceived impression.

5.3.3. Modeling via Ray Casting

As described in detail in Chap. 4, the computer implementation of these types of method employs a geometric 3D model of the scenery to be analyzed as well as an image generation via ray casting from the chosen observer position. This is shown in Fig. 80.

The 3D model is fitted with corresponding attributes such as luminance and color coordinates. The advantage of this procedure as compared to the analysis of video images lies in the parametric simulation with exact color coordinates as well as the automatic identification of object and environment pixels which form the basis for further analysis. The allocation of a pixel is simply added as a parameter to the image description.

5.3.4. Examples

This section describes the application of the presented model to real world advertising boards. For this purpose five different industry logos were generated as shown in Fig. 112. A given prerequisite was the use of a dark frame as well as the corresponding logo against a black background. The dimensions of the individual advertising boards remain the same; they differ only by the logo. The analysis was carried out for two different environments.

The simulation of Table 6 was based on the following parameters:

I. *One 3 x 3 retinal filter*
II. *4 cortical filters (horizontal, vertical, +45^0, –45^0)*
III. *Measured CIEcolor values (for instance: sky (5881, 0.315, 0.322))*
IV. *Ray cast image: 256 x 256 pixels*
V. *50 pixel environment*

The results of the visibility analysis are listed in Table 6 and can be interpreted as follows:

I. *The optical conspicuousness of all objects decreases against a structured background.*

II. The order of optical conspicuousness was shifted in favor of simple structures.

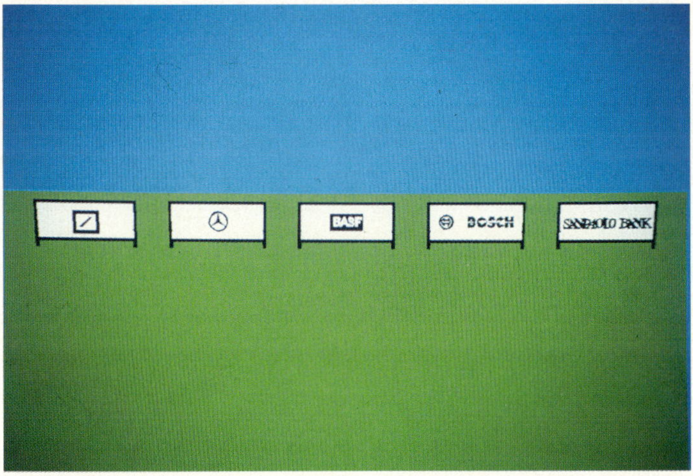

Figure 112: Environment 1: monochrome background (sky) and five boards with the respective logos. They are numbered from left to right w_1, w_2, w_3, w_4, w_5

Figure 113: Environment 2: simplified buildings of a pedestrian zone

The resulting trend confirms the qualitative statements of advertisement psychology fixing the differences in the texturing of object and background as an important measure for optical conspicuousness.

Table 6:
Results of the analysis

logo	*O* (environment 1)	*O* (environment 2)
W_1	4065	1827
W_2	3013	1619
W_3	4488	527
W_4	5257	987
W_5	5962	1966

5.4. Wavelets for Graphics and Imaging

The previous section has shown that oriented filters play an extremely important role in early visual processing and that they can be used successfully for early visual analysis. In recent years oriented filters have been used for image data coding, feature finding, and texture analysis [45, 163].

For this reason, the following section gives a detailed insight into a special type of linear transform, the wavelet transform. Since, in the two-dimensional case, the wavelet transform can be interpreted as an iterated oriented band-pass-filter, its relationship to the previous section is straightforward.

5.4.1. An Introduction to Wavelet Bases

Based on the work of [52, 107, 162] the wavelet transform has proved to be a promising approach for multiresolution data decomposition and analysis. Basically, the wavelet transform aims at analyzing and expanding a signal by means of basis functions, so-called wavelets, which are self-similar and can be derived only by scaling and translation of a prototype. In this way the wavelet transform (WT) gives a multiple view of the signal that is located both in time/ space and in frequency. This type of transform is of interest for non-stationary signals as an alternative to the classical Short-Time Fourier Transform [212] (STFT) or Gabor Transform (GT). But instead of using only a single analysis window, the wavelet transform employs short windows for high frequencies and long windows for low frequencies, which is in the spirit of the constant-quality or constant relative bandwidth analysis with bandpass filters. In this understanding, the wavelet can be interpreted as a pulse response of a band-pass filter and the transform itself can be implemented by a bank of filters that distinguish in scale and shift. Since the WT gives a multiple look on different scales, it is often referred to as a time-scale transform in signal analysis and as a space-scale transform in image analysis and vision. Although the basic idea of multiresolution signal representation was established long ago, strong unified mathematical frameworks were first provided by the above authors in the late 1980s. Due to the promising results the WT has been used in many applications, for instance in [225, 34].

There are different approaches to the wavelet formulation in the literature, and one of the mainstreams of basic research is to construct and implement wavelet bases. The WT and its mathematical description as a basis of $L^2(\mathbf{R})$, the Hilbert space of square integrable functions, and the discrete implementation of the pyramid by means of convolutions with quadrature mirror pair filters [6] can be used for the representation of data in *both computer graphics and imaging*. Therefore, 2D and 3D versions of the WT have to be constructed as in [52, 162, 180].

The following section introduces the reader to the formulation of the wavelet transform following the notations of [162], explaining the basic properties and describing the implementation of the WT. Furthermore, it elaborates on the 2D and 3D versions of the WT, as well as on nonorthogonal wavelets [107], which offer methods for modeling simple cortical neurons and therefore can be taken to characterize features in images, such as textures. Finally, applications for volume rendering and for image analysis are illustrated. Good representations of wavelet theory are provided in [212, 225, 45, 44]. Detailed mathematical analyses are given in [52, 53]. Implementations of QMF-pairs can be found in [6, 44]

5.4.2. General Description of the Continuous Wavelet Transform

In order to analyze non-stationary signals we have to find some kind of transform that gives us a sight both located in time and frequency. Unfortunately the well known Fourier transform is well located in the frequency domain but it does not provide information on time dependencies. Thus the FT is only appropriate for stationary signals $x(t)$ that can be decomposed into sine waves. In order to overcome this problem, the short-time Fourier transform (STFT) or Gabor transform has been developed as a windowed FT to give a time-frequency view of the signal. It is defined as follows:

$$STFT(\tau, f) = \int_{-\infty}^{\infty} x(t)g^*(t-\tau)e^{-j2\pi ft}dt \tag{81}$$

Where $g(t)$ is a time-limited window function. The success of the STFT depends strongly on the proper choice of $g(t)$ often taken as a Gaussian window. Due to the Heisenberg principle the lower bound of the time-frequency resolution $\Delta t\Delta f$ is given by Eq. (82)

$$\Delta t\Delta f \geq \frac{1}{4\pi} \tag{82}$$

and we have to find a trade-off between time and frequency resolution. The STFT, however, implies that one time window for the whole signal is accomplished with a fixed frequency resolution. This is illustrated in Fig. 114a.

The idea of the wavelet transform (WT) was now to overcome this resolution problem by letting Δt and Δf vary in the time-frequency plane and to obtain a multiresolution view of the signal. Therefore, we use basis functions founded on dilation and translation of only one prototype. Then the time-resolution increases with the central frequency of the corresponding filter. Supposing the relative bandwidth or "quality" Q is constant (as $Q = \Delta f/f = const.$) then the resolution cells of the analysis filters are regulary spread in a logarithmic scale or dyadic in a linear scale. This illustrated in Fig. 114b.

For low frequencies we have a high resolution in time and a low resolution in frequency and for high frequencies we have a high resolution in frequency and a low resolution in time. This corresponds to a flexible scheme. We still have to satisfy the Heisenberg principle, but the resolution products are now adaptive.

This is well suited for most real world signals consisting of high frequency components of short duration and low frequency components of long duration.

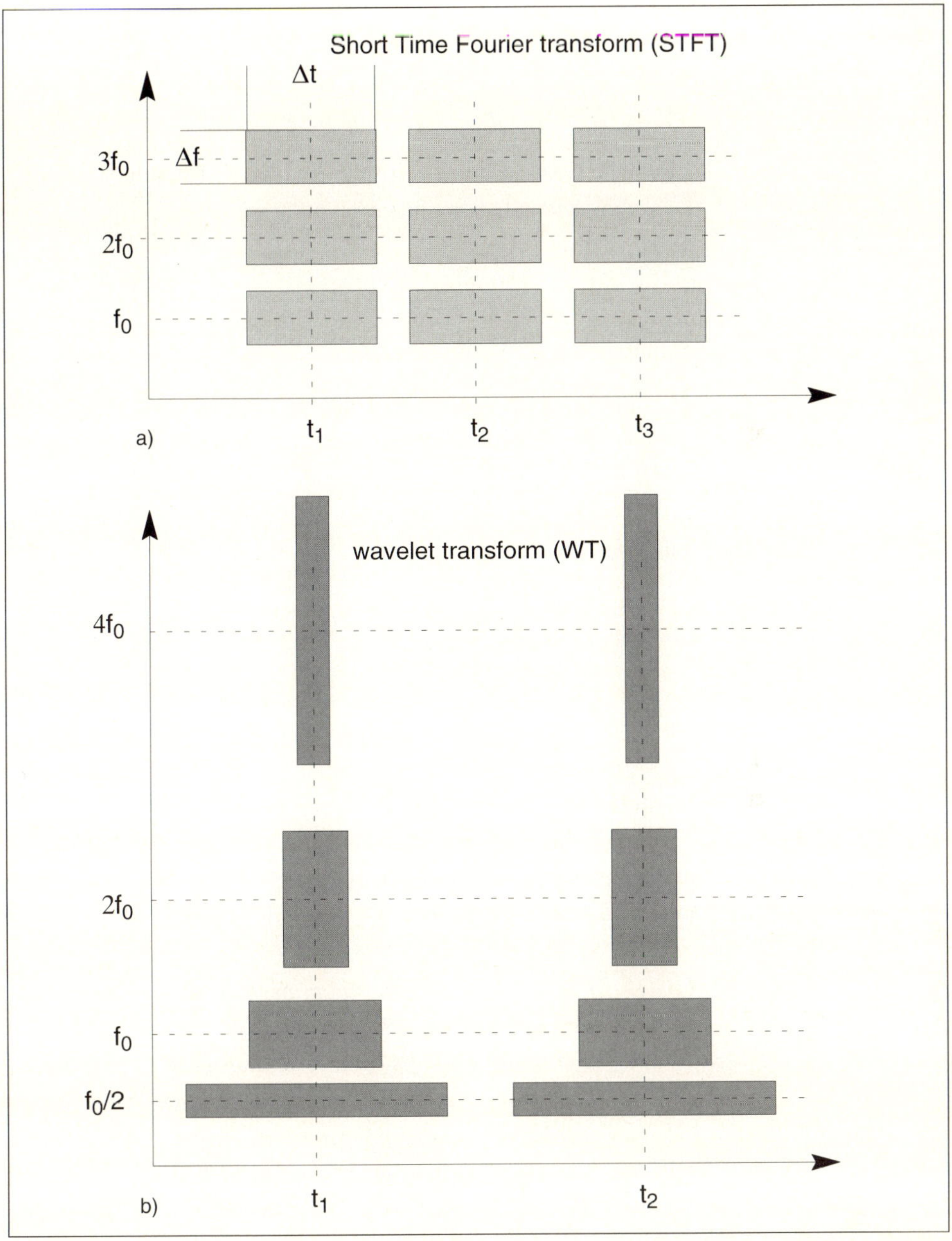

Figure 114:
Time-frequency plane and the resolution cells for a) the STFT b) the WT

The continuous wavelet transform CWT can be formulated as

$$CWT\ (\tau, a) = \frac{1}{\sqrt{|a|}} \int_{-\infty}^{\infty} x(t)\psi_{a\tau}(t)\ dt \qquad (83)$$

where the basis function $\psi_{a\tau}(t)$ can be derived from one prototype, by scaling with a factor a and translation with τ.

$$\psi_{a\tau}(t) = \frac{1}{\sqrt{|a|}}\psi\left(\frac{t-\tau}{a}\right) \qquad (84)$$

$\psi(t)$ is selected as any type of band-pass function. Since the local analysis is now limited to the scale factor a, the WT is often referred to as a time-scale (or in 2D and 3D a space-scale) transform. But to obtain optimal representations we have to find appropriate band-pass filters.

The Multiresolution Expression

Parallel to this signal analysis approach to the WT that has its origin in *constant-Q* methods, a rigorous mathematical approach has been set up by [162] and [52] that will be reviewed below.

Following the notation of [162], let $\mathbf{L}^2(\mathbf{R})$ be the vector space of measurable, square-integrable, one-dimensional functions $f(x)$. Let A_{2^j} be a linear operator with the following properties:

I. *It defines an orthonormal projection on a particular vector space* $V_{2^j} \subset \mathbf{L}^2(\mathbf{R})$. *Since* $A_{2^j}f(x)$ *describes an approximation of some* $f(x)$ *at a resolution* 2^j, V_{2^j} *can be interpreted as the set of all possible approximations at resolution* 2^j *of functions in* $\mathbf{L}^2(\mathbf{R})$.

II. *Due to the orthonormality it follows that the approximation* $A_{2^j}f(x)$ *is the most similar to* $f(x)$:

$$\forall g(x) \in V_{2^j},\ \| g(x) - f(x) \| \geq \| A_{2^j} f(x) - f(x) \| \qquad (85)$$

III. All information about a signal approximation at resolution 2^j is included in the approximation with the higher resolution 2^{j+1}. This is expressed by:

$$\forall j \in \mathbf{Z},\ V_{2^j} \subset V_{2^{j+1}} \tag{86}$$

IV. The spaces of approximated functions can be derived from one another by scaling each function according to its resolution:

$$\forall j \in \mathbf{Z}, \quad f(x) \in V_{2^j} \Leftrightarrow f(2x) \in V_{2^{j+1}} \tag{87}$$

V. The translation property can be formulated for the resolution at j=0 as follows:

$$\forall k \in \mathbf{Z},\ A_1 f_k(x) = A_1 f(x-k),\ \text{where}\ f_k(x) = f(x-k) \tag{88}$$

VI. Due to the orthonormal projections on the space V_{2^j} by the approximated signal at a resolution 2^j we can interpret the formulations

$$\lim_{j \to +\infty} V_{2^j} = \bigcup_{j=-\infty}^{+\infty} V_{2^j}\ \text{is dense in}\ \mathbf{L}^2(\mathbf{R}) \tag{89}$$

and

$$\lim_{j \to -\infty} V_{2^j} = \bigcap_{j=-\infty}^{+\infty} V_{2^j} = \{0\} \tag{90}$$

as the convergence of the approximation to the original signal with increasing resolution $\to\infty$ and the loss of any information as the resolution decreases to zero.

The set of vector spaces $(V_{2^j})_{j\in Z}$ satisfying I–VI is called a multiresolution approximation of $\boldsymbol{L}^2(\boldsymbol{R})$.

Construction of a Multiresolution Transform

The problem now is how to construct orthonormal bases of the set of multiresolution approximation spaces $(V_{2^j})_{j\in Z}$. In order to provide this, Mallat introduced the three theorems below.

Theorem 1:

Let $(V_{2^j})_{j\in Z}$ be a multiresolution approximation of $L^2(R)$. There exists a unique function $\phi(x)$ the so-called scaling function, that describes a set of self-similar functions

$$\left(\sqrt{2^{-j}}\ \phi_{2^j}\ (x - 2^{-j}n)\right)_{n\in Z} \tag{91}$$

forming an orthonormal basis of V_{2^j}. For this we set $\phi_{2^j}(x) = 2^j\phi(2^jx)$ for $j\in Z$ describing a dilation of $\phi(x)$ by 2^j. ❑

The theorem expresses that we can build an orthonormal basis of any V_{2^j} by dilating a function $\phi(x)$ with 2^j and translating the result on a grid with interval 2^{-j}. The scaling function itself cannot be derived from this theorem since different approximations can be based on different scaling functions. The constraints to specify it further are smoothness, continuous differentiability and exponential decrease. Basically $\phi(x)$ can be interpreted as a low-pass filter with special properties.

The projection V_{2^j} can be computed by decomposing the signal $f(x)$ on the orthonormal basis of Theorem 1.

$$\forall f(x) \in L^2(R),\ A_{2^j}f(x) = 2^{-j}\sum_{n=-\infty}^{+\infty}\left\langle f(u),\ \phi_{2^j}\ (u - 2^{-j}n)\right\rangle \phi_{2^j}\ (x - 2^{-j}n) \tag{92}$$

The inner product can be interpreted as a convolution product evaluated at a point $2^{-j}n$

The discrete approximation $A^d_{2^j} f$ of $f(x)$ at resolution 2^j can be written as

$$A^d_{2^j} f = \left(\left\langle f(u),\ \phi_{2^j}\ (u - 2^{-j}n)\right\rangle\right)_{n\in Z} \tag{93}$$

where < > denotes the inner product. Equation (93) has to be interpreted as a low-pass filtering of $f(x)$ followed by a uniform sampling at the rate 2^j suppressing the higher frequencies in f.

A further practical characterization of the scaling function is given by its Fourier transform with Theorem 2:

Theorem 2:

Let $\phi(x)$ be a scaling function and let H be a discrete filter with impulse response $h(n) = \langle \phi_{2^{-1}}(u), \phi(u-n) \rangle$, $n \in \mathbf{Z}$. Let $H(\omega)$ be the Fourier series defined by

$$H(\omega) = \sum_{n=-\infty}^{+\infty} h(n) e^{-in\omega} \tag{94}$$

$H(\omega)$ satisfies

$$|H(0)| = 1 \text{ and } h(n) = O(n^{-2}) \text{ at infinity} \tag{95}$$

$$|H(\omega)|^2 + |H(\omega + \pi)|^2 = 1 \tag{96}$$

Conversely let $H(\omega)$ be a Fourier series satisfying (95) and (96) and such that

$$|H(\omega)| \neq 0 \text{ for } \omega \in [0, \pi/2] \tag{97}$$

The function defined by

$$\hat{\phi}(\omega) = \prod_{p=1}^{+\infty} H(2^{-p}\omega) \tag{98}$$

is the Fourier transform of a scaling function. ❑

The filters satisfying (96) are called conjugate filters and can be found in any signal-processing literature [6]. For practical purposes one can now choose a $H(\omega)$ according to localization properties in spatial and frequency domains.

Implementation of Discrete Orthogonal Wavelet Transforms

So far, we have described a multiresolution approximation where at each resolution 2^j all the information about lower resolutions is contained. The goal is to extract the difference of information between two resolution steps 2^j and 2^{j+1} which is coded in the detail signal at resolution 2^j. This detail signal can be obtained by the orthogonal projection of the original signal on the orthogonal complement of V_{2^j} in $V_{2^{j+1}}$. Let O_{2^j} be this orthogonal complement with the properties

- O_{2^j} *is orthogonal to* V_{2^j}
- $O_{2^j} \oplus V_{2^j} = V_{2^{j+1}}$

The problem of calculating this projection is strongly related to that of finding an orthonormal basis of O_{2^j}. Corresponding to Theorem 1, Mallat shows in the following theorem that such a basis can be built by scaling and shifting one basis function $\psi(x)$.

Theorem 3:

Let $(V_{2^j})_{j \in Z}$ be a multiresolution vector space sequence, $\phi(x)$ the scaling function and $H(\omega)$ the corresponding discrete conjugate filter. Let $\psi(x)$ be a function whose Fourier transform is given by

$$\hat{\psi}(\omega) = G\left(\frac{\omega}{2}\right) \hat{\phi}\left(\frac{\omega}{2}\right) \tag{99}$$

$$\text{with} \quad G(\omega) = e^{-i\omega}\, \overline{H(\omega + \pi)}$$

Let $\psi_{2^j}(x) = 2^j \psi(2^j x)$ denote the dilation of $\psi(x)$ by 2^j. Then

$$\left(\sqrt{2^{-j}}\ \psi_{2^j}\ (x - 2^{-j}n)\right)_{n \in Z} \tag{100}$$

is an orthonormal basis of O_{2^j} and

$$\left(\sqrt{2^{-j}}\ \psi_{2^j}\ (x - 2^{-j}n)\right)_{(n,j) \in Z^2} \tag{101}$$

is an orthonormal basis of $L^2(R)$. $\psi(x)$ is called an orthogonal wavelet. ❑

The discrete detail signal at the resolution 2^j is called $D_{2^j} f$ and is computed by uniform sampling of $(f(u)*\psi_{2^j}(-u))(x)$ at the rate 2^j.

$$D_{2^j} f = ((f(u) * \psi_{2^j}(-u))(2^{-j}n))_{n \in Z} \qquad (102)$$

The wavelet $\psi(x)$ can be interpreted as a bandpass filter whose frequency bands are approximately equal to $[-2\pi, -\pi] \cup [\pi, 2\pi]$. The detail signals $D_{2^j} f$ describe $f(x)$ in the bands $[-2^{-j+1}\pi, -2^{-j}\pi] \cup [2^{-j}\pi, 2^{-j+1}\pi]$. Finally it is stated that the original measured discrete signal at resolution 1, $A^d_1 f$, is represented by

$$(A^d_{2^{-J}} f,\ (D_{2^j} f)_{-J \le j \le -1}) \qquad (103)$$

The set in (103) is the orthogonal wavelet representation. The wavelet representation can be interpreted as a decomposition of a signal in independent frequency channels giving an intermediate view located both in spatial and in frequency domains. Due to the orthogonality of the transform, the representation is compact and the overlap in the frequency domain is minimized. This is not always fulfilled when selecting nonorthogonal bases, for instance, the Morlet wavelets. Basically, (103) gives a pyramidal description of $f(x)$.

The implementation is provided by a pyramidal algorithm convolving $A^d_{2^{j+1}} f$ with two discrete filters $\overline{G}(\omega)$ and $\overline{H}(\omega)$ and subsampling to obtain $D_{2^j} f$ and $A^d_{2^j} f$ respectively. The impulse responses of $\overline{G}$ and $\overline{H}$ are related as follows:

$$g(n) = (-1)^{1-n}\, h(1-n)$$

$$\bar{g}(n) = g(-n) \qquad (104)$$

$$\bar{h}(n) = h(-n)$$

G and H are quadrature mirror filter pairs (QMF).

The whole transform is then obtained by an iterated filter bank as shown in Fig. 115 where the QMF filters are applied successively on $A^d_1 f$ followed by a subsampling of 2 for any $-J \le j \le -1$.

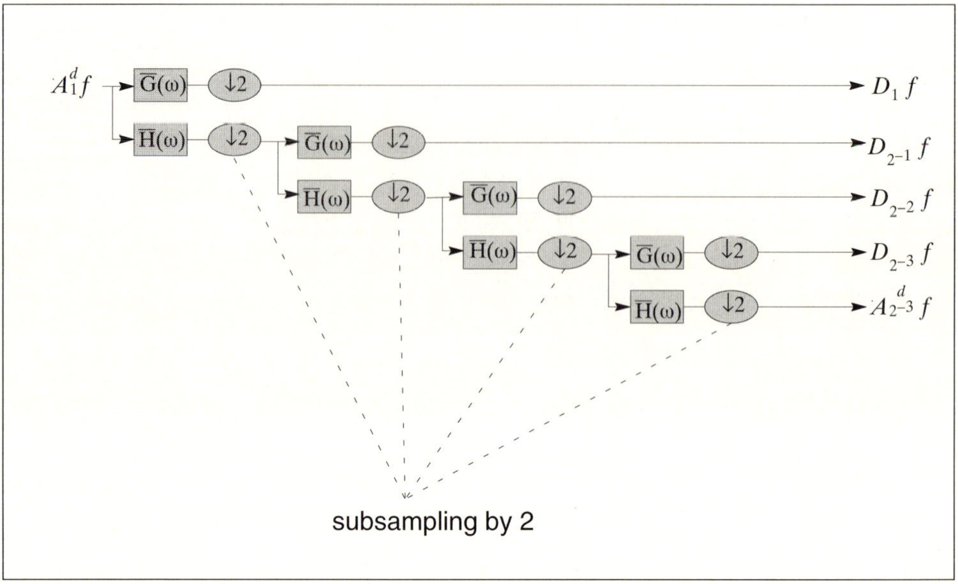

Figure 115: Decomposition of a discrete signal $A^d_1 f$ with a quadrature mirror filter pyramid to obtain the detail signals. The boxes indicate that the sequence is subsampled by the factor 2

This scheme corresponds to subband coding as stated in [212]. If the original signal has N samples, due to orthogonality, the wavelet representation

$$(A^d_{2^{-J}} f,\ (D_{2^j} f)_{-J \le j \le -1}) \qquad (105)$$

has the same total number of samples as the original approximated signal $A^d_1 f$.

Figure 115 shows that the wavelet transform of a discrete representation $A^d_1 f$ can be implemented by an iterated pyramidal filter bank using QMF pairs. Each filter step at resolution 2^j subsamples the remaining signal $A^d_{2^{j+1}} f$ by 2 and decomposes it into a difference signal $D_{2^j} f$ and a low pass signal $A^d_1 f$ which will be further processed. The process corresponds also to a pyramidal octave band splitting of the initial spectrum $F(\omega)$ using a low-pass and a band-pass filter in each step. This is illustrated in Fig. 116.

Since the wavelet representation is complete, we are able to reconstruct the original signal by upsampling and filtering. This is illustrated in Fig. 117 where the signal approximation $A^d_{2^{j+1}} f$ at resolution 2^{j+1} is implemented by upsampling (putting zeros between each sample) using the filters $H(\omega)$ and $G(\omega)$, respectively.

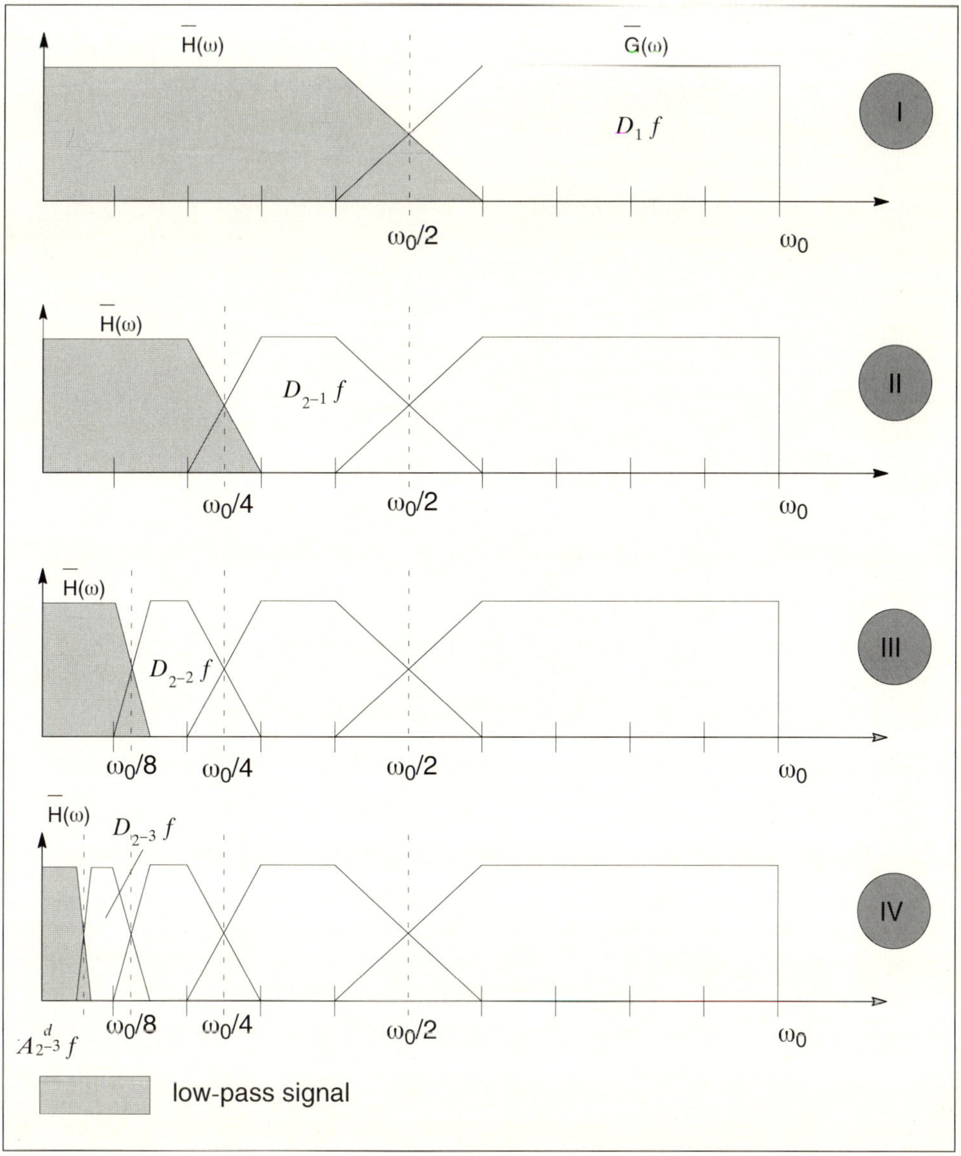

Figure 116:
Octave band splitting of a signal with a wavelet transform

The continuous form approximation $A^d_{2^{j+1}} f$ can be calculated using the approximation at resolution step $A^d_{2^j} f$ and the orthogonal projection $P_{\mathbf{O}_{2^j}} f$ onto the vector space $\mathbf{O}_{2^j}$:

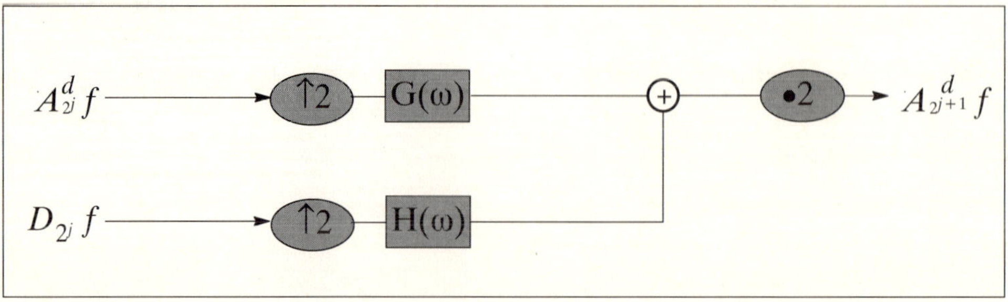

Figure 117: Reconstruction pyramid using upsampling and the filter pairs G and H respectively

$$A_{2^{j+1}} f = A_{2^j} f + P_{0_{2^j}} f$$

$$= \sum_{n=-\infty}^{\infty} (A^d_{2^j} f)_n \ \phi\ (2^j x - n) \qquad (106)$$

$$+ \sum_{n=-\infty}^{\infty} (D_{2^j} f)_n \ \psi\ (2^j x - n)$$

This equation expresses that $A^d_{2^{j+1}} f$ can be computed from its discrete low-pass function $A^d_{2^j} f$ and from the difference signal $D_{2^j} f$ using the scaling function $\phi(x)$ and the wavelet $\psi(x)$.

Resuming the statements above according to [163] the relationship between the QMF decomposition pairs G and H and their corresponding reconstruction pairs G and H can be expressed according to [199] as:

$$H(\omega) = \bar{H}(-\omega) \qquad (107)$$

$$G(\omega) - \bar{G}(-\omega) = e^{-i\omega}\ \overline{H(\omega + \pi)}$$

and the design problem reduces to:

$$|H(\omega)|^2 + |H(\omega + \pi)|^2 = 1 \qquad (108)$$

Wavelet Bases

The sections above have explained how to implement a wavelet transform by means of an iterated filter bank of QMF. The properties of the basis wavelet depend on the proper choice of the filter characteristics $H(\omega)$. In the literature there are several filters proposed for wavelet analysis. The constraints are a good location in space and frequency domain, on the one hand, and smoothness, differentiability, and exponential decay on the other hand. The following sections give examples proposed for different applications. Although all filters discussed below are given by their discrete pulse response $h(n)$, most authors use the FFT to implement the filter banks.

Mallat [163], for instance, proposes a filter for multiresolution approximations built from polynomial spines. Table 7 shows an example for a 31-tap symmetrical filter. The corresponding mirror pair $g(n)$ is also represented. This filter impulse response $h(n)$ is symmetric at $n = 0$.

Table 7: The Battle–Lemarie filter for wavelet approximation from cubic splines (from [163])

n	*h(n)*	*g(n)*
–1	0.30683	0.541736
0	0.54173	–0.30683
1	0.30683	–0.035498
2	–0.035498	0.0778079
3	–0.077807	0.0226846
4	0.022684	–0.0297468
5	0.0297468	–0.0121455
6	–0.0121455	0.0127154
7	–0.0127154	0.00614143
8	0.00614143	–0.00579932
9	0.005799	–0.00307863
10	–0.00307863	0.00274529
11	–0.00274529	0.00154624
12	0.00154624	–0.00133087
13	0.00133087	–0.000780461
14	–0.000780461	0.000655628
15	–0.000655628	0.000395934
(–16)	(0.000395934)	(0.000655628)

Another 9-tap filter was proposed in [235] and is given in [199] and specified in Table 8:

Table 8:
Filter proposed by Adelson and Simoncelli (from [199])

n	*g(n)*	*h(n)*
–4	0.02807382	0.02807382
–3	0.060944743	–0.060944743
–2	–0.073386624	–0.073386624
–1	–0.41472545	0.41472545
0	0.7973934	0.7973934
1	–0.41472545	0.41472545
2	–0.073386624	–0.073386624
3	0.060944743	–0.060944743
4	0.02807382	0.02807382

Daubechies wavelets can be constructed using the filters given in [6] that offer a large variety of one dimensional QMF-filters to be used for signal analysis. Some examples are given in Table 9.

Table 9:
Coiflet PR-QMF filters: coefficients for taps of 6, 12, 18 and 24 ([6])

n	*h(n)*	*h(n)*	*h(n)*	*h(n)*
0	0.000630961046	–0.002682418671	0.011587596739	–0.051429728471
1	–0.001152224852	0.005503126709	–0.029320137980	0.238929728471
2	–0.005194524026	0.016583560479	–0.047639590310	0.602859456942
3	0.011362459244	–0.046507764479	0.273021046535	0.272140543058
4	0.018867235378	–0.043220763560	0.574682393857	–0.051429972874
5	–0.057464234429	0.286503335274	0.294867193696	–0.011070271529
6	–0.039652648517	0.561285256870	–0.054085607092	
7	0.293667390895	0.302983571773	–0.042026480461	
8	0.553126452562	–0.050770140755	0.016744410163	
9	0.307157326198	–0.058196250762	0.003967883613	
10	–0.047112738865	0.024434094321	–0.001289203356	
11	–0.068038127051	0.011229240962	–0.000509505539	
12	0.027813640153	–0.006369601011		
13	0.017735837438	–0.001820458916		
14	–0.010756318517	0.000790205101		
15	–0.004001012886	0.000329665174		
16	0.002652665946	–0.000050192775		
17	0.000895594529	–0.000024465734		
18	–0.000416500571			
19	–0.000183829769			
20	0.000044080354			
21	0.000022082857			
22	–0.000002304942			
23	–0.000001262175			

The different properties of the filters are discussed by the authors. Thus the choice of an appropriate filter depends on the application. For visualization [180, 199] and for imaging [163] both types in Table 7 and Table 8 have been used successfully. Finally Fig. 118a illustrates the curvature of a 1D scaling function obtained by the filter of Table 9. It was constructed using cubic splines. The corresponding wavelet is shown in Fig. 118b (from [153]).

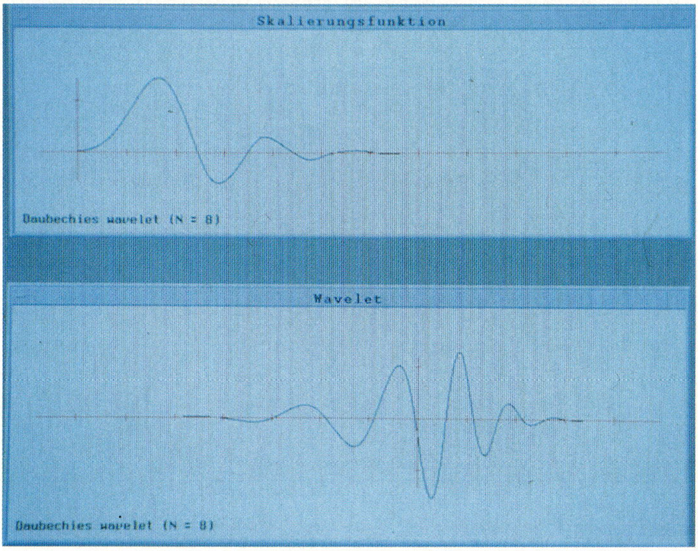

Figure 118:
a) 1D scaling function obtained from a Daubechies filter
b) Corresponding 1D wavelet

The 2D and 3D Wavelet Transform

In order to apply the wavelet transform to computer graphics and to image processing, 2D and 3D extensions of the one-dimensional version have to be found. In these cases we have to find multiresolution approximations of either $\boldsymbol{L}^2(\boldsymbol{R}^2)$ or $\boldsymbol{L}^2(\boldsymbol{R}^3)$, where the signal functions are $f(x,y) \in \boldsymbol{L}^2(\boldsymbol{R}^2)$ and $f(x,y,z) \in \boldsymbol{L}^2(\boldsymbol{R}^3)$, respectively.

In most cases separable versions of the approximations are formulated, where each vector space V_{2^j} can be decomposed as a tensor product of two identical subspaces of $\boldsymbol{L}^2(\boldsymbol{R}^2)$ or as a tensor product of three identical subspaces of $\boldsymbol{L}^2(\boldsymbol{R}^3)$.

Let us first consider the 2D case for image processing applications.

The vector space $V^2_{2^j}$ is decomposed according to (109) using the tensor products

$$V^2_{2^j} = V^1_{2^j} \otimes V^1_{2^j} \tag{109}$$

$V^2_{2^{j+1}}$ can be written as

$$V^1_{2^{j+1}} = V^1_{2^j} \oplus O^1_{2^j} \tag{110}$$

We obtain the following decomposition of $V^2_{2^{j+1}}$

$$\begin{aligned} V^2_{2^{j+1}} &= (V^1_{2^j} \oplus O^1_{2^j}) \otimes (V^1_{2^j} \oplus O^1_{2^j}) \\ &= (V^1_{2^j} \otimes V^1_{2^j}) \\ &\oplus (V^1_{2^j} \otimes O^1_{2^j}) \\ &\oplus (O^1_{2^j} \otimes V^1_{2^j}) \\ &\oplus (O^1_{2^j} \otimes O^1_{2^j}) \end{aligned} \tag{111}$$

Thus we can also define a 2D scaling function $\Phi(x,y)$ that can be written as

$$\Phi(x, y) = \phi(x)\ \phi(y) \tag{112}$$

where $\phi(x)$ is the one-dimensional scaling function of $(V^1_{2^j})_{j \subset \mathbf{Z}}$. The two-dimensional basis of O_{2^j} can now be built by using a simple extension of Theorem 3. The three wavelets

$$\begin{aligned} \Psi^1(x, y) &= \phi(x)\ \psi(y) \\ \Psi^2(x, y) &= \psi(x)\ \phi(y) \\ \Psi^3(x, y) &= \psi(x)\ \psi(y) \end{aligned} \tag{113}$$

are used to build an orthonormal basis of $L^2(R^2)$. In this separable formulation of the 2D wavelet transform special emphasis is given to the horizontal, vertical, and diagonal directions in the image. Border problems are handled by supposing the original image to be symmetric with respect to the vertical and horizontal borders.

This orthonormal basis can be written as:

$$\begin{aligned} &2^{-j}\,\Psi^1_{2^j}\,(x - 2^{-j}n, y - 2^{-j}m),\\ &2^{-j}\,\Psi^2_{2^j}\,(x - 2^{-j}n, y - 2^{-j}m), \qquad (114)\\ &2^{-j}\,\Psi^3_{2^j}\,(x - 2^{-j}n, y - 2^{-j}m)_{(j,\,n,\,m)\,\in Z^3} \end{aligned}$$

As in Fig. 115, the 2D wavelet decomposition can be implemented by a filter pyramid of two-dimensional separable QM filters. This is illustrated in Fig. 119.

Figure 119: Separable 2D filter bank that implements a 2D wavelet transform with a resolution change by 4 (2 in each direction); this cascade splits the frequency plane into four subbands for each resolution step. Low-pass signal, vertical high-pass, horizontal high-pass and low-pass

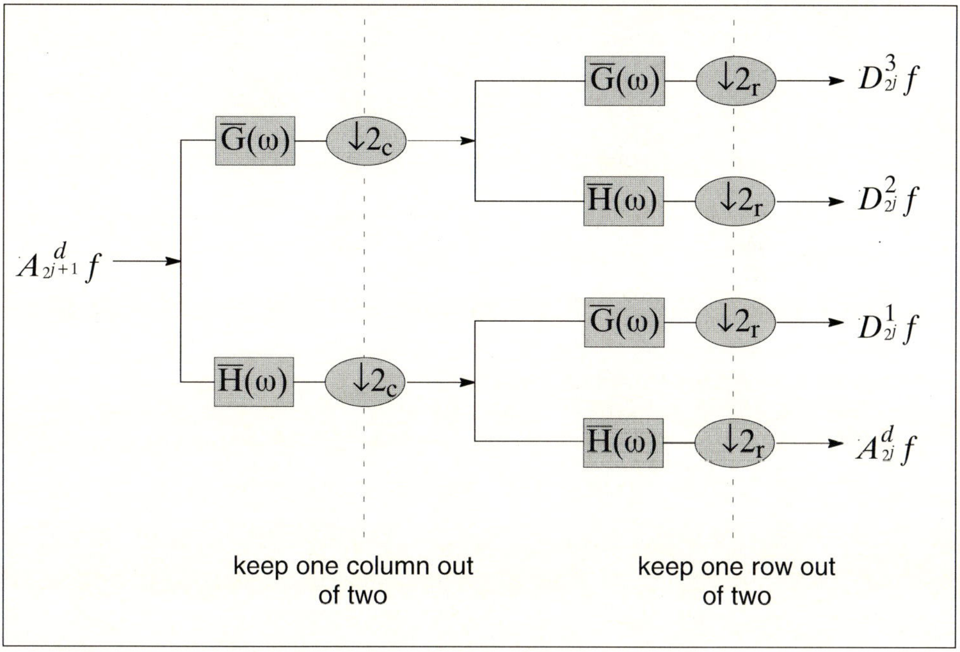

In other words the information $A^d_{2^{j+1}} f$ at resolution step 2^{j+1} is split into a low-pass $A^d_{2^j} f$ and into three detail images $D^1_{2^j} f$, $D^2_{2^j} f$ and $D^3_{2^j} f$, each emphasizing oriented high-pass information.

This is illustrated in Fig. 120, showing how the frequency plane is decomposed into the corresponding subbands.

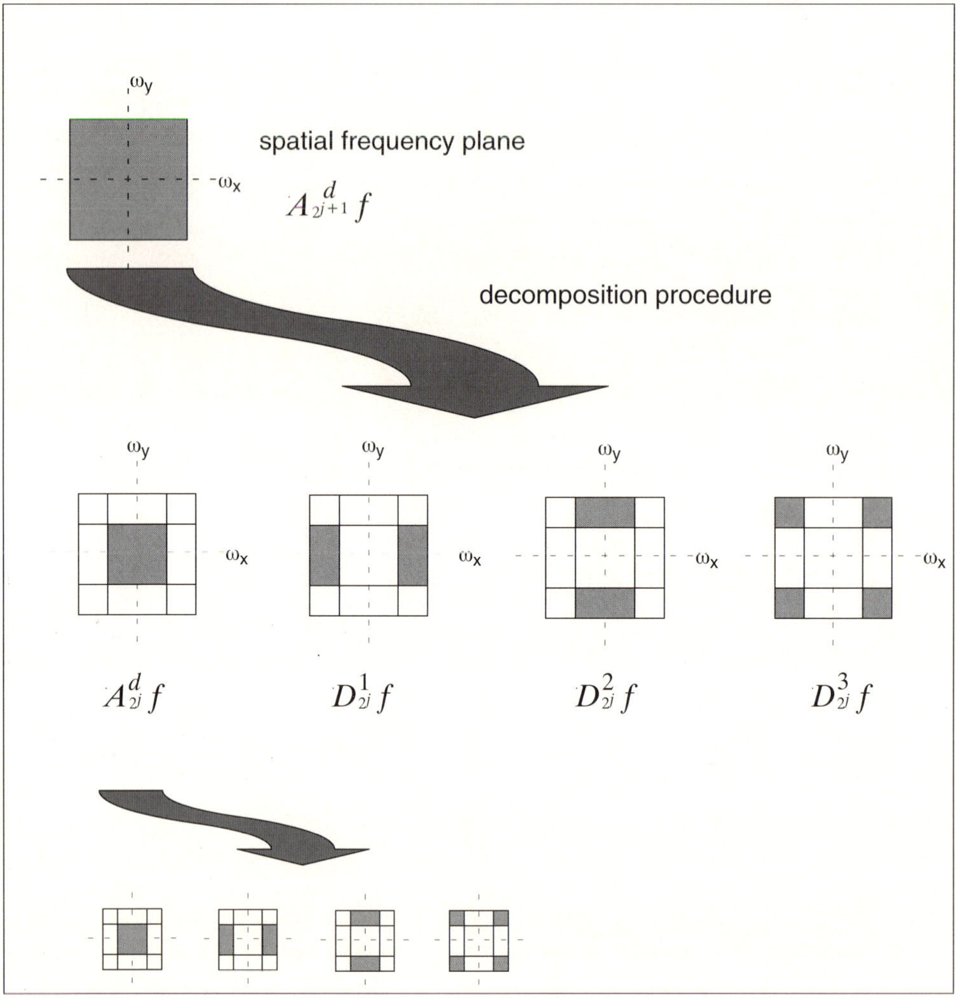

Figure 120: Iterated decomposition of the initial image frequency plane into different subbands

The corresponding inner products can be written as:

$$A^d_{2^j} f =$$

$$((f(x,y) * \phi_{2^j}(-x)\ \phi_{2^j}(-y))\ (2^{-j}n, 2^{-j}m))_{(n,m) \in Z^2}$$

$$D^1_{2^j} f =$$

$$((f(x,y) * \phi_{2^j}(-x)\ \psi_{2^j}(-y))\ (2^{-j}n, 2^{-j}m))_{(n,m) \in Z^2}$$

$$D^2_{2^j} f = \qquad (115)$$

$$((f(x,y) * \psi_{2^j}(-x)\ \phi_{2^j}(-y))\ (2^{-j}n, 2^{-j}m))_{(n,m) \in Z^2}$$

$$D^3_{2^j} f =$$

$$((f(x,y) * \psi_{2^j}(-x)\ \psi_{2^j}(-y))\ (2^{-j}n, 2^{-j}m))_{(n,m) \in Z^2}$$

The decomposition can also be interpreted as a signal representation by means of independent, spatially oriented frequency channels.

The 2D-QMF filters can easily be constructed from the tables above by cartesian products of the mirror pairs $h(n)$ and $g(n)$. Thus we obtain the low-pass by $h(x) \otimes h(y)$, the vertical high-pass by $h(x) \otimes g(y)$, the horizontal high-pass by $g(x) \otimes h(y)$ and the diagonal high-pass by $g(x) \otimes g(y)$.

From this representation, the continuous approximation at resolution step 2^{j+1} can be reconstructed using

$$A_{2^{j+1}} f(x,y) = \sum_{m,n} (A^d_{2^j} f)_{m,n}\ \Phi(2^j x - n, 2^j y - m) \qquad (116)$$

$$+ \sum_{m,n} [(D^1_{2^j} f)_{m,n}\ \Psi^1(2^j x - n, 2^j y - m)$$

$$(D^2_{2^j} f)_{m,n}\ \Psi^2(2^j x - n, 2^j y - m)$$

$$(D^3_{2^j} f)_{m,n}\ \Psi^3(2^j x - n, 2^j y - m)]$$

The whole image can be reconstructed from the pyramid by shifted and dilated versions of 4 functions Φ, Ψ^1, Ψ^2, and Ψ^3 and their corresponding coefficients.

Due to the orthogonality of the representation, the set

$$\left\{A^d_{2^{-J}}f,\ (D^1_{2^j}f,\ D^2_{2^j}f,\ D^3_{2^j}f)_{-J\leq j\leq 1}\right\} \tag{117}$$

represents the whole image using $3J+1$ images, where J denotes the depth of the pyramid. Due to the localization of the WT both in space and in frequency, it is possible to adjust the resolution of reconstructed images according to the local area of interest.

The elucidations above are limited to the separable case. The more interesting, since nontrivial, non-separable 2D wavelet transform has also been investigated by several authors, e.g., [212]. Where in the separable case we have always a resolution shift of 4 (2 in each direction) the non-separable WT can be constructed with an overall subsampling of 2. The samples are then arranged on a so-called quincunx sublattice of $\boldsymbol{R}^2$.

The separable extension of the wavelet transform to 3D is straightforward and explained for instance in [180].

We define a separable version of V_{2^j} as a multiresolution approximation of $L^2(\boldsymbol{R}^3)$ using

$$V^3_{2^j} = V^1_{2^j} \otimes V^1_{2^j} \otimes V^1_{2^j} \tag{118}$$

and write $V^3_{2^{j+1}}$ as

$$\begin{aligned} V^3_{2^{j+1}} &= (V^1_{2^j} \oplus O^1_{2^j}) \otimes (V^1_{2^j} \oplus O^1_{2^j}) \otimes (V^1_{2^j} \oplus O^1_{2^j}) \\ &= (V^1_{2^j} \otimes V^1_{2^j} \otimes V^1_{2^j}) \\ &\oplus (V^1_{2^j} \otimes V^1_{2^j} \otimes O^1_{2^j}) \\ &\oplus (V^1_{2^j} \otimes O^1_{2^j} \otimes V^1_{2^j}) \\ &\oplus (V^1_{2^j} \otimes O^1_{2^j} \otimes O^1_{2^j}) \\ &\oplus (O^1_{2^j} \otimes V^1_{2^j} \otimes V^1_{2^j}) \\ &\oplus (O^1_{2^j} \otimes V^1_{2^j} \otimes O^1_{2^j}) \\ &\oplus (O^1_{2^j} \otimes O^1_{2^j} \otimes O^1_{2^j}) \\ &\oplus (O^1_{2^j} \otimes O^1_{2^j} \otimes V^1_{2^j}) \end{aligned} \tag{119}$$

The scaling function $\Phi(x,y,z)$ can then be defined as

$$\Phi(x,y,z) \; - \; \phi(x)\,\phi(y)\,\phi(z) \qquad (120)$$

and the corresponding wavelets

$$\begin{aligned}
\Psi^1\,(x,y,z) &= \phi(x)\,\phi(y)\,\psi(z),\\
\Psi^2\,(x,y,z) &= \phi(x)\,\psi(y)\,\phi(z),\\
\Psi^3\,(x,y,z) &= \phi(x)\,\psi(y)\,\psi(z),\\
\Psi^4\,(x,y,z) &= \psi(x)\,\phi(y)\,\phi(z),\\
\Psi^5\,(x,y,z) &= \psi(x)\,\phi(y)\,\psi(z),\\
\Psi^6\,(x,y,z) &= \psi(x)\,\psi(y)\,\phi(z),\\
\Psi^7\,(x,y,z) &= \psi(x)\,\psi(y)\,\psi(z).
\end{aligned} \qquad (121)$$

In the same way we can reconstruct an approximation at resolution 2^{j+1} with

$$\begin{aligned}
P_{o_{2^j}} f(x,y,z) = \sum_{n,m,l} [\,
&(D^1_{2^j} f)_{(n,m,l)}\,\Psi^1\,(2^j x - n,\, 2^j y - m,\, 2^j z - l)\\
+\,&(D^2_{2^j} f)_{(n,m,l)}\,\Psi^2\,(2^j x - n,\, 2^j y - m,\, 2^j z - l)\\
+\,&(D^3_{2^j} f)_{(n,m,l)}\,\Psi^3\,(2^j x - n,\, 2^j y - m,\, 2^j z - l)\\
+\,&(D^4_{2^j} f)_{(n,m,l)}\,\Psi^4\,(2^j x - n,\, 2^j y - m,\, 2^j z - l)\\
+\,&(D^5_{2^j} f)_{(n,m,l)}\,\Psi^5\,(2^j x - n,\, 2^j y - m,\, 2^j z - l)\\
+\,&(D^6_{2^j} f)_{(n,m,l)}\,\Psi^6\,(2^j x - n,\, 2^j y - m,\, 2^j z - l)\\
+\,&(D^7_{2^j} f)_{(n,m,l)}\,\Psi^7\,(2^j x - n,\, 2^j y - m,\, 2^j z - l)\,].
\end{aligned} \qquad (122)$$

where

$$A_{2^{j+1}} f(x,y,z) = A_{2^j} f(x,y,z) + P_{o_{2^j}} f(x,y,z) \qquad (123)$$

Applying the 3D wavelet transform on volume data the resulting filter cascade has to be constructed using 7 oriented high-pass filters and one low-pass. This is illustrated in Fig. 121. The volume data is then decomposed into eight subvolumes at each resolution step representing the low-pass and the oriented high-pass filters respectively (see also Fig. 122).

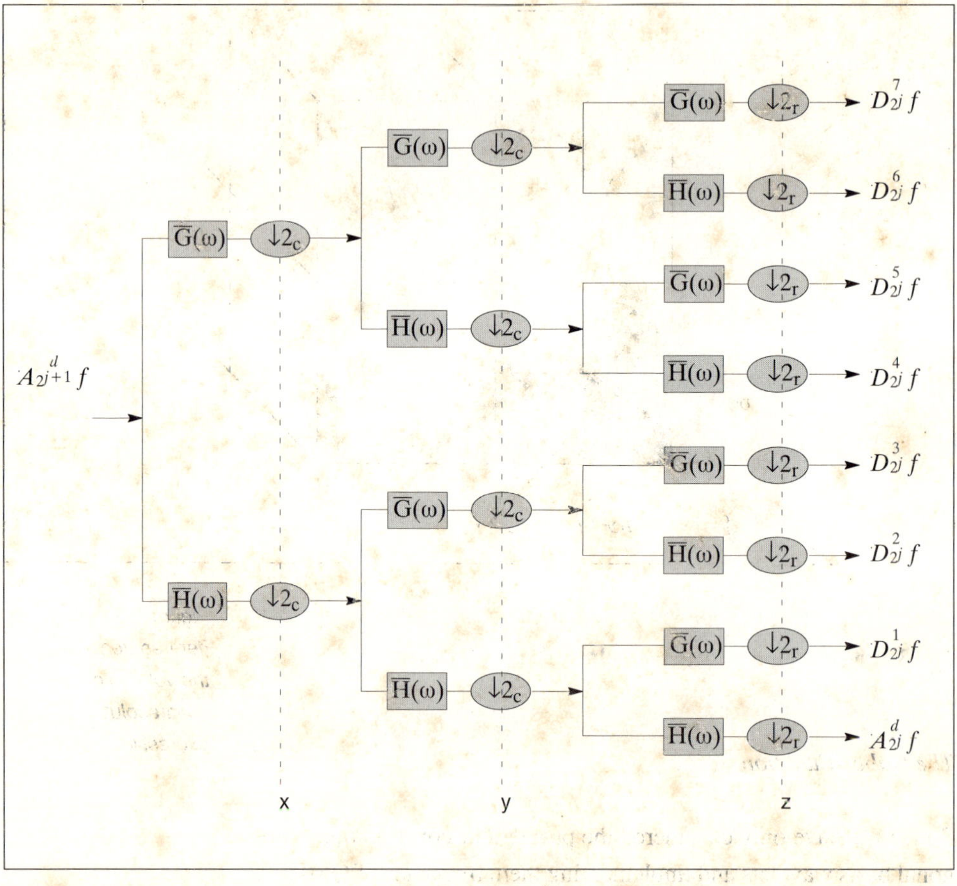

Figure 121: Implementation of the 3D wavelet transform with a three-level filter pyramid: $A^d_{2^{j+1}}f$ is decomposed into a low-pass volume $A^d_{2^j}f$ and seven detail volumes $D^1_{2^j}f$ to $D^7_{2^j}f$

Basically, wavelet representations can also be used to compress data, since the contribution of each detail signal depends both on the coefficient and on the frequency channel.

In the pyramid we can introduce a psychophysically based coding concept according to the spatial frequency sensitivity of human vision (see Fig. 43). The coefficients could be weighted with their corresponding sensitivity and thus ordered from the highest contribution to the lowest one. Such a scheme would minimize the perceived error in a reconstruction conforming to current JPEC standards.

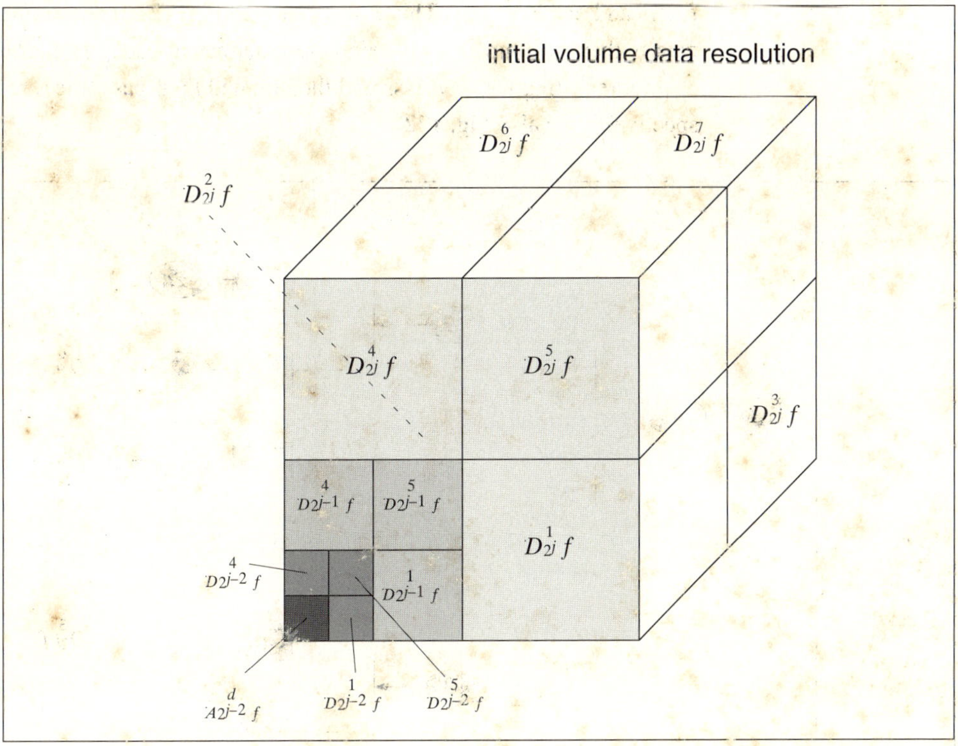

Figure 122: Iterated decomposition of the volume data into a multiresolution expression

5.4.3. Nonorthogonal Wavelets

The Gabor Function

So far, we have only considered the problem of constructing orthogonal basis wavelets and implementing them by means of QMFs. If we remember Sect. 5.4.1, the generic formulation of the wavelet transform is by no means limited to a special type of wavelet. Moreover, we can choose any band-pass function $\psi(x)$ and its dilated and translated versions to build a wavelet representation. Thus the band-passes may overlap in the spectrum and the transform will not always provide an optimal, compact, representation of the data. But on the other hand, depending on the application, a non-orthogonal data representation could yield interesting information. In particular, due to the fact that the image representation in the visual cortex is processed by simple cells that can be interpreted as oriented band-passes, WTs have generated interest in the field of modeling human visual processing. Nowadays, the response of these cells is increasingly modeled using Gabor functions [150], which are among the most popular functions for building non-orthogonal wavelet transforms. These types of wavelets have been introduced by [107] and have been used in many signal and image processing applications [34]. The Gabor function itself is a sine or cosine function affected by a Gaussian window. It can be written according to (124) or (125):

$$h(x) = \sin(\omega x)\, e^{-\frac{x^2}{2\sigma^2}} \tag{124}$$

or

$$h(x) = \cos(\omega x)\, e^{-\frac{x^2}{2\sigma^2}} \tag{125}$$

where ω describes the frequency of the oscillation and σ the width of the Gaussian. The number of waves per σ can be expressed by

$$\frac{\omega\sigma}{2\pi} \tag{126}$$

The complex version that is often used can be formulated as

$$h(x) = e^{i\omega x}\, e^{-\frac{x^2}{2\sigma^2}} \tag{127}$$

The extension to 2D and 3D separable versions of the Gabor function is straightforward. A 2D version can be described as

$$h(x, y) = e^{i\omega_x x} e^{-\frac{x^2}{2\sigma_x^2}} e^{i\omega_y y} e^{-\frac{y^2}{2\sigma_y^2}}$$

with *(128)*

$$\omega = \begin{pmatrix} \omega_x \\ \omega_y \end{pmatrix} = |\omega| \begin{pmatrix} \cos\varsigma \\ \sin\varsigma \end{pmatrix}$$

ς: *phase angle*

The Gabor function describes an attenuated oscillation. Using Gabor functions as the window functions of a STFT such as in Sect. 5.4.1. we obtain the so-called Gabor transform. We remember that this type of transform is well adapted for signals that have a locally constant spectrum. In image processing and graphics, elements with a locally coherent spectrum are in particular textures. Therefore it is straightforward to employ wavelets for texture analysis.

Gabor Wavelets

Non-orthogonal wavelet bases can easily be built from the Gabor function by scaling and translation as formulated in Eq. (83) for the one-dimensional case. The interesting 2D extensions for imaging will be elucidated briefly below. Due to the rotational symmetry of the Gaussian for $\sigma_x = \sigma_y$ it is useful to build the wavelets by translation, rotation, and scaling. The resulting 2D Gabor functions can be interpreted as simple oriented band-pass filters.

Let ς express the rotation, $a = \sigma$ express the scale and $\boldsymbol{x} - \boldsymbol{x}'$, with $\boldsymbol{x} = (x,y)$ the translation, then we obtain the wavelet family according to the following equation.

The discrete version of the transform can be written as follows: with

$$h_{a,\varsigma}(\boldsymbol{x}) = \frac{1}{\sqrt{\pi}\, a} e^{i|\omega| \begin{pmatrix} \cos\varsigma \\ \sin\varsigma \end{pmatrix} x} e^{-\frac{x^2}{2\sigma^2}} \qquad (129)$$

we obtain

$$h_{a,\varsigma}(\boldsymbol{x}) = \frac{1}{\sqrt{\pi}\, a} e^{i|\omega|(x\cos\varsigma + y\cos\varsigma)} e^{-\frac{(x^2+y^2)}{2\sigma^2}} \tag{130}$$

and the discrete representation of ω

$$\omega = \omega\,(j, l) = \frac{2\pi}{N}\sqrt{2}^{\,j}\begin{bmatrix}\cos\left(\frac{2\pi l}{L}\right)\\ \sin\left(\frac{2\pi l}{L}\right)\end{bmatrix} \tag{131}$$

where l and j describe the sampling of the frequency space for rotation and scale respectively. L is the discretization in rotation and $l \in \{0,..., L/2-1\}$, and $j \in \{0,..., 2\log_2(N-1)\}$ where N is the size of an image to be transformed.

Let $I(\boldsymbol{x})$ be a discrete image function, then the WT $g_{WT}(\boldsymbol{x})$ is given by the discrete convolution

$$g_{WT}(\boldsymbol{x}) = \sum_{x \in I} h_{a,\varsigma}(\boldsymbol{x} - \boldsymbol{x}')I(\boldsymbol{x}) \tag{132}$$

and

$$\boldsymbol{x}' = \boldsymbol{x}'(j, m, n) = a\sqrt{2}^{\,-j}\begin{pmatrix} m \\ n \end{pmatrix} \tag{133}$$

The example of Fig. 124 illustrates a set of convolution kernels of the Gabor function for the orientations 0, $\pi/4$, $\pi/2$ and 3 $\pi/4$, respectively. Only the real component is illustrated.

5.4.4. Wavelets for Volume Rendering

The subband coding scheme provided by the QMF implementations of the wavelet transform can be used for the development of efficient volume ray tracers. This was first proposed in [180] and can be sketched as follows. If we suppose the resolution of the volume data set to be N^3, we can write the volume function as:

$$A_1 f(x, y, z) = \sum_{j=1}^{N^3} c_j \, \tau_j \, (x, y, z) \tag{134}$$

where c_j are the coefficients of the 3D wavelet transform of the intensity values of the volume and $\tau_j(x,y,z)$ are the respective version of the 3D scaling function Φ and of the wavelets Ψ.

To obtain the isosurface of the threshold T in the volume, we simply write:

$$T = \sum_{j=1}^{N^3} c_j \, \tau_j \, (x, y, z) \tag{135}$$

This expression contains an implicit function as far as we suppose continous approximations for the τ_j (for instance splines). They can be ray traced using the techniques of [132]. In order to obtain an efficient scheme, the c_j can be ordered according to their significance and the less important ones can be neglected. This leads to a decrease in the resolution of the isosurface to be presented. Due to the spatial location of the wavelet transform it is possible to vary the resolution spatially, i.e., to emphasize areas important for particular applications in the volume by adding the corresponding c_j.

The other advantage of this method is the improved computation of the surface gradient for illumination and shading. If, however, a volume density integration [151] is required the proposed method has to be extended, as in [57] and [153].

The following pictures in Fig. 123 illustrate the effect of volume rendering in wavelet spaces. In Figs. 123a–c a Gaussian density function of 32^3 voxels was rendered using the threshold 0.5 for defining the isosurface. In this case a hybrid rendering scheme (see also [57]) was employed to visualize both the implicit surface and the surrounding translucency. Figures 123e–g show the same scheme using a voxelized model of the object in Fig. 123d. By summing up more and more of the high-pass-coefficients and wavelets, the image gets more and more detailed. In both cases, Coiflet 6-tap wavelets were used.

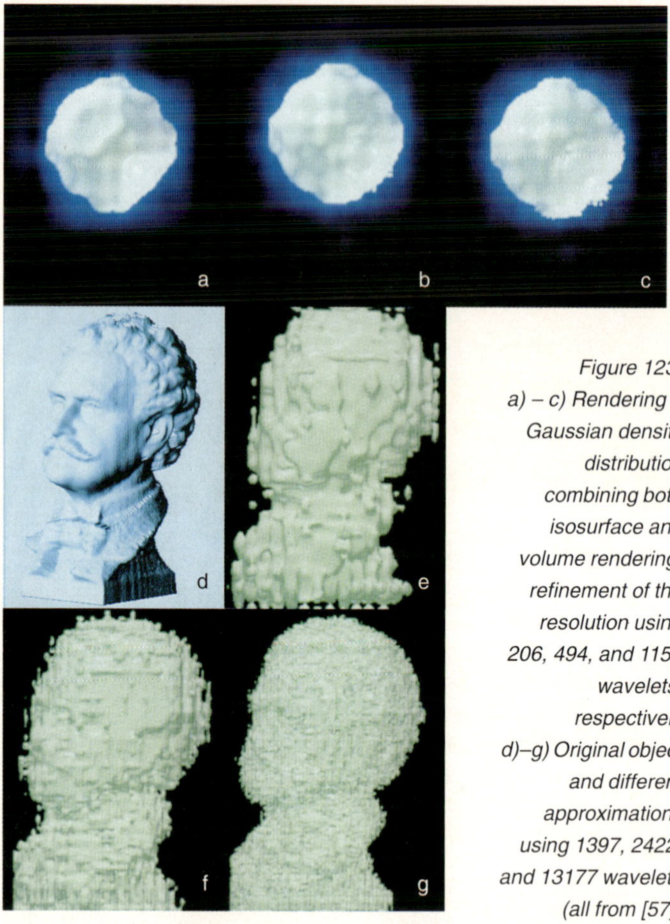

Figure 123:
a) – c) Rendering a Gaussian density distribution combining both isosurface and volume rendering; refinement of the resolution using 206, 494, and 1154 wavelets, respectively
d)–g) Original object and different approximations using 1397, 2422, and 13177 wavelets (all from [57])

5.4.5. Wavelets for Texture Analysis

The WT can also be used for the extraction of local texture features from images or volumes and can serve for further texture analysis methods. [138], for instance uses Gabor wavelets to describe local texture features. Where orthogonal wavelets have to be employed for compact coding and data representation, local texture analysis requires an overlap in the frequency domain and a dense staggering of the filter orientations. This is also supported by the fact that the cortical simple cells as oriented band-pass filters are staggered by 10° [124]. Unfortunately, non-orthogonal wavelets require redundancy.

Figure 124:
Illustration of the convolution kernels of different Gabor functions used for the WT

Figure 125:
System for image texture analysis based on multiresolution descriptions (see [138])

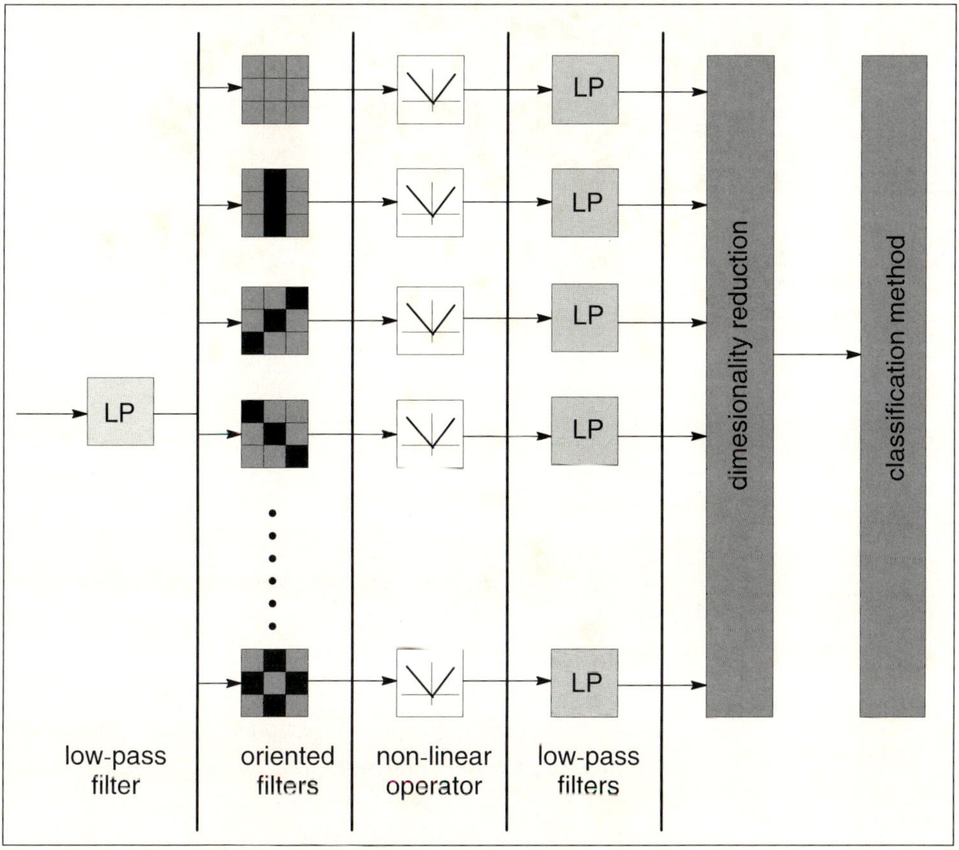

During the last few decades numerous operators have been proposed for characterizing textures [114]. The most promising, however, are multiresolution analyses [163, 31, 245] combined with nonlinear post-processing. Such schemes are illustrated in Fig. 125.

Finally, Fig. 126 illustrates again the capabilities of the WT. In this case a simple face image is shown (a) as well as its decomposition into orthogonal wavelet pyramids (b and c). Due to the local support of the WT, it is possible to reconstruct the image from the pyramid by adapting the spatial resolution around the eyes (d and e). In Fig. 127 a test sample for texture segmentation is shown as well as its segmentation (b) using a two-level Gabor pyramid with 8 different orientations. Since the textures are oriented and limited in the spectrum the different Gabors are well suited to discriminate them (see also Fig. 127c).

Since wavelets seem to provide both efficient methods for data representation and analysis, [153] proposes an integrated scheme for volume data visualization and analysis.

5.5. Shape from Stereo

5.5.1. Introductory Remarks

The previous chapters have elucidated computational models for early visual processing in the human retina and in the brain. The higher-order mechanisms of visual perception, namely the recognition of objects and the recovery of 3D shape from images, require different methods, usually based on the early models. A research area dealing with these problems has been established during the last two decades and is called *computational vision, computer vision,* or simply *vision*. Computer vision has to make use *both of graphics and imaging techniques* to handle its algorithms mathematically. The most famous methods to recover shape from images are stereo matching, shape from shading, shape from texture and shape from motion. There have been many attempts [165, 8, 122] to integrate these features into a unique model for human vision. This section aims to give an insight into higher-order computer vision methods, exemplified by an algorithm for automatic stereo matching based on simulated annealing optimization [1].

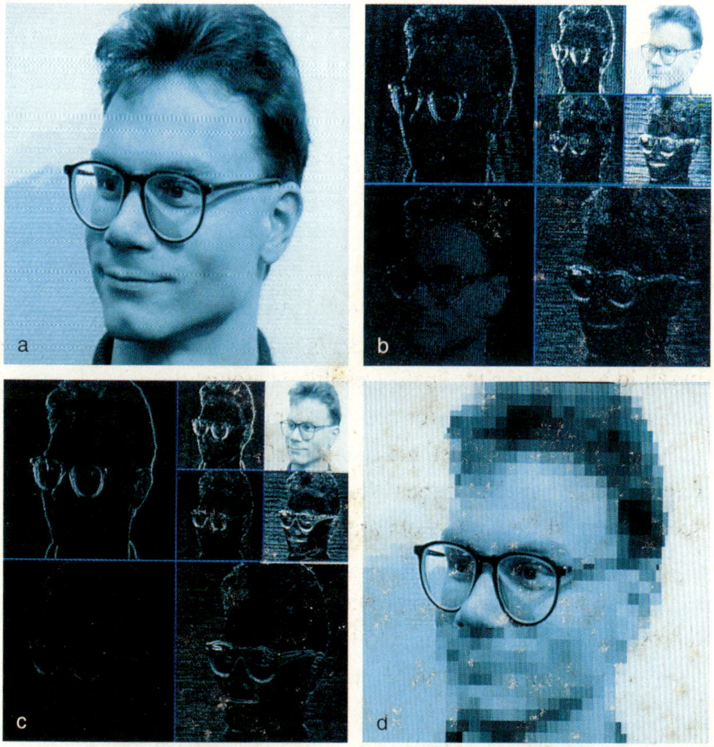

Figure 126:
a) Face image
b), c) Image pyramid constructed with Haar (b) and Daubechies 8-tap (c) wavelets
d), e) Image reconstruction enhancing the eyes of the person for Haar (d) and Daubechies (e) wavelets
(all from [153])

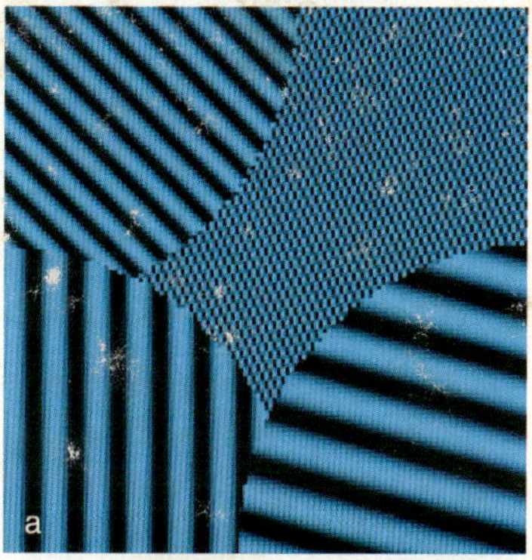

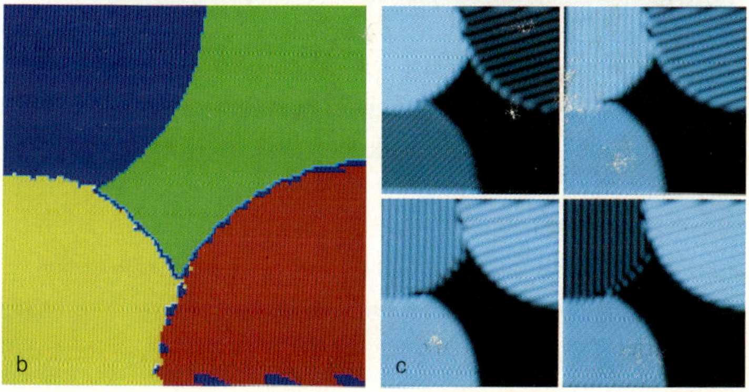

Figure 127:
a) Test textures
b) Segmentation based on Gabor wavelets
c) Reaction of different Gabor wavelets to the different orientations of the textures (all from [138])

The automatic recovery of depth from disparent stereoscopic image pairs has been of fundamental importance in computer vision and machine perception, and is being studied by many researchers in this field. Although the task of stereo matching is accomplished so well by the human visual system (see Chap. 3) most computational approaches have shortcomings with regard to solving ambiguities in the matching process and reconstructing the shape based on a disparity map. Basically the process of stereo matching can be taken as a problem of discrete optimization and faces the associated problems of being captured in local minima. Although electronic photogrammetry [152] provides active sensing methods, for instance laser range finding or structured light approaches, stereo matching is still a challenging problem either with regard to the costs of a recognition system or with regard to digital terrain modeling from remote sensing data.

Early work on stereo matching stems from electronic photogrammetry [113] where first techniques involved grey level correlation of remotely sensed images. These approaches are based on area matching of locally coherent parts of the image pairs and render a dense grid of depth points, in contrast to feature based matching that provides scattered data. Biologically based fundamental work in this area was done by Marr [165] who introduced both a neural network approach [167] and matching based on features of preprocessed image pairs via edge detectors and coarse–fine strategies. But implementations [83] have also shown the limits of these approaches. Later algorithms are based on symbolic feature matching [15] or on structured templates [17] and others [21, 241]. Some work has also been proposed on stochastic methods [20]. Good reviews on stereo matching can be found in [19].

This section gives a survey of computational stereo and proposes a new matching technique for disparate image pairs combining the advantages of several of the above methods. It is based on the three-pass process: In order to reduce the possible matches the images are first preprocessed with edge detectors of different sizes in a hierarchical approach. The matching itself is handled for each edge size as a variational problem where the information about the matches on the coarser levels is used to reduce the finer-level ambiguities. The optimization is solved by simulated annealing of the initial disparity. Finally, the shape is reconstructed by scattered data interpolation (see also Chap. 4).

The section first introduces the generic problem of stereo matching and provides definitions as well as illustrations of the matching pipeline and of the camera model for data acquisition. Then the matching strategy is explained in detail for the three parts and the accuracy of the matching is investigated by means of random dot stereograms.

5.5.2. Automatic Stereo Matching

The Matching Pipeline

Basically, stereo matching algorithms aim to calculate the disparities of the two input images by finding corresponding pixels or symbolic features. The result of this process is usually a disparity map where the different disparities stand for the differences in depth. The process of stereo vision can be taken as a pipeline of different tasks to be solved. This is illustrated in Fig. 128.

The six important steps, namely image acquisition, camera modeling, feature extraction, image matching, depth computation, and interpolation are explained in the following subsections.

Image Acquisition and the Camera Model

Stereo images can be acquired in many different ways. They can be recorded either simultaneously or successively, the camera positions can differ by large or small amounts, and distortions may arise from daylight or atmospheric conditions. In general, the acquisition strongly depends on the application, for instance:

I. *Digital terrain modeling using aerial photographs*
II. *Control and collision detection of robots*
III. *Automatic modeling for computer graphics applications (i.e. CAD)*
IV. *etc.*

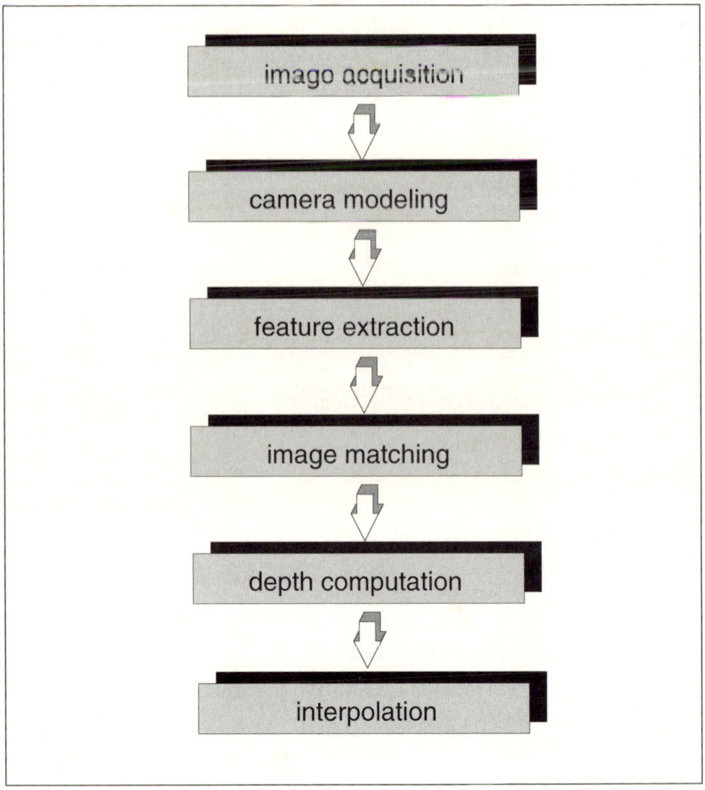

Figure 128: The stereo vision pipeline and its components

The most important and significant differences in stereo images are lighting conditions that arise from differences in the illumination when taking the photos successively. This is for example done by the SPOT satellite [152]. Another important issue is that of the contents of the images. Whereas large scale satellite images usually contain only natural boundaries and features, such as forest areas, water, and so on, small scale photos contain mostly artificial structures such as buildings and so on with periodic features that may decrease the performance of the matching algorithm. Thus most matching techniques introduced so far are adopted for particular scene types.

The camera model is crucial for the accuracy of any matching process. Position, orientation and the physical properties of the camera are the parameters that control the mapping from corresponding image pixels to 3D depth information. In most applications we can distinguish between two types of camera model, namely convergent and non-convergent ones. They are shown in Figs. 129 and 130 respectively. As we know from Chap. 3, the human visual system makes use of a convergent model. Based on the geometry of the camera model we are able to specify the mapping from the image coordinate system *(x,y)* to the 3D world coordinate system (X_w, Y_w, Z_w). The distance between the coordinate centers of the two images is called the baseline *L*.

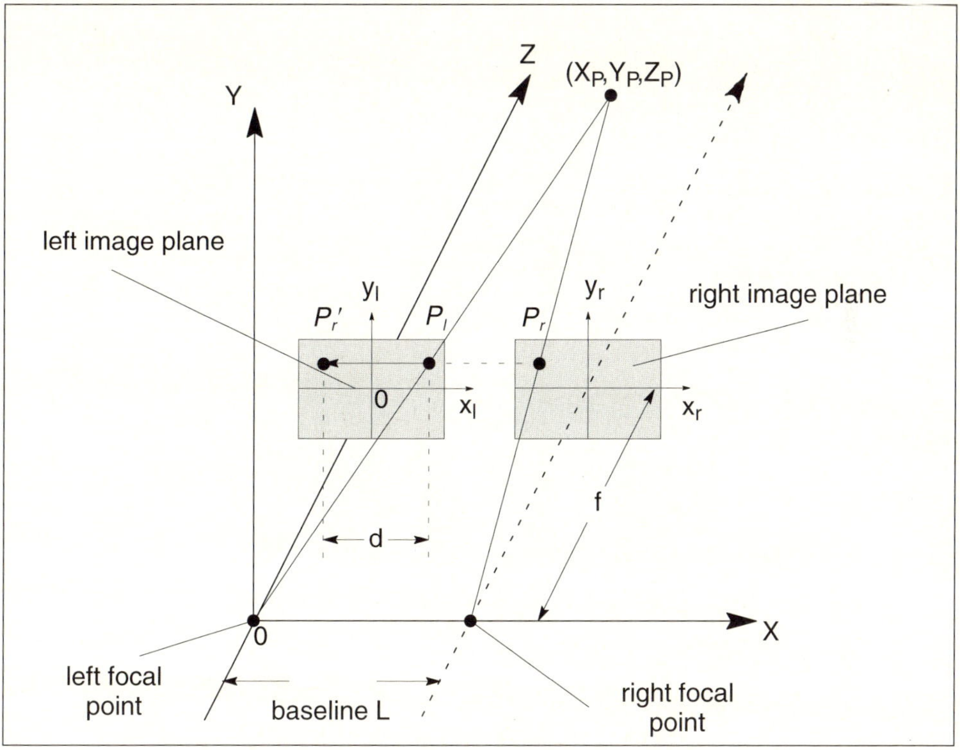

Figure 129: Non-convergent binocular camera model

Another very interesting aspect is the reduction of the searching for corresponding image pixels into one dimension by means of the epipolar constraint. Every point (X_P, Y_P, Z_P) defines together with the optical centers of the two camera systems a plane that intersects both images. This intersection is called the epipolar line and reduces the possible correspondences of a particular projection onto all pixels lying on that line. Each point in the left image can only correspond to a pixel lying on the epipolar line in the right image and we obtain an enormous reduction of possible matches. If the stereo cameras are only translated horizontally then the epipolar lines are also horizontal and fall on the scan lines of the image. Such a camera

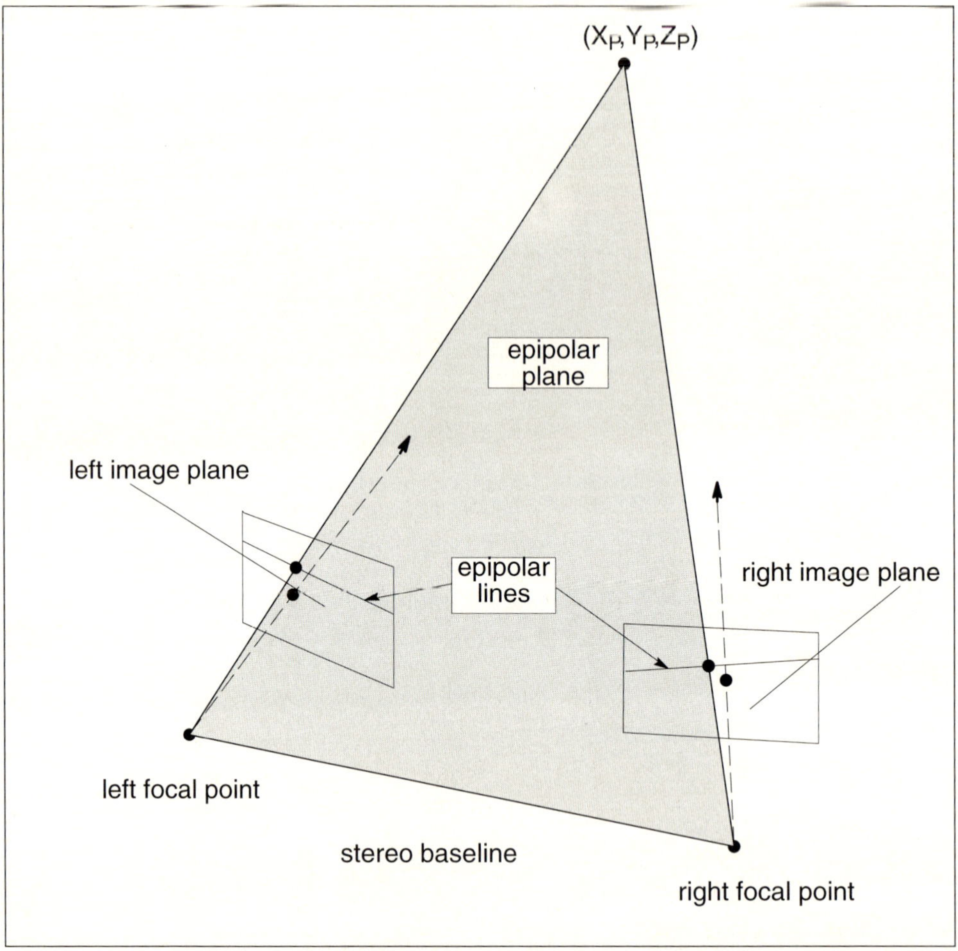

Figure 130: Convergent camera model and the epipolar constraint

arrangement reduces also the computation costs. In aerial photogrammetry the stereo cameras usually differ by up to 2° – 3° vertically and the stereo images have to be adjusted. Using a camera model as in Fig. 129 the depth is computed relative to the origin of the world coordinate system employed. In the stereo matching algorithm below, the model from Fig. 129 will be used, but there are also more complex models in the literature that handle nonlinear distortions arising from the camera optics.

Feature Extraction and Matching

In order to label pixels that correspond in the two images most stereo vision algorithms use preprocessing techniques to extract symbolic or iconic features. Thus special operators can be defined as in [113] or [178] to correlate subareas to be matched. In most cases pointwise features are extracted in order to avoid problems of perspective projections. A very common method to extract low level features in images are edge-detectors [15, 17]. The most popular edge-detector that is also biologically based is the Marr–Hildreth operator [166] (see also Fig. 102) that approximates the second order derivative of the image intensity to extract an edge. It is described in detail in the previous section. The advantage of this operator is the adjustable bandwidth and frequency range of operation. This allows the construction of coarse-fine strategies, where at the beginning low-pass edges are matched and the result is used to match the higher frequency edges. In real world images due to the *causality principle* each edge can be taken as a spatial transition of an intensity that is more or less smooth. The smoothness or low-pass characteristics of this transition differs for different types of edge. For this reason it is useful to define several operators, each reacting to a special type of edge.

The matching process itself reduces to finding corresponding features in the left and the right images and to estimating the disparity between them. But, unfortunately, this process is confronted with the problem of ambiguities. Depending on the features extracted we have often more than one possible match for one particular pixel on the corresponding epipolar line in the other image. The more complex the features are the more reliably the matching can be accomplished. We distinguish between:

I. **Area matching:** *These approaches use local neighborhoods for pixel-based matching. They imply another very important condition, the so-called continuity constraint, which says that based on the limitations of the resolution most stereo images describe continuous depth maps and thus each discontinuity (and edge of a building, etc.) is modeled by a continuous depth surface. The results of these pre-assumptions are two antagonistic constraints,* *namely the equality in the image intensity and the spatial gradient of the disparity map, that can be handled using variational approaches [20, 204]. Neighboring pixels in these methods represent neighboring areas in 3D. This can be seen as an extension of traditional correlation based matching. Area matching generates a dense disparity map.*

II. ***Feature matching:*** *As explained above, feature matching is based on finding corresponding symbolic features in the images. In contrast to a pixel based approach, the features stem from more or less complex preprocessing and they are by no means arranged on a regular grid. Moreover, they are scattered over the image and the matching methods based on these features usually generate sparse disparity maps. Depending on the complexity of the features, the corresponding points found do not provide sufficient depth information. Then we may apply area matching that uses the previously matched points to constrain the matching process further. In any case feature matching is confronted with the problem of interpolation of sparse scattered data maps.*

Computation of Depth and Interpolation

Based on the disparity map generated in the previous step the final task is now to compute the depth for each pixel. Due to distortions and errors during the matching, this task requires also a careful processing. Basically, the error in the distance map is influenced by the length of the baseline and by the positioning of matched pixels. The larger the baseline the larger the disparity range to be considered for possible matches. In order to enhance the accuracy of the matching, subpixel-interpolations can be provided and multiple views can be calculated [178]. The latter is useful when dealing with noisy data.

In the algorithm described below, the non-convergent camera model of Fig. 129 is employed. The world coordinate system corresponds to the local coordinates of the left camera and the right camera system is translated by L along the X-axis. Let (xp_l, yp_l) and $(xp_r,$

y_{Pr}) be the coordinates of the point in the left and right image respectively, then:

$$\frac{d}{L} = \frac{f}{Z_P} \tag{136}$$

$$\frac{x_{Pl}}{f} = \frac{X_P}{Z_P} \tag{137}$$

$$\frac{y_{Pl}}{f} = \frac{Y_P}{Z_P} \tag{138}$$

In order to obtain the coordinates (X_P, Y_P, Z_P) of an arbitrary point P in space we combine (136) – (138).

The term $(d = x_{Pr} - x_{Pl})$ is called the disparity of the point P. It is easy to see that the disparity range to be handled depends on the length of the baseline L.

The final step in the stereo vision pipeline is the interpolation of the depth map. In particular the feature matching techniques only provide sparse disparity information and the depth maps arising can be taken as a scattered data matrix. Thus we have to introduce interpolation methods to compute the range at each point of the image. The traditional approaches suppose continuous depth functions [167] and can be applied successfully on large scale aerial photos to recover terrain models. But to deal with discontinuities arising from large buildings or from hidden edges we have to extend the traditional interpolation methods [83, 27]. There are also combinations between stereo matching and shape from shading [122, 8].

5.5.3. Formulation of a Matching Algorithm

The Concept

The following stereo matching algorithm proposed by [257] is based on a three-pass process illustrated in Fig. 131. First, both images to be matched are convolved with Marr–Hildreth operators of different sizes. This corresponds to an approximation of the second order derivative of the image intensity and provides the extremes of the first derivative. After this, the exact position of the edge has to be found by searching for the so-called zero-crossings, the transitions from positive to negative values in the second derivative or vice versa. The result of this step is a set of images that represents the edges of different frequency characteristics where the coarsest filter usually renders the most sparse edge map.

Based on this preprocessing the matching is performed by means of a stochastic simulated annealing approach [20] where we begin with the coarsest filter and use the results to constrain the matching of the finer ones. This strategy helps to reduce the large number of ambiguities arising with very fine filter sets. In the algorithm described here we use three filter types but the extension to more than three is straightforward. Finally the disparity value that is obtained at each zero-crossing is interpolated.

Edge Detection as a Preprocessor

As we see from Fig. 131 the edge detection is itself a two-pass process. Once we have computed the second derivative of the intensity by means of the algorithm introduced in Sect. 5.2.2 we have to search for the zero crossings that indicate the maximum of the intensity gradient. This can be accomplished by the operation illustrated in Fig. 132.

The reader is inviteded to compare it to the examples shown in Figs. 102 – 107

Due to the isotropic characteristics of the operator we have to detect a change of the sign in any direction for a current pixel. The arrows in Fig. 132 stand for the directions of the searching method. The bold arrows describe a zero-crossing that lies in the middle between the positive and the negative pixel. The resulting zero-crossing map always defines a grid between the original image pixels. Another important constraint is the direction of the zero-crossing which can either go from positive to negative or from negative to positive values.

In the current implementation of the matching method we only search in the direction of the scan line (x-axis). This leads to small holes in the edges but it avoids ambiguities arising from edges aligned with the scan lines. Implicitly we have defined an anisotropic operator only extracting anisotropic edges. Figure 137 shows the edges extracted from a random dot stereo image.

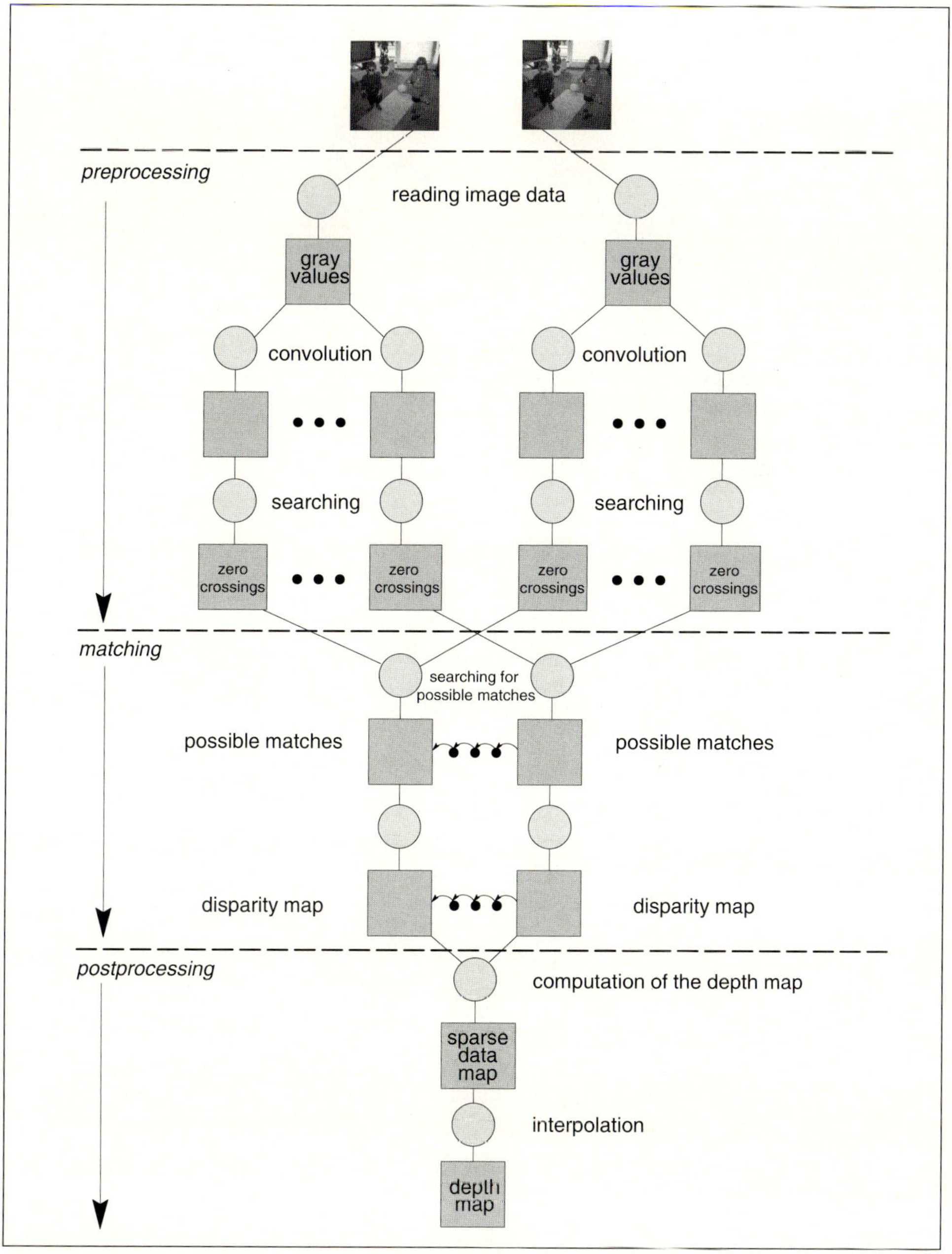

Figure 131:
Illustration of the matching strategy introduced according to [257]

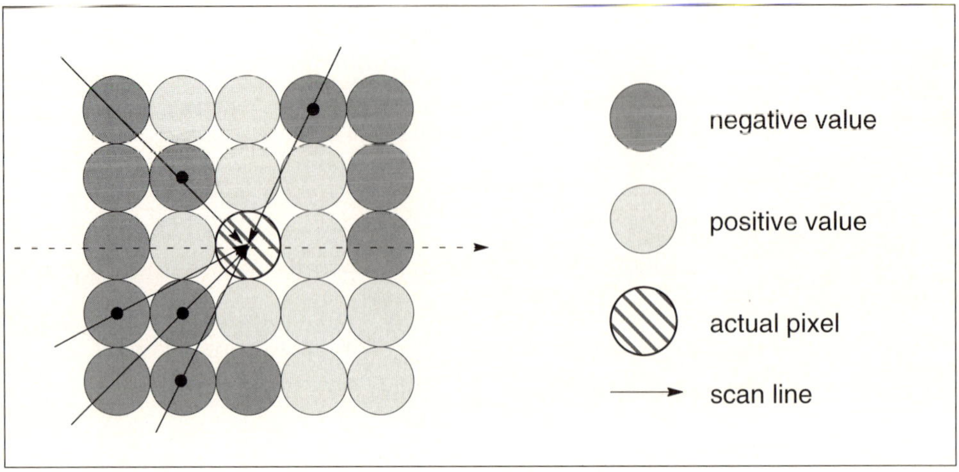

Figure 132: Searching for zero-crossings in the isotropic second derivative of the image intensity function

Stochastic Matching using Simulated Annealing

The matching method used to solve the correspondence problem is based on a simulated annealing technique [1] derived from physics. This method can be used for a large variety of optimization problems, for instance in neural networks (see Chap. 6). Since stereo matching can be considered as a constraint optimization problem, simulated annealing was first proposed by Banard [20]. But in contrast to his method that interacts directly on the image, the proposed algorithm uses the zero-crossing representations of the images, and includes them in a hierarchical solution. Thus only the image positions of the zero-crossings are matched and the number of possible matches is strongly reduced. On the other hand, the final depth map has to be interpolated from the scattered matches.

The zero-crossings are represented as pixel chains where each element of a particular chain in the left image is related to its possible matches in the right image. This is illustrated in Fig. 133.

During the initialization of the method these relations are built up. The number of possible correspondences in the right image is limited by making use of the following constraints:

I. *The epipolar constraint causes possible matches lying on the same scan-line (see Fig. 133)*

II. *Since the disparity range $D_r(i)$ for possible matches depends on the bandwidth and size of filter i and is limited we can introduce the following definition:*

$$D_r(i) = \omega_{2Di}\ 2.0\ const. \qquad (139)$$

const.: *disparity range factor*

Thus only pixels lying in this range have to be considered and the maximum disparity depends on the size of the filter and vice versa.

III. *The zero-crossings can be distinguished by the sign expressing their intensity gradient, either from + to – or from – to +, and only zero-crossings with the same sign can be matched.*

The relationship and mapping built during the initialization is not unique and pixels in the right image can be associated several times in the left one. But this is necessary because hidden edges in one image might lead to such configurations.

Figure 133: Relation of zero-crossing elements in the left image to possible matches in the right image

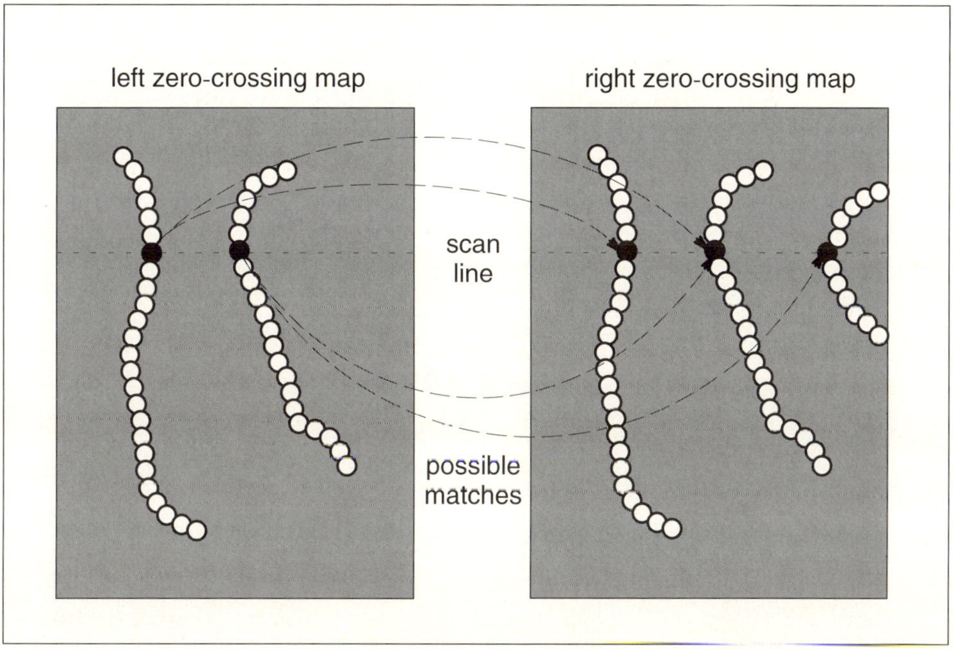

Simulated annealing itself [1] originated in statistical physics but can be used to solve any kind of optimization and minimization problem that has a convex solution space (see also Sect. 6.3.4). It uses an energy function that expresses the problem to be solved and that has to be minimized during the simulation. The principle is based on the Metropolis algorithm [174] that calculates a temperature equilibrium. For any system in equilibrium its stages are described by a Boltzmann distribution:

$$P(E) = e^{-E/T} \tag{140}$$

E expresses the system's energy, $P(E)$ the probability of a state of energy E and T the system's temperature. The Metropolis algorithm leads the system into equilibrium by providing small random state transitions that cause a change of the energy. These transitions are accepted if they lead to a decrease in the energy function. If, however, the change leads to a higher value of the energy they are only accepted with the Boltzmann probability.

The simulated annealing method starts with a high temperature and uses the Metropolis algorithm to achieve equilibrium. Then the temperature is gradually reduced and for each T_i the equilibrium is simulated down to a very low temperature. This procedure aims at avoiding local minima by giving a probability to jump out from them, i.e., to accept positive changes in the energy. A pseudocode for simulated annealing is given below:

```
Select a random state S
Select a sufficiently high starting temperature T
while T > 0 do
        Make a random state change: S' ← R(S)
        ΔE ← E(S') − E(S)
        if     ΔE ≤ 0      then
                /* Accept lower energy states */
                S ← S'
        else
                /* Accept higher energy states with probability P */
                P ← e^(-ΔE/T)
                       x ←random number in [0, 1]
                if x < P then
                       S ← S'
if there has been no significant decrease in E for many iterations then
                lower the temperature T
```

The problem with this algorithm is how to define the energy or cost function for a specific problem.

Suppose that we start with a left and right zero-crossing image with L_k and R_k and $k = \{ i, j \}$, $0 \le i, j \le N-1$. For the left image intensity $I_L(k) = I_L(i, j)$ there exists a disparity $d(k)$ that defines the correct match $I_R(i, j + d(k))$ to the corresponding pixel in the right image R_k. The problem is now to find the disparities $d(k)$ for all k that satisfy the constraints of intensity and smoothness. If, for instance the disparity range extends from $d_{min} = 0$ to $d_{max} = 9$ and $N = 128$ we have $(d_{max} - d_{min} + 1)^{N2} = 10^{16384}$ different states. This illustrates the requirement to reduce the amount of data by edge-detection. In order to satisfy the two antagonistic constraints, namely the similarity of the intensities $I_L(i,j) = I_R(i,j + d(k))$ and continuity, the following energy function can be used:

$$E = \sum_k \| I_L(k) - I_R(i,j + d(k)) \| + \lambda \| \nabla d(k) \| \qquad (141)$$

This is a variational approach, where the first term represents the intensity constraint and the second one the smoothness. The parameter λ controls the relative influence of the smoothness. The disparity gradient $\|\nabla d(k)\|$ can be obtained by computing the differences of the actual disparity $d(k)$ to the others within a local neighborhood $N(k)$ according to:

$$\| \nabla d(k) \| = \sum_{n \in N(k)} \| d(k) - d_n(k) \| \qquad (142)$$

This illustrated in Fig. 134. Due to the sparse data map derived from edge detection, it is possible to extend the neighborhood on a relatively large area.

To take into account the distance to the actual position it is possible to weight the disparities with a Gaussian.

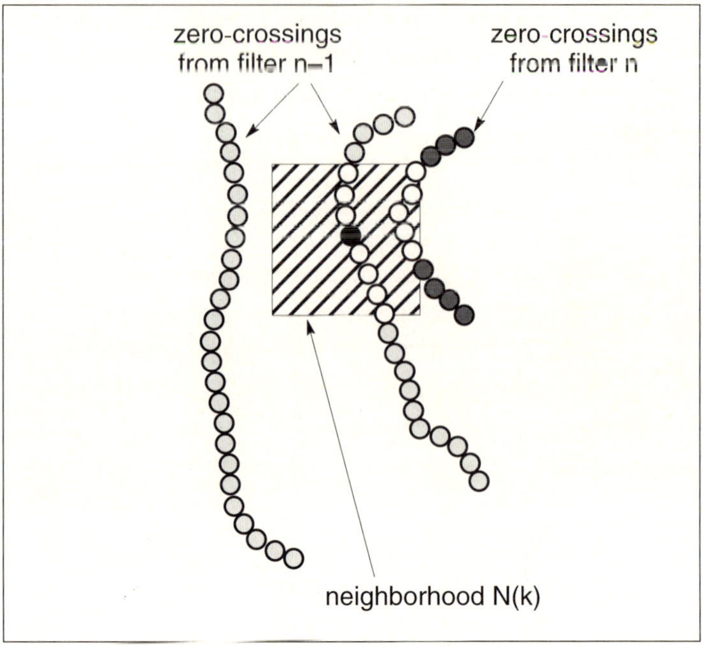

Figure 134: Neighborhood and Gaussian weighting

$$g(r) = \sigma^2 e^{-\frac{r^2}{2\sigma^2}} \tag{143}$$

where we suppose a $1/e$-ratio at the boundaries. The maximum radius r_{max} thus obtained is

$$r_{max} = \sigma \sqrt{2 + 4 \ln\sigma} \tag{144}$$

The parameters σ should follow the filter size of the corresponding Marr–Hildreth operator for the edge detection.

During the initialization every disparity value in the left image will be associated to one of its possible matches in the right one. The state changes of the system are then performed by selecting any k and by changing the possible match. The change of the energy function is computed with Eq. (141) and follows the rules of simulated annealing. The decrease of T is performed after a specific number of random changes.

Since this algorithm employs a coarse–fine strategy in a first run only the coarsest zero-crossings are matched. The results in terms of disparities are used as additional information for the computation of the disparity gradients in the filters. This hierarchical method supports a reduction of ambiguities in the dense maps of the fine filters by using information from previous runs. Furthermore, it generates a more dense disparity map depending on the number of filters used.

The computation of the depth from the disparity map is straightforward and follows the geometry of our simple camera model. Once we know the depth Z_P for at least one disparity d_P then we can formulate for any k:

$$Z_P \frac{d_P}{L} = Z(k)\, \frac{d(k)}{L} \qquad (145)$$

This is a very simple way, however, and thus associated with error problems.

The interpolation of the depth map appears to be a scattered data problem that can be solved with standard Shepard or Franke methods [69].

5.5.4. Examples

The following examples illustrate the efficiency of the matching method by computing on a random dot stereogram. The method was applied on 256 x 256 pixel images with 40% black pixels as illustrated in Fig. 137. Since the algorithm has to be tuned carefully with regard to the parameters for preprocessing and matching, the following table gives an overview of the values found to yield good results.

	panel width	**mask radius factor**	**mask size of LOG operator**
filter 1	5	1.8	17
filter 2	6		21
filter 3	7		25

annealing factor	0.95
λ-factor	1.0
matching duration	10
starting temperature	100°
stopping temperature	1°

Table 10: Parameters chosen for filtering and matching

After initialization the annealing method works only on those candidates that have more than one potential match. All others will be matched immediately. Since the proposed technique works on a coarse-fine-strategy the annealing behavior will be improved with smaller filter sizes. Figure 138 shows the decrease of energy *E(T)* as a function of the simulation temperature *T* recorded after each decrease of *T*.

We see that the energy can also increase locally, allowing the system to escape from local minima. Figure 135 illustrates the annealing behavior for the three successively applied filters. The grey bar represents the starting energy, the black bar the stop energy.

Figure 136 illustrates the distribution of the computed disparities for each run on a logarithmic scale. We see that the values 0 and 8 are the most common. This results from the random dots that have only either 0 or 8 units disparity. The peak at value 16 for the first filter indicates a too-large filter size.

Figure 135: Annealing behavior for different filters

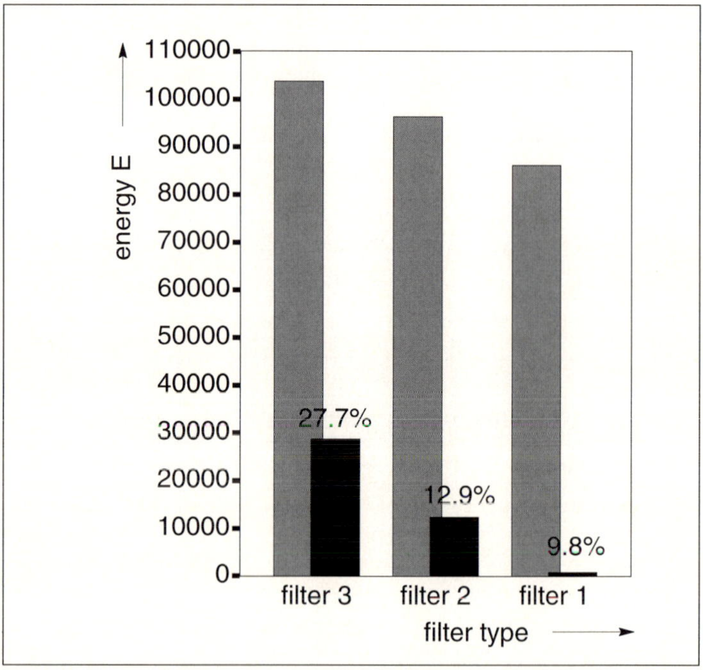

The white bars in Fig. 136 stand for candidates that have 0 units disparity, the grey bar for those that have 8 units. The total percentage of correct matches is also presented. The total number of computed matches increases from filter 3 to filter 1.

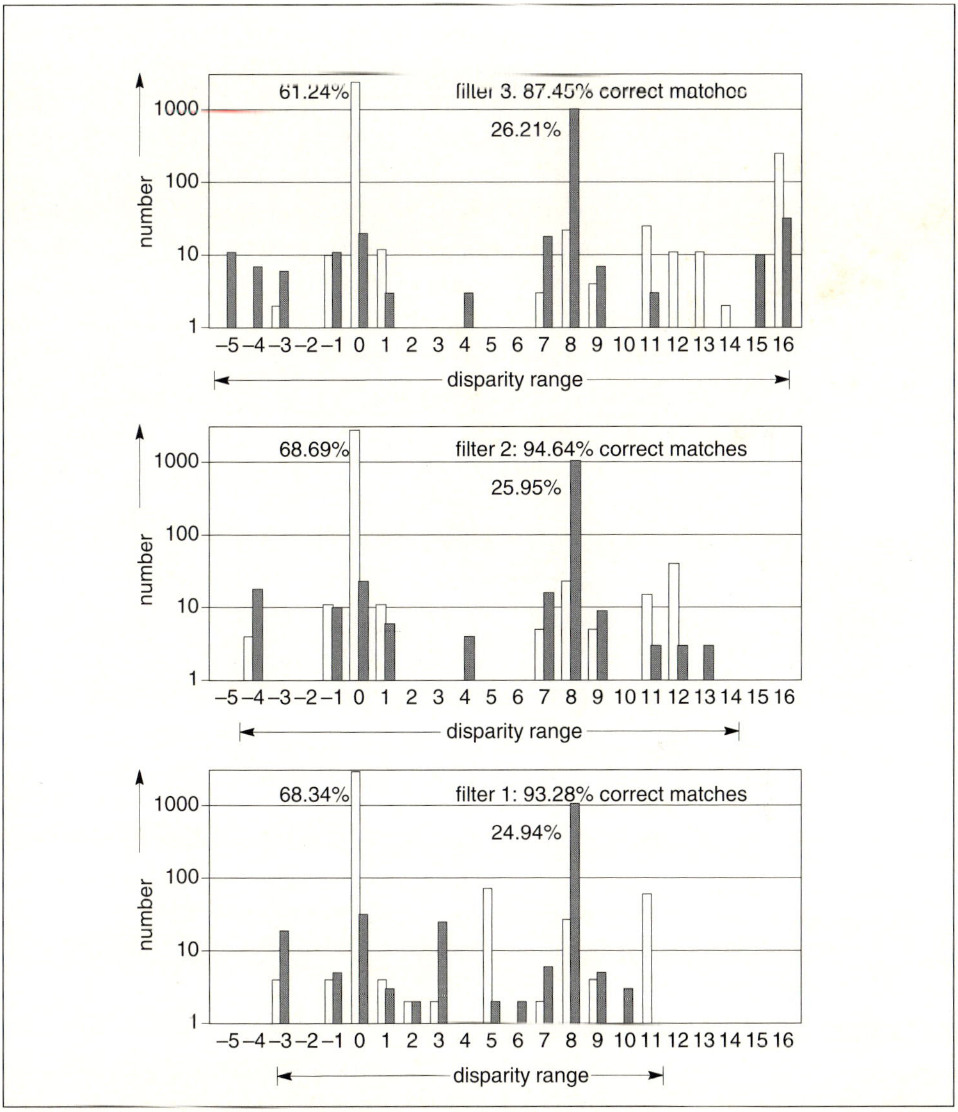

Figure 136: Distribution of the computed disparity ranges with respect to the value 0 (white bar) and the value 8 (grey bar)

5.6. Active Light Approaches: Laser Scanners

Aside from the solutions discussed for the standard computer vision problems of computing depth from images, there are numerous methods stemming from electronic phtogrammetry that use active light to recover range. Some of these techniques, reviewed for instance in [152], use structured light such as Moiré patterns or bars of different size and orientation, others employ differently colored light sources to illuminate the object. But the basic idea is to ease the identification of a particular feature point in the image and its position in 3D space. Apart from this there are also methods based on laser Doppler effects or radar waves, depending on the problem they are tailored for. Radar scanners can be found in satellites, for example. We should note here that these systems strictly speaking cannot be seen as real 3D scanners, since they do not provide any information about the interior of an object. This is only possible with CT- or MR-tomography, which are briefly reviewed later.

Active range finding is well suited for fast and accurate 3D modeling in computer graphics. For this purpose there are some sophisticated hardware systems available nowadays. Figure 139 shows for instance a Cyberware 3D laser scanner that allows the computation of range and color maps of rotation-symmetric objects, like human heads (see also [252]).

The basic principle of a range finder is illustrated in Fig. 140 from [246]. The computation of a particular 3D point in space follows a simple algebra. A laser lighting system projects a simple thin bar of a specific color (red) on the surface of the object to be scanned. A calibrated sensor array records a 2D image of the object. Drawing a line from a pixel location found in the image sensor array through the camera lens center to the object surface determines a ray in space. Knowing the exact positions, orientations, and other parameters of the imaging system and identifying the position of the projected bar we can easily build a triangulation and find the solution quickly and accurately. By moving the system around the object, we can compute stripwise the range of the object in question. Additional filters can also help to facilitate the identification of the projected bar in the imaging sensor array.

In the industrial realization of the system, a coherent light bar is generated by a laser and the size of the system is minimized by special mirrors. Furthermore, a CCD sensor records the color associated with the respective range points. The recording time of the scanner in Fig. 139 is about 20 sec for a human head and accuracies up to 0.1 mm can be reached. In order to avoid artifacts arising from the motion of the platform, [246] extended this concept for plastic surgery applications. They use 6 different stationary lighting

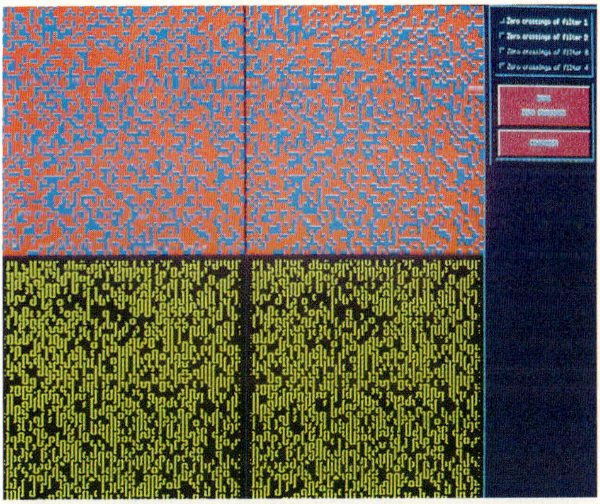

Figure 137:
Vertical edges extracted from a random dot stereogram

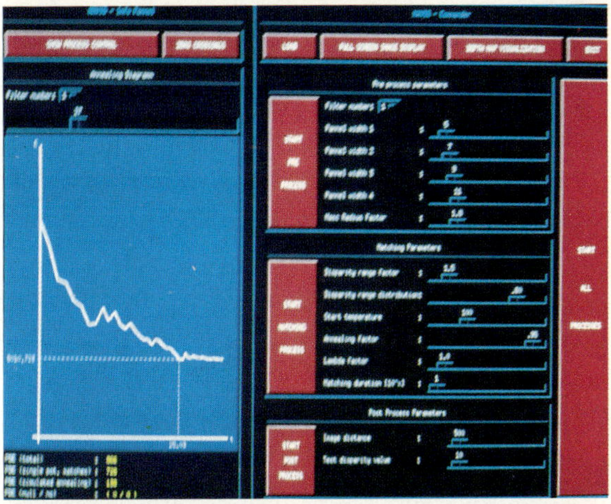

Figure 138:
System energy E as a function of the temperature T

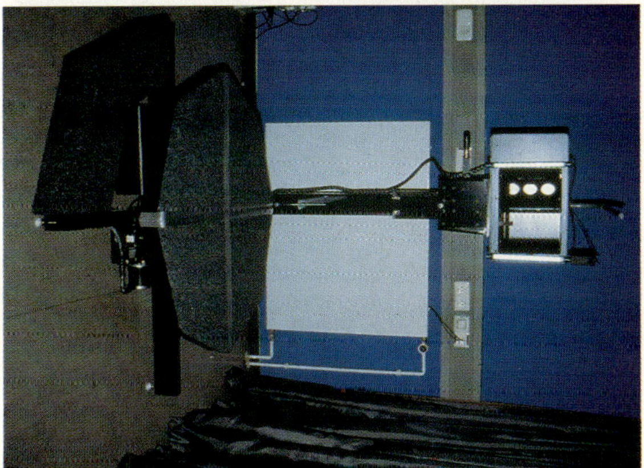

Figure 139:
3D laser scanner of Cyberware on a rotation-symmetric platform

systems that simultaneously project bars of different patterns on the human head. Ambiguities stemming from the multiple bars are re-

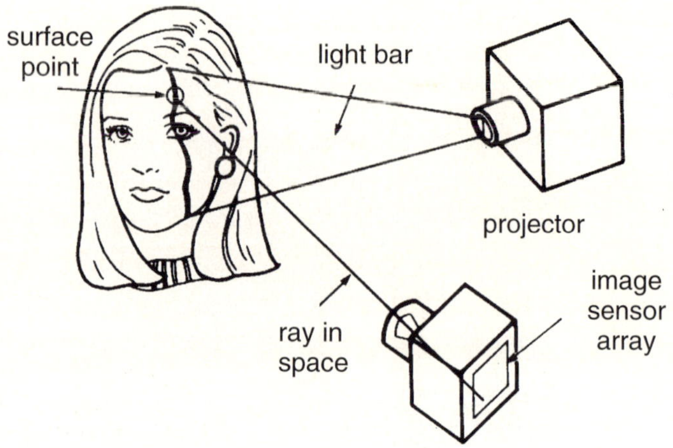

Figure 140:
Basic principle of the determination of range using an active light pattern (from [246])

Figure 141:
Range data from the scanner

Figure 142:
Phong shaded model:
a) without
b) with pseudcolor distance coding

Figure 143:
Front and side view with color texture mapping

Figure 144:
Cylindrical projection

Figure 145:
Surface model of the face data:
a) wireframe model
b) shaded and textured model

solved by coding them with different patterns and by a simple pattern analysis technique. In this case incoherent light is employed.

In order to give an idea of the possibilities arising with these methods in the field of graphics and imaging, the following pictures show some experiments with human faces. Figure 141 first shows the raw range data from a head scan. In Fig. 142 highlighted range data representations are shown with and without pseudocolor–distance coding. Figure 143 presents a front and a side view of the scan including the color information. A cylindrical projection is shown in Fig. 144, respectively, and a surface model after tesselation and data reduction is illustrated in Fig. 145.

In particular, the 3D scanning of human faces offers a large variety of applications, for instance face models for telecommunications and video conferencing [7], or face animation [252]. Other applications include plastic surgery, 3D face editing, 3D face recognition, and simulation of aging.

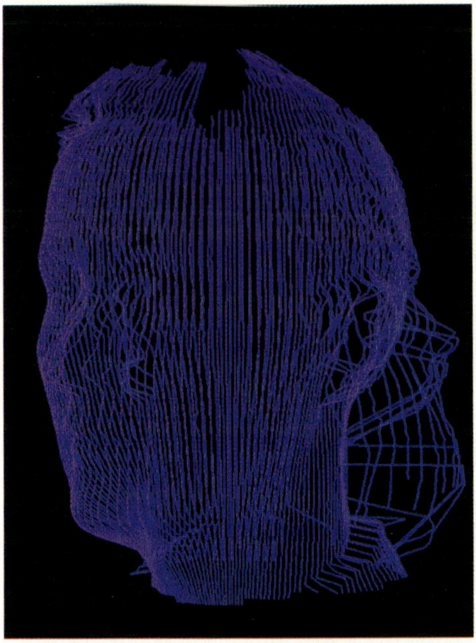

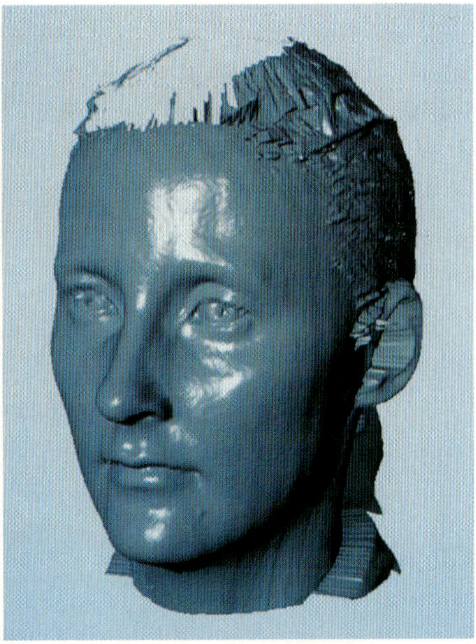

Figure 141, 142a

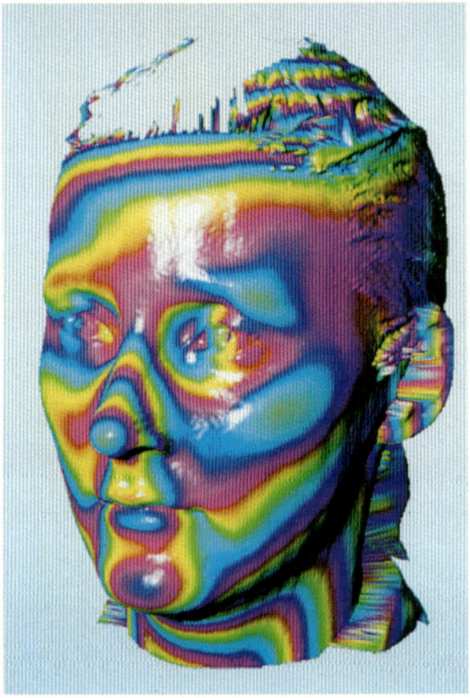

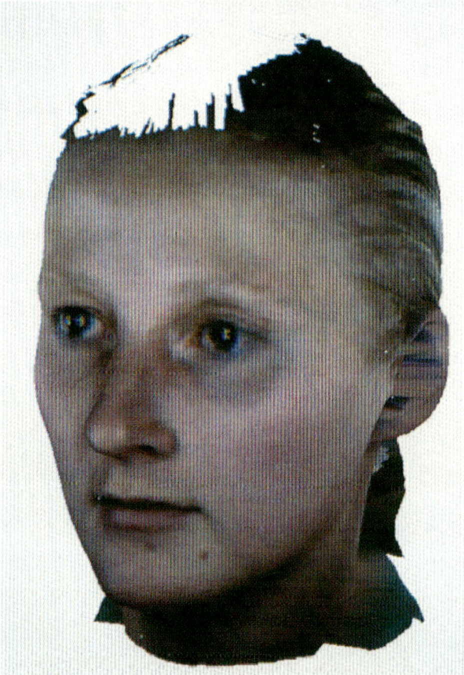

Figure 142b, 143a

Figure 143b, 144

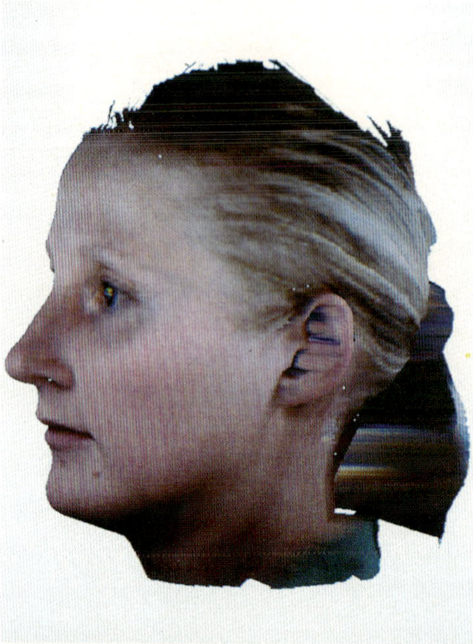

Figure 145

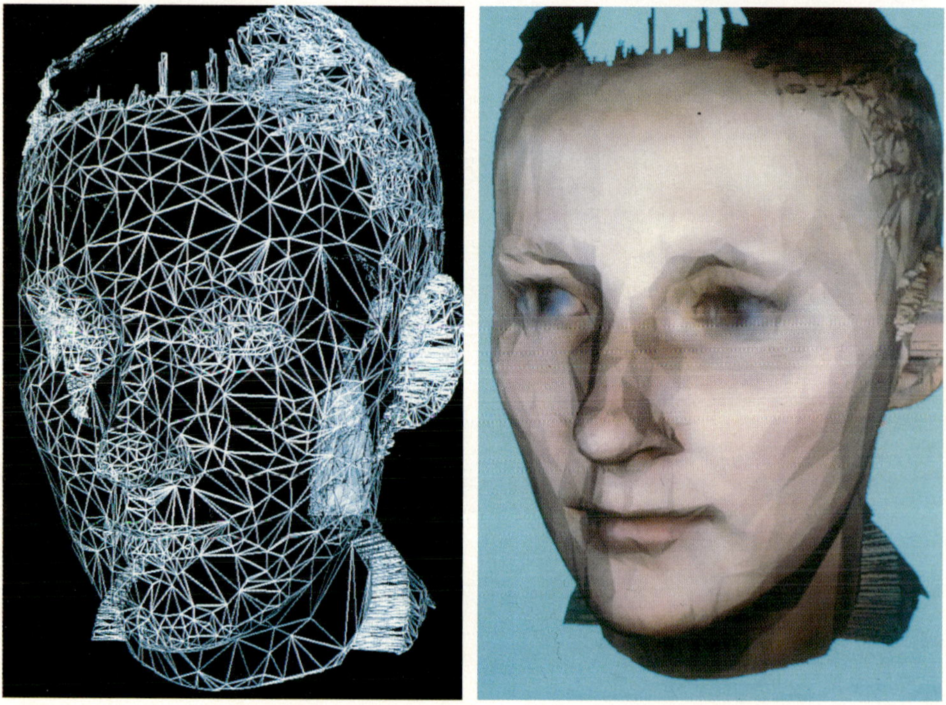

6. Image Analysis and Neural Networks

6.1. Introductory Remarks

In the applications presented so far, there was a strong requirement for imaging algorithms that implement basic functions in human visual perception like edge detection or shape from stereo. The idea was to employ these techniques as sophisticated solutions for complex modeling problems. However, aside from these strictly visual analysis techniques, there is another subject that is even more general in the sense that it stands for intelligent behavior, such as decision making and classification. Each of us knows that human beings perform these tasks very well even if the underlying facts are unclear or fuzzy. In visualization, for instance, segmentation and cluster analysis are extremely important for the prefiltering of large data sets. Moreover, in imaging and even more in artificial intelligence in general [24] one of the mainstream working areas turns out to be segmentation and classification.

Due to the complexity and nonlinearity of this task, mathematical statistics has developed numerous methods in the past [71, 58]. Unfortunately, most effective techniques are quite complex in computation time and mathematical background.

Apart from these classical methods, during the last decade, there has been increasing research activity in the field of artificial neural networks. Based on neurophysiological models the goal is to find paradigms that approximate biological neural networks by means of parallel and distributed processing. Artificial neural networks proved to be very capable of solving tasks such as complex control, nonlinear function approximation and estimation, clustering, classification, and associative memory. As a result they are often employed as an interesting alternative to classical techniques.

The goal of this chapter is to give an introduction to the principles of statistical data analysis, emphasizing classical techniques like vector quantization and c-means clustering as well as principal component analysis. Furthermore, the most popular neural network types are explained and extensions for visualization and image processing are clarified.

6.2. Mathematical Foundations

6.2.1. Cluster Analysis and Vector Quantization

The basic goal of cluster analysis, also known as non–supervised classification, is to find a set of mean vectors $\boldsymbol{m}_i$, $i = 1..c$, that optimally presents any given density function $p(\boldsymbol{x})$ of a given N-dimensional data vector $\boldsymbol{x}$, using a specific optimization criterion. The mean vectors $\boldsymbol{m}_i$ then perform a vector quantization of the data space. They can be interpreted as a discrete set of codebook vectors that describe $p(\boldsymbol{x})$. Although many different approaches have been set up, the standard criterion function is usually a mean-square error E to be minimized. Thus, for metric spaces, we can describe an error function E as follows:

$$E = \int \| \boldsymbol{x} - \boldsymbol{m}_k \|^2 \, p(\boldsymbol{x}) \, d\boldsymbol{x} \tag{146}$$

$$\boldsymbol{m}_i^T = (m_{i1},..,m_{iN})$$
$$\boldsymbol{x}^T = (x_1,..,x_N)$$

where E has to be minimized in a way that the mean vector $\boldsymbol{m}_k$ presents the samples $\boldsymbol{x}$ of the data set in a sense that:

$$\| \boldsymbol{x} - \boldsymbol{m}_k \| = \min_i \{ \| \boldsymbol{x} - \boldsymbol{m}_i \| \} \qquad (147)$$

Let Φ be a discrete set of vectors $\boldsymbol{x}$ in the N-dimensional feature space, we can describe the problem as:

$$E = \sum_{i=1}^{c} \sum_{x \in \Phi_i} \| \boldsymbol{x} - \boldsymbol{m}_i \|^2 \rightarrow \min \qquad (148)$$

These descriptions imply that we divide the feature space given by s samples into exactly c disjoint subsets $\Phi_1,..,\Phi_c$, the so-called clusters, with means or cluster centroids, where

$$\boldsymbol{m}_i = \frac{1}{s_i} \sum_{x \in \Phi_i} \boldsymbol{x} \qquad (149)$$

and s_i is the number of samples in Φ_i. The cluster centroids $\boldsymbol{m}_i$ represent the samples best in the sense that the sum of the square lengths of the error vectors $\boldsymbol{x} - \boldsymbol{m}_i$ is minimized. However, the problem arises of how to divide the feature space into c partitions receiving a global minimum of E, where there are approximately $c^s/c!$ [58] ways to do.

The problem above is a classical application for discrete optimization techniques, which can be performed using interactive hill climbing techniques or stochastic methods. The variety of definitions of the boundaries between two clusters and their centroids is also illustrated for a 2-dimensional data space in Fig. 146. One of the popular undirected methods for optimizing the energy function of Eq. (148) can be discribed as follows.

If we introduce a partitional error E_i with

$$E_i = \sum_{x \in \Phi_i} \| \boldsymbol{x} - \boldsymbol{m}_i \|^2 \quad \textit{and} \quad E = \sum_{i-1}^{c} E_i \qquad (150)$$

then we obtain the following change of the means $\boldsymbol{m}_i$ and $\boldsymbol{m}_j$ when moving a sample $\bar{\boldsymbol{x}}$ from Φ_i to Φ_j

$$\boldsymbol{m}_i^* = \boldsymbol{m}_i - \frac{\bar{\boldsymbol{x}} - \boldsymbol{m}_i}{s_i - 1} \qquad (151)$$

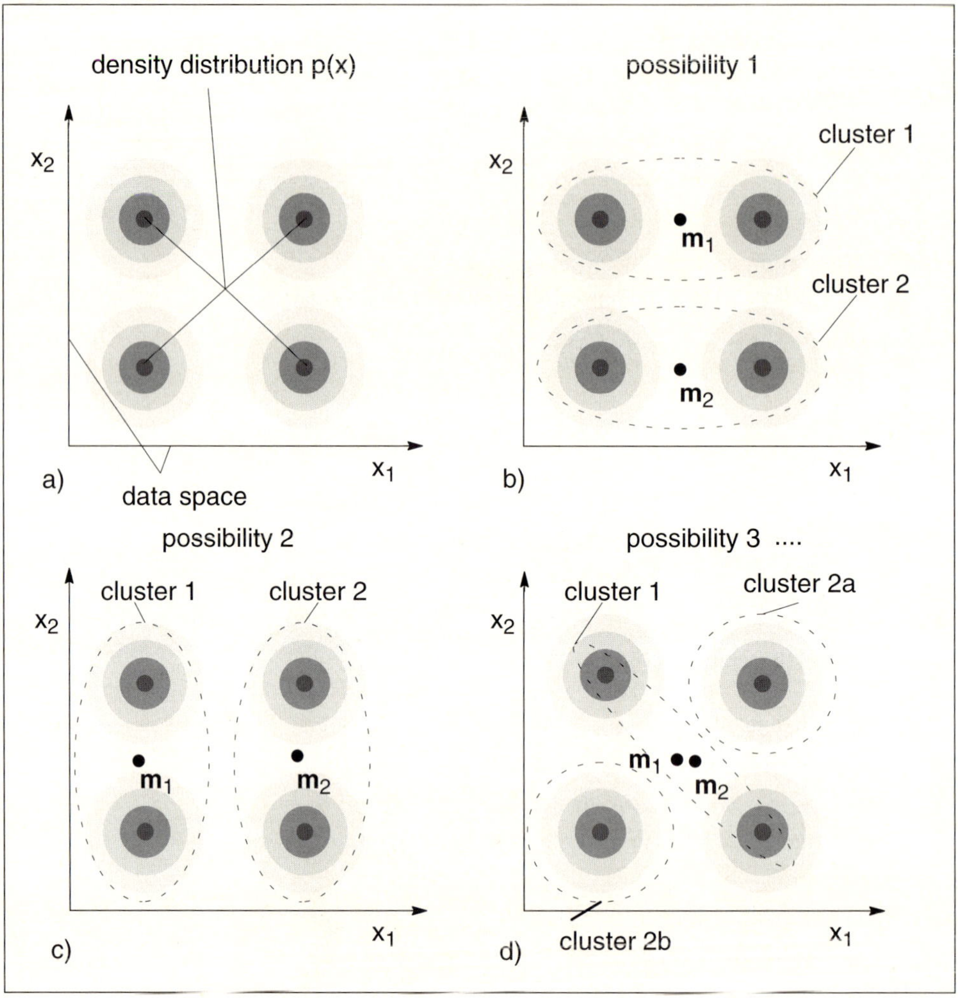

Figure 146: Defining two clusters and centroids in a 2 dimensional space. a) Input data set b), c), d) Possible clusters

$$m_j^* = m_j + \frac{\bar{x} - m_j}{s_j + 1} \qquad (152)$$

The corresponding partitional error functions change with

$$E_i^* = E_i - \underbrace{\frac{s_i}{s_i - 1} \| \bar{x} - m_i \|^2}_{a} \qquad (153)$$

$$E_j^* = E_j + \underbrace{\frac{s_j}{s_j + 1} \| \bar{x} - m_j \|^2}_{b} \qquad (154)$$

and if $a > b$ we obtain a total decrease in error. s_i and s_j are the numbers of samples in Φ_i and Φ_j respectively.

This suggests the following interative (c-means clustering) technique that is written in a pseudocode below:

```
initialize_clusters (s,c);              # initial partitions Φi of s samples in c clusters
X = {x};                                # all samples included
do {
        Φi = get_subset (Φ,X);          # get a subset Φi with a x ∈ Φi and x ∈ X
        x̄  = get_sample (Φi);           # get a sample x̄ ∈ Φi
        for all subsets Φj with j != i  # compute all changes bj of the errors Ej for sample x̄
                bj = error_part_b (x̄,Ej);

        a = error_part_a (x̄,Ei);        # compute change a of the error Ei
        bk = min (bj);                  # get the minimum of all b-changes
        if (bk < a) {                   # if the error decreases ...
                sub_sample (x̄,Φi);      # put x̄ out of Φi
                add_sample (x̄,Φk);      # put x̄ into Φk
                X = {x};                # include again all samples
                }
        else    X = X - x̄;              # exclude x̄ from X
        }
while (X != {});                        # do until X is empty
```

This vector quantization method of a certain multidimensional data space refers directly to the well-known concept of Voronoi tessellation in computational geometry [108], which creates a partition of $\boldsymbol{R}^n$ into regions where all $\boldsymbol{x}$ have the same $\boldsymbol{m}_i$ as their next neighbor. The corresponding boundaries are performed by hyperplanes perpendicular to the lines connecting two cluster centers $\boldsymbol{m}_i$ and $\boldsymbol{m}_j$. This is illustrated in Fig. 147 for a 2-dimensional example.

Aside from minimizing the mean square of the Euclidean distances, many other criteria can be taken into consideration such as variances or correlation functions (see also [58]).

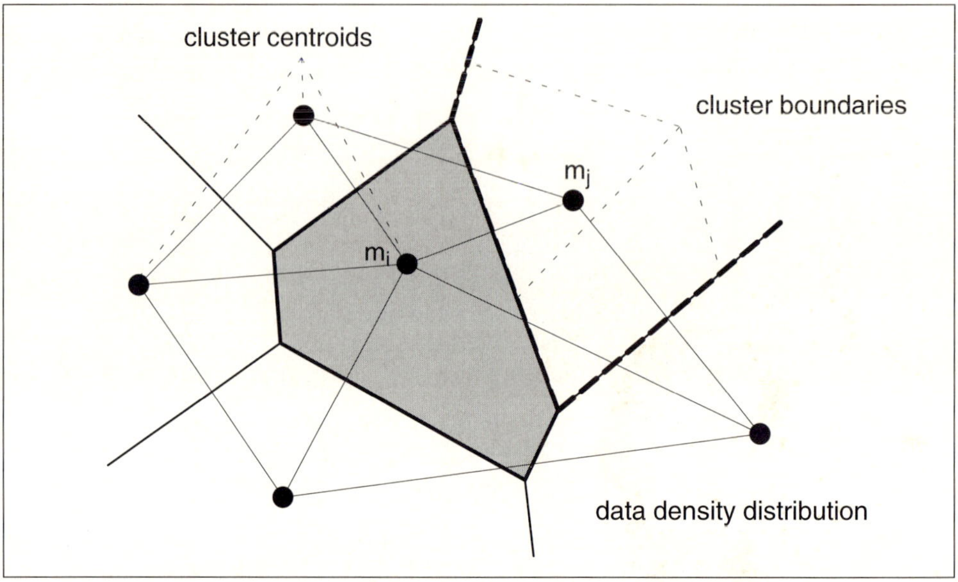

Figure 147:
Voronoi tessellation as a clusterization for the 2-dimensional case [94]

6.2.2. *N*-Tree Clustering

The *c*-means methods have the shortcoming of selecting an appropriate *c* in advance: the total number of clusters is fixed and cannot be adapted on the underlying density function $p(\boldsymbol{x})$. For this reason another very popular clustering method had been established, namely clustering using *N*-dimensional trees (see also [62]). Since trees have been proven to provide efficient data structures for data management and retrieval [240] they have been very well examined in computer science.

The following figure illustrates the basic principle of *N*-tree clustering for the 2-dimensional case. The density function $p(\boldsymbol{x})$ is divided into subregions by a simple quadtree-tessellation.

Let $\boldsymbol{x}_i$: i=1,..,s be the set of data samples and the global criterion for subdivision of the *N*-tree cells will be:

$$\frac{P_j(\boldsymbol{x})}{\Delta V_j} \leq \delta_{\max} \qquad (155)$$

$P_j(\boldsymbol{x})$ represents the a priori probability of $\boldsymbol{x}$ in a tree-cell j, δ_{max} a threshold density for subdividing the cell into 2^N daughter cells, and ΔV_j the hypervolume of the cell.

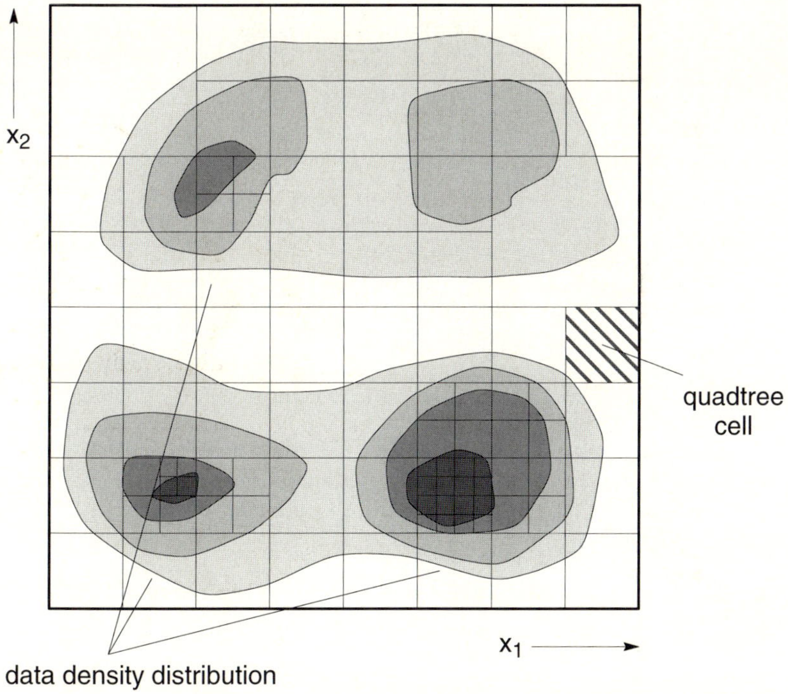

Figure 148:
*N-tree tessellation of a data density function p(**x**) for N = 2*

This assumes that the amount of data samples will be accumulated up to a limit δ_{max} and then the cell will be subdivided.

The rule for generating the *N*-tree can be written in pseudocode as follows:

After defining the *N*-tree, the respective centroids $\boldsymbol{m}_j$ can be computed easily for each cell *j* with

$$\boldsymbol{m}_j = \sum_{i=1}^{s_j} \frac{\boldsymbol{x}_{i,j}}{s_j} \qquad (156)$$

s_j: *number of data samples in cell j*
$\boldsymbol{x}_{i,j}$: *data sample i in cell j*

```
init_octree ();
    create_first cell ();
    while (!eof)
      {
        read (x);
          actual_cell=root_of_octree;
          while (child (actual_cell) )                          /* search the octree branch for x */
              actual_cell=son_cell  (x, actual_cell);
          while ( delta (actual_cell) >= DELTA_MAX )
          {                                           /*divide this branch into sons if
                split_cell_into_sons (actual_cell);       data limit is reached           */
                 transfer_data_into_sons (actual_cell); /* transfer all data to the new son */
                actual_cell=son_cell (x, actual_cell);
           }

          if (delta (actual_cell) < DELTA_MAX)
                write_x_into_actual_cell;
        }
```

The number of centroids depends then only on the choice of δ_{max} and on the underlying density distribution. Due to the efficient implementation of this scheme, it provides a fast and flexible clustering method.

6.2.3. Dimensionality Reduction and Rank Ordering

One of the basic problems of analyzing and visualizing multidimensional data sets is the representation of the data and its structure in a low-dimensional subspace. The general approach to this problem is to represent the data in such a way that the distances of the sample points in the low-dimensional space correspond as much as possible to the dissimilarities between points in the original space. This process is also called multidimensional scaling.

Let us formulate the problem in the following way: if $\boldsymbol{x}$ are the original data samples $\boldsymbol{x}_1,..,\boldsymbol{x}_s$ and $\boldsymbol{y}$ are the lower dimensional representatives $\boldsymbol{y}_1,..,\boldsymbol{y}_s$, then the goal has to be to look for a configuration where the $s(s-1)/2$ interpoint distances $d_{ij} = \| y_j - y_i \|$ are as close as possible to the corresponding data distances $\delta_{ij} = \| x_j - x_i \|$. Since it is not in general possible to find a configuration where $\delta_{ij} = d_{ij}$ for all i and j, it is usual to set up a criterion function E_D to evaluate the match; for instance,

$$E_D = \frac{1}{\sum_{i<j} \delta_{ij}} \sum_{i<j} \frac{(d_{ij} - \delta_{ij})^2}{\delta_{ij}} \qquad (157)$$

yields a good compromise between the largest error and the fractional error [58]. An optimal configuration can then be sought using gradient descent methods. The gradient of E_D with respect to $\mathbf{y}_k$ is obtained by

$$\nabla_{\mathbf{y}_k} E_D = \frac{2}{\sum_{i<j} \delta_{ij}} \sum_{j \neq k} \frac{(d_{kj} - \delta_{kj})}{\delta_{kj}} \frac{(\mathbf{y}_k - \mathbf{y}_j)}{d_{kj}} \qquad (158)$$

and represents a unit vector in the direction of $\mathbf{y}_k - \mathbf{y}_j$.
A second criterion important for nonmetric spaces is a rank ordering of the distances, where the preserving of ranks can be formulated as follows: If we can order the $g = s(s-1)/2$ dissimilarities in such a way that $\delta_{i1,j1} <,..,< \delta_{ig,jg}$ and we define numbers $\bar{d}_{ij}$ satisfying the monotonicity constraint as $\bar{d}_{i1,j1} <,..,< \bar{d}_{ig,jg}$, the degree to which the d_{ij} match this criterion can be estimated by

$$E_{mon} = \frac{1}{\sum_{i<j} d_{ij}} \min_{\bar{d}_{ij}} \sum_{i<j} (d_{ij} - \bar{d}_{ij})^2 \qquad (159)$$

The minimization of this criterion function will provide an optimal configuration in a subspace satisfying the constraint of topological ordering. These dimensionality scaling techniques are also applied in the field of experimental psychology [74].

6.2.4. Principal Components and Subspaces

The section above has shown that dimensionality reduction is strongly connected with finding subspaces satisfying respective optimization criteria. In statistical data analysis [71], we can find several techniques for this task. One of the most famous methods, taking the optimization as an eigenvalue problem, is the principal component analysis or Karhunen–Loeve expansion. In general, this method aims to find a subset of principal directions in a data set of any statistical distribution. The corresponding basis vectors satisfy the constraint of orthonormality and the subspace defined by these vectors optimally takes into account the data correlation. The transformation of an initial data set into the space of principal components minimizes the cross-correlation of the single data samples. Mathematically, this method can be formulated as follows.

Let $\boldsymbol{x}_j : j = 1 ,.., s$ be a data set of the dimension N and $\boldsymbol{m}$ a mean vector:

$$\boldsymbol{m} = \frac{1}{s}\sum_{j=1}^{s} \boldsymbol{x}_j \qquad (160)$$

The difference vectors $\boldsymbol{d}_j$ can be calculated with

$$\boldsymbol{d}_j = \boldsymbol{x}_j - \boldsymbol{m} \qquad (161)$$

We can now apply the principal component analysis, that seeks a set of orthonormal vectors $\boldsymbol{u}_k$ with the constraint

$$\lambda_k = \frac{1}{s}\sum_{j=1}^{s} (\boldsymbol{u}_k^T \boldsymbol{d}_j)^2 \overset{!}{=} \max \qquad (162)$$

and

$$\boldsymbol{u}_l^T \boldsymbol{u}_k = \delta = \begin{cases} 1, & \text{if } l = k \\ 0, & \text{otherwise} \end{cases} \qquad (163)$$

$\boldsymbol{u}_k$ and λ_k represent the eigenvectors and eigenvalues of the covariance matrix $\boldsymbol{C}$, with

$$\boldsymbol{C} = \frac{1}{s}\sum_{j=1}^{s} \boldsymbol{d}_j \, \boldsymbol{d}_j^T \qquad (164)$$

There are numerous methods for numerically handling this approach. Since the dimension of $\boldsymbol{C}$ is given with N^2, a popular way to do it [137] follows by decomposition of $\boldsymbol{C}$ writing

$$\begin{aligned} \boldsymbol{C} &= \boldsymbol{A}\,\boldsymbol{A}^T \\ \boldsymbol{A} &= (\boldsymbol{d}_1,..,\boldsymbol{d}_s) \end{aligned} \qquad (165)$$

and we consider the eigenvectors $\boldsymbol{v}_i$ of $\boldsymbol{A}^T\boldsymbol{A}$ such that

$$A^T A v_i = \mu_i v_i \tag{166}$$

Multiplying both sides by A from the left we obtain

$$A A^T A v_i = \mu_i A v_i \tag{167}$$

where Av_i corresponds to the eigenvectors of $C = AA^T$.

This scheme constructs an s x s matrix $A^T A$ which we can easily compute the eigenvectors v_i with standard methods [208] and then obtain the u_k of C by linear combinations of the s training vectors:

$$u_k = \sum_{j=1}^{s} v_{kj} d_j \qquad k{:}\ 1,..,s \tag{168}$$

Since $s << N^2$ for most cases the problem has now become manageable.

After solving this eigenvector problem, any datum x can be projected into this eigenspace spanned by the u_k:

$$\omega_k = u_k^T (x - m) \tag{169}$$

where ω are the coordinates in the eigenspace.

Conversely, any datum x can be expanded as a linear combination of u_k and ω_k

$$x = m + \frac{1}{s} \sum_{k=1}^{s} \omega_k u_k \tag{170}$$

ω_k describes the contribution of each eigenvector.

The dimensionality reduction can now be achieved by ordering the eigenvectors u_k according to the absolute value of their corresponding eigenvalue λ_k and by taking only the $s - r$ largest ones for the data expansion in Eq. (170).

The vector $\Omega^T = (\omega_1, \omega_2,.., \omega_{s-r})$ can be interpreted as a feature vector describing statistical properties of the data set.

The result of this process is that the $s - r$ eigenvectors define a subspace that minimizes the average error of information lost by the reduction of the number of dimensions with respect to Eq. (170).

Finally, it can be stated that the cluster analysis described above can also be thought of as a grouping of several dimensions of the data set with highly correlated features. Thus a lower dimensional subset can be produced.

6.2.5. Image Coding Using the KL-Transform

This method is very popular for image coding, i.e. for removing correlation from highly correlated data like face images. This was proposed first by [137, 236] and adapted by several other authors [244]. Figure 149 shows a set of 20 face images, and Fig. 150 shows the principal axes of this data set. In this example, we took the images pixelwise as data vectors of the dimension 64 x 64. The resulting principal axes $\boldsymbol{u}_k$ can also be visualized as images of the same pixel size. In Fig. 150 it is indicated that different eigenvectors emphasize the local variances in the grey values of the image data set. The images are ordered according to the size of the associated eigenvalue. In the upper left corner, we can see the mean image.

Using Eq. (170) we are able to reconstruct any image of the data set by means of a limited set of derived eigenvectors. This corresponds to a coding scheme and is illustrated in Figs. 151, 152, and 153, which show the efficiency of the coding when using different numbers of eigenvectors.

Although the pictorial interpretation of the eigenvectors presented in Fig. 150 somehow reveals a correspondence between the regions emphasized by particular vectors and by symbolic facial features such as hair, eyes, or nose, it must be stated that only iconic statistical properties are visualized. This should also be noted when estimating the quality of reconstruction and coding.

This section has shown that analyzing multidimensional data sets strongly correlates with discrete, iterative optimization of constraint cost functions. The following sections reveal artificial neural networks as a reciprocal approach and implementation to this problem. Many investigations document the relationship between neural network training and principal components [195, 196].

Figure 149:
Initial data set of 20 face images

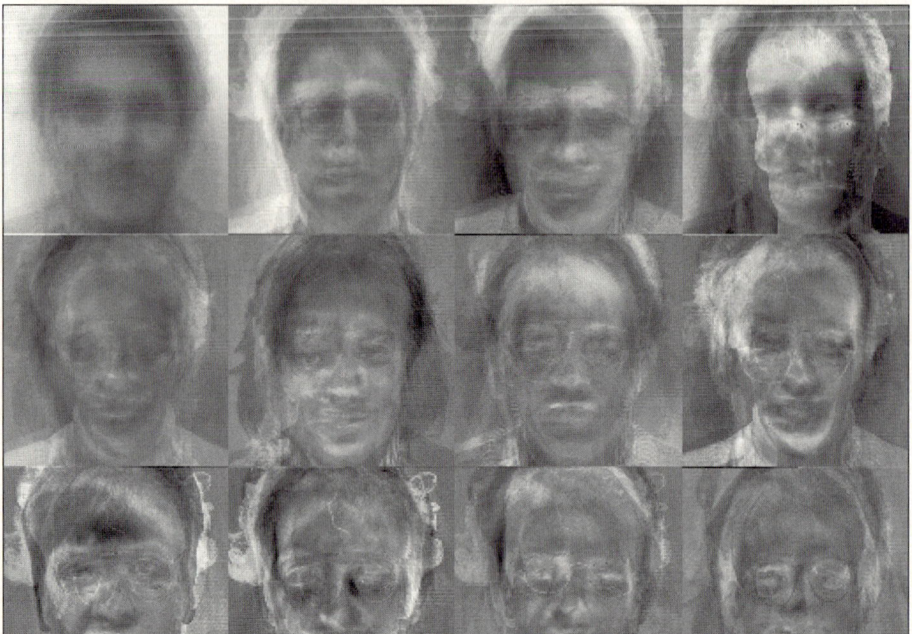

Figure 150:
Mean vector (upper left) and eigenvectors of the data set of Fig. 149

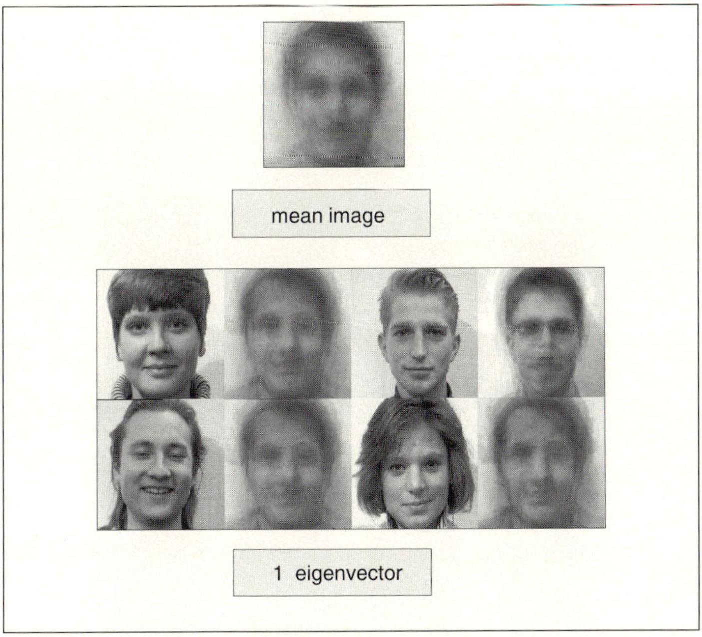

Figure 151:
4 face images and their reconstructions using 1 eigenvector

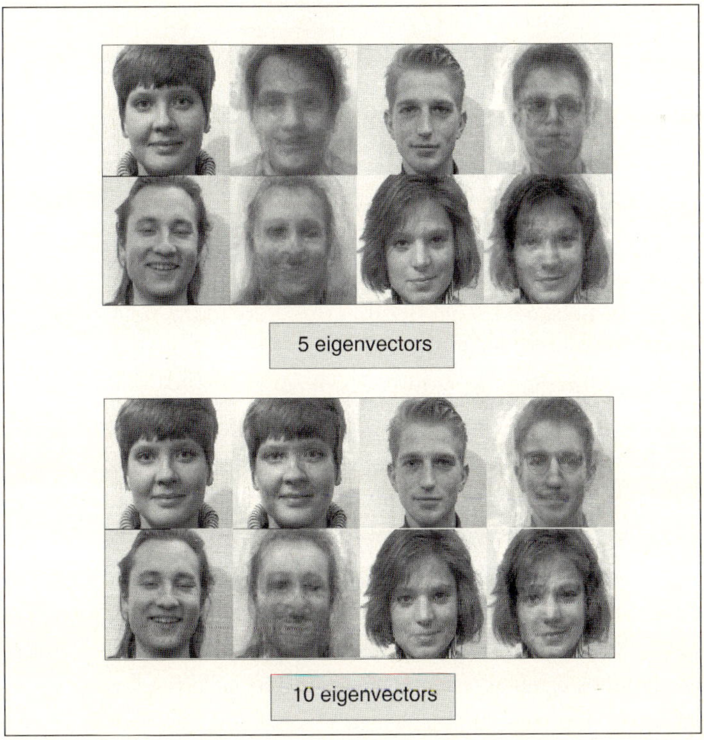

Figure 152:
4 face images and their reconstructions using 5 and 10 eigenvectors

Figure 153:
4 face images and their reconstructions using 15 and 20 eigenvectors

6.2.6. Supervised Classification Methods

A major task in image analysis is the segmentation and classification of an image into its components based on pixel or object properties to be presented. This feature also refers to the field of pattern recognition [189] and can be performed by several algorithms introduced in the past. A survey of these techniques is given as an example in [128]. The interested reader can also find detailed discussions of classification techniques in [58]. Where segmentation is related to the described clustering techniques, classification always has to be supervised by an instructor.

Classification and decision making is a generic task in artificial intelligence and is used in various applications, all the way from multispectral satellite data via handwritten characters up to gestures produced by a data glove, and interpreted by an advanced user interface [66]. The basic approach is to adapt a specific classifier via test samples and their class assignments, where the samples have to represent the statistical data distribution.

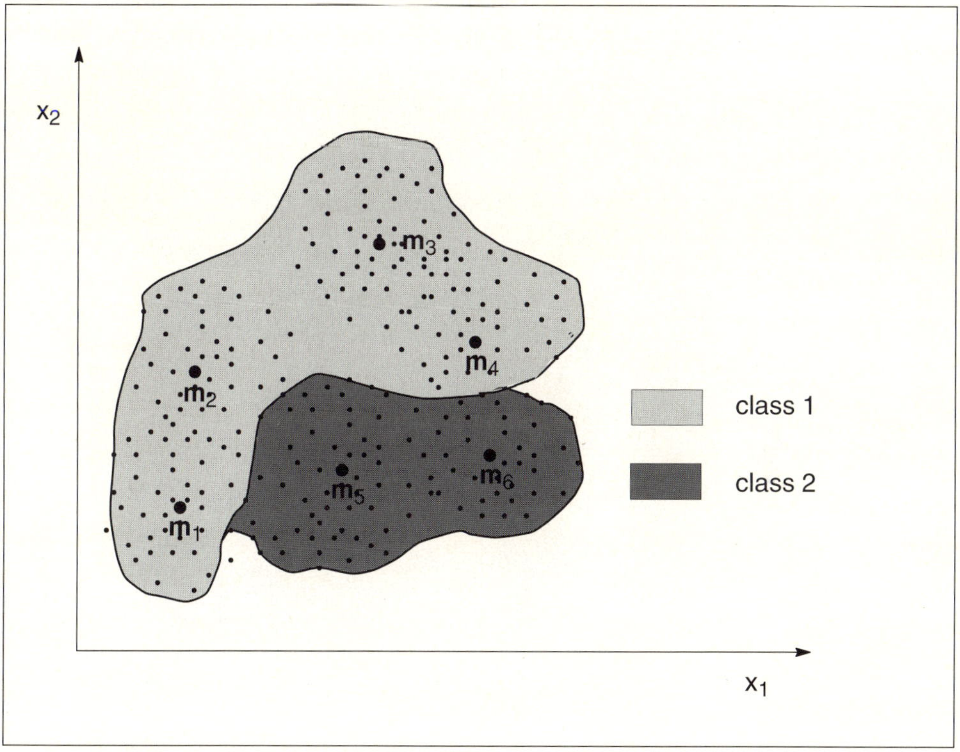

Figure 154: Clusters and class boundaries in a 2-dimensional feature space

Classification techniques aim at separating classes by defining decision boundaries in a feature space (see Fig. 154). Suppose there are K different classes and N features available, where $\boldsymbol{x}$ represents the feature vector for each object (pixel) to be classified. One of the fundamental functions is the discriminant function $g_k(\boldsymbol{x})$, which takes the maximum value if $\boldsymbol{x}$ belongs to the class k and for which the decision rule is simply

$$g_k(\boldsymbol{x}) > g_i(\boldsymbol{x}) \qquad k \neq i \quad , i: 1,..,K \tag{171}$$

Based on this understanding, the discriminant function divides the feature space into K regions. This is shown in Fig. 154 for a 2-dimensional space. The decision boundaries defined by the classifier are usually nonlinear and often nonconvex. In this sense classification turns out to be an approximation problem, where the goal is to approximate the optimal decision boundaries.

Unfortunately, in most real applications the clusters of different classes are overlapping and thus difficult to separate. There are numerous mathematical approaches to handle this problem, yet one of the fundamental rules is the Bayes decision rule. It postulates a decision boundary b, where the error probability P_E for any classification problem is minimized. This is illustrated for the one-dimensional case by the example in Fig. 155.

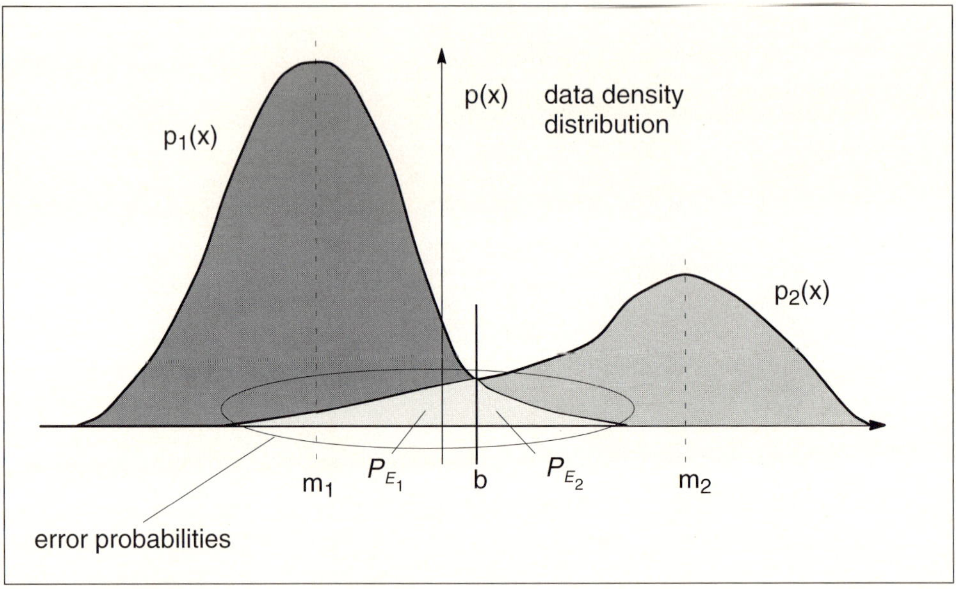

Figure 155: Minimum error decision boundary value b in the one-dimensional case

Let b be the decision boundary and P_{E_2} be

$$P_{E_2} = prob \{ \boldsymbol{x} \in C_1 \mid \boldsymbol{x} \to C_2 \} = \int_b^{\infty} p_1(\boldsymbol{x})d\boldsymbol{x} \tag{172}$$

i.e., the probability of $\boldsymbol{x}$ belonging to class C_1 but being assigned to class C_2 and similarly

$$P_{E_1} = \int_{-\infty}^{b} p_2(\boldsymbol{x})d\boldsymbol{x} \tag{173}$$

we get the overall error P_E

$$P_E = P_{E_1} + P_{E_2} \doteq min \qquad (174)$$

where $p_1(\boldsymbol{x})$ and $p_2(\boldsymbol{x})$ are the a priori probability density functions for C_1 and C_2. In order to minimize P_E, b has to follow the rule:

$$p_1(x_b) - p_2(x_b) = 0 \ ! \qquad (175)$$

In general, this means that the difference between the a priori density functions of the neighboring classes C_1 and C_2 to be distinguished from each other drops to zero at the so-called Bayesian border. The task is now to find a discrimination function that yields a good approximation of the Bayes border for an arbitrary data density distribution $p(\boldsymbol{x})$. The following section sketches the most popular statistical classifiers (see also [62, 93]).

Next Neighbor Classifiers

The central idea of this method consists of calculating the Euclidian distance d from the vector $\boldsymbol{x}$ that has to be classified to all feature vectors $\boldsymbol{x}_j$ $(j = 1,..,s)$ out of the training set with Eq. (176). The class C of the vector $\boldsymbol{x}_j$ with the shortest distance to $\boldsymbol{x}$ will be set as the classification result.

$$d(\boldsymbol{x}_j, \boldsymbol{x}) = \sqrt{(x_{j1}-x_1)^2 + (x_{j2}-x_2)^2 + \ldots + (x_{jN}-x_N)^2} \qquad (176)$$

with the dimension N of the feature space.

The disadvantage that a few bad feature vectors in the training set may influence the result inefficiently can be avoided by taking a vote on an odd number of nearest neighbors. The discriminant functions $g_i(\boldsymbol{x})$, whose maximum determines the resulting class C are:

$$g_i(\boldsymbol{x}) = \frac{nearest\ neighbors\ of\ class\ C_i}{nearest\ neighbors}, \quad i = 1,..,K \qquad (177)$$

This method does not have to be trained since it uses the whole training set during the working phase. The disadvantage arises when dealing with large training sets. In these cases, it is better to calculate centroids $\boldsymbol{m}_j$ via cluster analysis and to assign them to the respective classes.

Regression Methods and Polynomial Classifiers

Regression analysis is a minimum squared error procedure [58]. The discriminant functions $g_i(\boldsymbol{x})$ are optimized in a way that the *expectation of the quadratic error* between $g_i(\boldsymbol{x})$ and the target z_i is *minimized*. The variable z_i has the value 1 if $\boldsymbol{x}$ belongs to class C_i, otherwise, it has the value 0. The discriminant functions are approximated by polynomial functions. Usually, linear discriminant functions are preferred with regard to complexity. They are set up as follows:

$$g_i(\boldsymbol{x}) \quad = \quad w_{i0} + w_{i1}x_1 + w_{i2}x_2 + \cdots + w_{iN}x_N \tag{178}$$

The coefficients w_{ij} are determined by the feature vectors in the training set and consequently the problem is reduced to finding the solution of a set of linear equations. The classification result is found by a maximum decision over all discriminant functions $g_i(\boldsymbol{x})$.

Since the linear approximation of the discriminant functions only provides a reliable scheme for problems that are linearly separable, higher-order polynomials have been employed. Unfortunately, this leads to a nonlinear system of equations that is computationally expensive.

Maximum Likelihood Estimation and Bayes Classifiers

A common statistical method for classification is the maximum likelihood estimation. It is based on the decision rules of Bayes [58] and aims to define decision boundaries in such a way that the probability of false classification will be minimized. For this purpose, the *a posteriori probability* $P(C_i|\boldsymbol{x})$ is computed by the Bayes formula (Eq. (179) and a maximum decision for the class assignment of $\boldsymbol{x}$ is taken:

$$\boldsymbol{x} \mapsto C_i \mid P(C_i|\boldsymbol{x}) \;\geq\; P(C_j|\boldsymbol{x}) \;\forall\; i \neq j \tag{179}$$

The Bayes formula states that the a posteriori probability $P(C_i|\boldsymbol{x})$ can be computed from the *state conditional probability density function* $P(\boldsymbol{x}|C_i)$ for $\boldsymbol{x}$, the *a priori probability* of class C_i and the density function $p(\boldsymbol{x})$

$$P(C_i|\boldsymbol{x}) = \frac{p(\boldsymbol{x}|C_i)\ P(C_i)}{p(\boldsymbol{x})} \tag{180}$$

where

$$p(\boldsymbol{x}) = \sum_{i=1}^{K} p(\boldsymbol{x}|C_i)\ P(C_i) \tag{181}$$

Furthermore, if we assume that the classes have the same a priori probability $P(C_i)$ then we can simply set the discriminant function $g_i(\boldsymbol{x}) = p(\boldsymbol{x}|C_i)$. In order to compute the class density function, we have to select an underlying model for the data distribution. If multivariate Gaussian distributions are employed $g_i(\boldsymbol{x})$ is given by:

$$p(\boldsymbol{x}|C_i) = \frac{1}{(2\pi)^{N/2}\ |\boldsymbol{C}|^{\frac{1}{2}}}\ e^{-\frac{1}{2}(x-m_i)^T C^{-1} (x-m_i)} \tag{182}$$

where $\boldsymbol{m}_i$ is the mean of the feature vectors in C_i and $\boldsymbol{C}$ is the covariance matrix $N \times N$. The above method is able to approximate decision boundaries by means of second-order hypersurfaces such as hyperparaboloids, hyperellipsoids, hyperbolas, etc. Complex and non-convex areas can only be discriminated using extensions of the maximum likelihood estimation. In these cases, a cluster analysis can subdivide each class into subclasses that are supposed to have Gaussian distributions. The final class boundary is then given by superimposing the second-order boundary of each class.

This method has been applied very often in imaging, specifically for satellite image classification [237].

6.3. Neural Networks

6.3.1. An Introduction

Artificial neural networks or connectionist models have been developed to make use of the organization and information processing principles of the human brain. Although the processing time of the brain's neurons is much slower than silicon chips, it performs – due to its specific architecture – some computations many times faster. The idea of modeling neural behavior by machines has quite a long tradition. First attempts can be found in [172] and several other papers before 1958, when Rosenblatt introduced the perceptron and opened the classical period of artificial neural systems [220]. However, a decade later Minsky and Papert in their famous book *Perceptrons* [177] exposed the limitations of these types of networks. That is when the dark ages of neural network research began. Although basic work was done with success by [140, 250, 72] and others, the breakthrough came with Rumelhart and the back-propagation algorithm [223, 224].

During the last decade, there has been increasing research activity in the field of neural networks [154] and interesting relationships have been discovered. For instance, Amari [13, 12] provides mathematical analysis of neural learning and shows the relationship between internal data coding and principle components [18]. Others extend neural networks in terms of fuzzy logic [109, 142] or even wavelets [266]. Latest research results also include genetic algorithms and evolution strategies [78].

The basic applications for which neural networks are adapted are clustering, classification, topological mapping, and approximation [54]. The advantages are that neural networks usually do not make any assumptions on the underlying cluster morphology, they are easy to use and implement, and they can be parallelized. Generally speaking, they are able to approximate any nonlinear problem just from observations, even if there is no mathematical formulation for it. The disadvantages, on the other hand, are that for most nonlinear models there is no unique mathematical analysis of the internal dynamics during training. Furthermore, for complex applications hill-climbing training rules can get stuck in local minima [177]. Al-

though there are different opinions on the overall capabilities of neural networks, there have been countless applications during the last years, particularly in the field of image processing and recognition [34, 35, 105]. In some cases, advantages in terms of accuracy and computation time have been proved.
For example, [88, 104, 38] reported on successful use of neural networks in scientific visualization. Dimensionality reduction and topological mapping can be performed by Kohonen maps. Others [149] applied genetic algorithms and evolution strategies for global illumination problems.

Anyway, neural networks are based on basic principles of human information processing and therefore they have to be considered in the scope of this book. In this sense they can be taken as models for *the integration of human perception, graphics, and imaging.*

For this reason the following section provides an introduction to the functionality of the most popular neural network types which can be distinguished as follows: supervised trained networks that refer to classification, and unsupervised networks that stand for cluster analysis and topological mapping. It should be noted, however, that for most of the models introduced here there exist both supervised and nonsupervised training algorithms.

Basically, neural networks are characterized by massive parallel computation and distributed memory. They typically consist of basic processing units, the neurons, and of interconnections between them. The weights of the interconnections can be adjusted during training. Figure 156 shows a model of an artificial neuron.

The input channels can be referred as the dendrites of the neuron, which are usually connected to other neurons. The connection strength is given by the weights $w_{j0},..,w_{jn}$. The neuron body performs a weighed sum S_j over the inputs, and employs a nonlinear threshold function to compute the output. The output signal x_j is transferred to the dendrites of all other neurons connected with it. The output channel represents the axon of a biological neuron.

For instance, the perceptron [177] simply checks whether the weighed sum is larger or smaller than a threshold value τ and produces a binary output signal x according to Eq. (183):

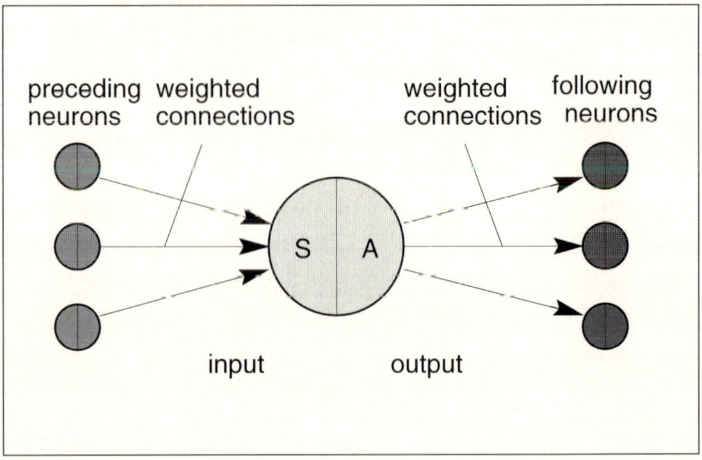

Figure 156: Basic processing unit of an artificial neural network

$$\begin{aligned} &if \quad S_j > \tau \quad then \quad x_j = 1 \\ &if \quad S_j \le \tau \quad then \quad x_j = 0 \end{aligned} \tag{183}$$

The network itself is characterized by its topology. The following classical example is a two-layered perceptron as shown in Fig. 157.

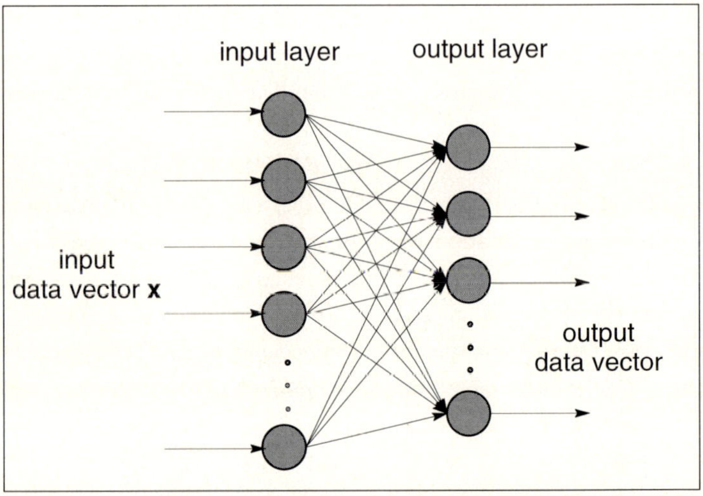

Figure 157: Network topology of a 2-layered perceptron

This topology employs an input and an output layer of neurons. Each neuron of the input layer is interconnected to all neurons of the output layer. Incoming signals, for example a feature vector or a part of an image, are fed into the input layer and each output layer neuron may represent one class when making decisions.

Since the weights of the interconnections store the knowledge the network has learnt, they have to be adjusted according to the task that is to be performed; they have to be trained using a training set of patterns similar to supervised classification methods. A basic learning rule for the connection of a weight w_{ji} between a binary neuron j and a binary input i exemplifies the ideas and is given by:

$$w_{ji}^{new} = w_{ji}^{old} + \eta(T_j - x_j)a_i \qquad (184)$$

where

η : *small constant (the learning rate)*

$(T_j - x_j) = 1$ *if* T_j *is* 1 *and* $x_j = 0$

0 *if* $T_j = x_j$

-1 *if* T_j *is* 0 *and* x_j $i = 1$

T_j : *target output value*

a_i : 1 *or* 0, *the value of input unit* i

The problem arises when considering perceptrons with more than two layers and classification problems which are not linearly separable in feature space. These limitations and capabilities are shown in [177]. The problem of training the hidden units in multi-layered perceptrons was first satisfactory solved by [223] who proposed an efficient hill-climbing method, called back-propagation.

6.3.2. Self-Organizing Neural Networks: The Kohonen Map

Topology and Training Rules

The Kohonen map, introduced in [139, 140], is a self-organizing network which is trained without supervision. It aims at an organization of the input patterns to a topological structure represented by its neurons, where the relations between different patterns are preserved as much as possible.

The Kohonen map is a two-layered network. The first layer of neurons can be considered as like a group of sensors picking up the data, entirely connected to a second, two-dimensional layer: the competitive layer. Figure 158 shows the topology of the network. The weights associated with the connections are adjusted during training where only one single neuron in the competitive layer can be active at a time. This neuron represents the cluster to which the data set belongs in the spirit of c-means clustering. Due to the training rules explained below, the Euclidian distance between two neurons reacting on different input patterns can be a measure that determines the similarity of the two patterns.

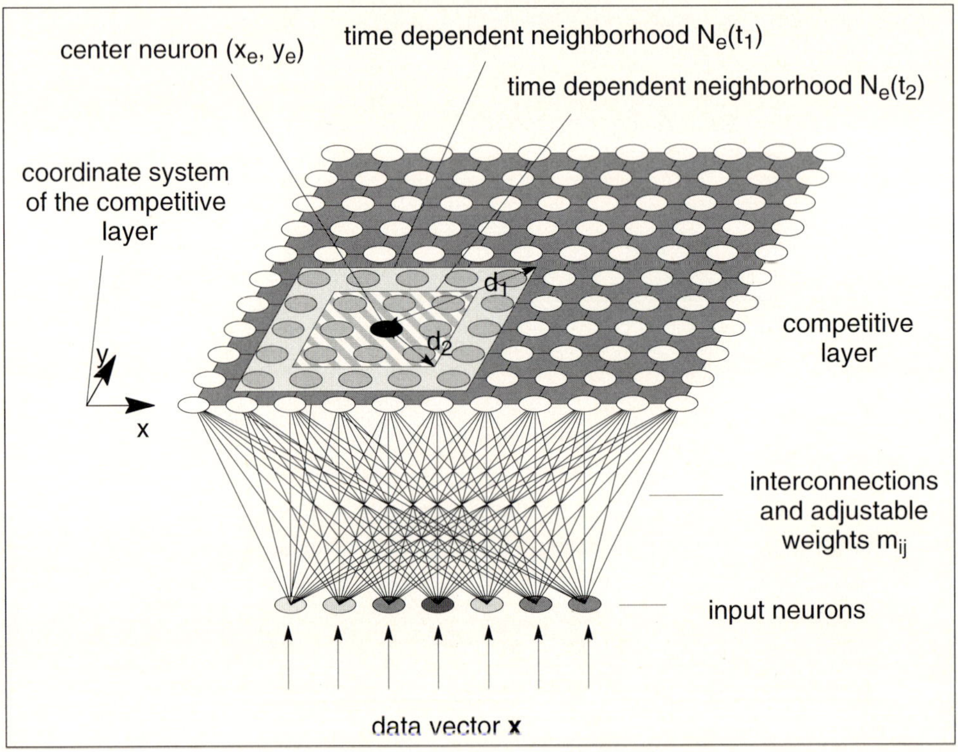

Figure 158: Topology of the Kohonen map and its 2D competitive layer with a time dependent neighborhood $N_e(t)$ of a neuron e

The training of the network is figured out by presenting data vectors $\boldsymbol{x}$ to the input layer of the network whose connection weight vectors $\boldsymbol{m}_i$ of all competitive neurons i are initialized by random values. If N is the dimension of the data vectors, we choose N input neurons and define an Euclidean distance d_i between $\boldsymbol{x}$ and $\boldsymbol{m}_i$ with

$$d_i = \| \boldsymbol{x} - \boldsymbol{m}_i \| = \sqrt{\sum_{j=1}^{N} (x_j - m_{ij})^2} \qquad (185)$$

The neuron e with the minimum distance is then activated, where

$$d_e = \min_i(d_i) \tag{186}$$

The updating of the weights m_{ij} associated with the neurons is only performed within a proximity ($i \in N_e(t)$) of e. This proximity $N_e(t)$ is reduced with increasing training time t. The updating conforms to Eq. (187), where $\eta(t)$ represents a time-dependent learning rate:

$$m_{ij}^{(t+1)} = m_{ij}^{(t)} + \Delta m_{ij}^{(t)} \tag{187}$$

$$\Delta m_{ij}^{(t)} = \begin{cases} \eta(t)(x_j - m_{ij}^{(t)}), & \text{if neuron } i \in N_e(t) \\ 0, & \text{otherwise} \end{cases} \tag{188}$$

$$\eta(t) = \eta_0(1 - \frac{t}{T_{max}}), \quad t \in [0, .., T_{max}] \tag{189}$$

This rule refers directly to c-means clustering [58], where the $\boldsymbol{m}_i$ represent the centroids. The time-dependent neighborhood, which is also illustrated in Fig. 158, can be described for rectangular areas as follows:

$$\begin{aligned} x_e - d(t) < x < x_e + d(t) \\ y_e - d(t) < y < y_e + d(t) \end{aligned} \tag{190}$$

where

$$d(t) = d_0(1 - \frac{t}{T_{\max}}), \quad t \in [0, .., T_{\max}] \tag{191}$$

The network performs two features during the training that are strongly related to the previous analysis techniques:

I. *A separation, i.e. cluster analysis of the presented data by mean vectors* $\mathbf{m}_i$ *that are associated as weights to the neurons.*

II. *A topological ordering of the competitive neurons in a sense that neighboring neurons in the layer represent similar clusters in multidimensional space and thus a dimensionality reduction.*

This can also be interpreted as a nonlinear, topology preserving, associative mapping process. Figure 159 once again illustrates this property. But aside from a linear scaling of η and d according to Eqs. (189) and (191) there are also nonlinear functions possible, for instance, Gaussians. [139] reports that this does not affect the results very much.

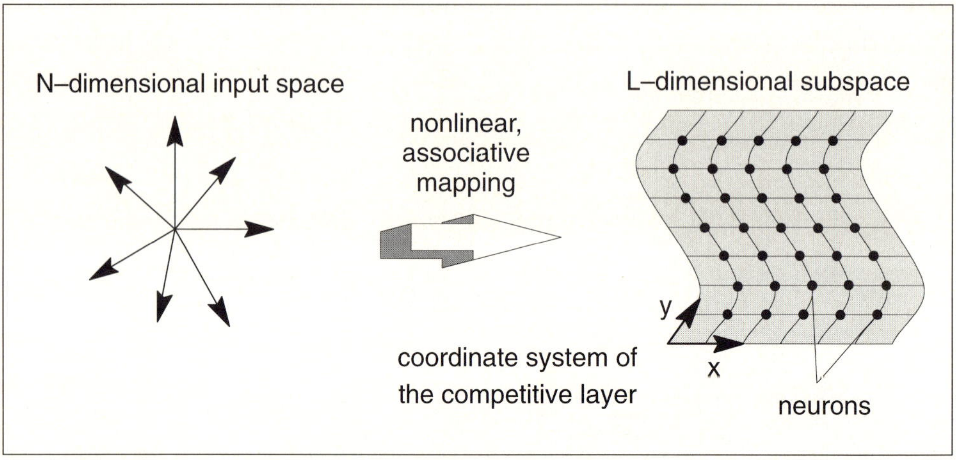

Figure 159: Associative mapping process

Generally, the Kohonen map refers to the classical iterative optimization techniques, well known from c-means clustering.

3D Extensions for Visualization

In the previous section it was explained that the standard Kohonen map can be used to reduce the dimensionality of data sets to be trained with. To do so, the number of input neurons has to be equal to the dimension of the input data, where each data vector is simultaneously presented to the net. Since the neurons in the competitive layer are ordered topologically, neighboring neurons react to similar data vectors in the input space. The mapping can be interpreted as reduction of any N-dimensional space into 2 dimensions, preserving the topology of the data as much as possible (see also previous sections). The resolution of this discrete 2D space is given by the number of competitive neurons, i.e., by the clusters.

This fact can be used for visualizing multidimensional data sets. Depending on the degree of freedom available, as color, transparency, shape, etc., any mapping from N to L dimensions, with L

$\leq N$ can be required. Thus, [94] proposed an L-dimensional hypercube of competitive neurons as an extension to this concept.

Figure 160 shows a model for $N = 9$ and $L = 3$ and a direct mapping of the neurons into the R, G, B color space. Other mappings depending on the problem, with $L > 3$, including transparency, and other features are straightforward and can easily be generalized from this example.

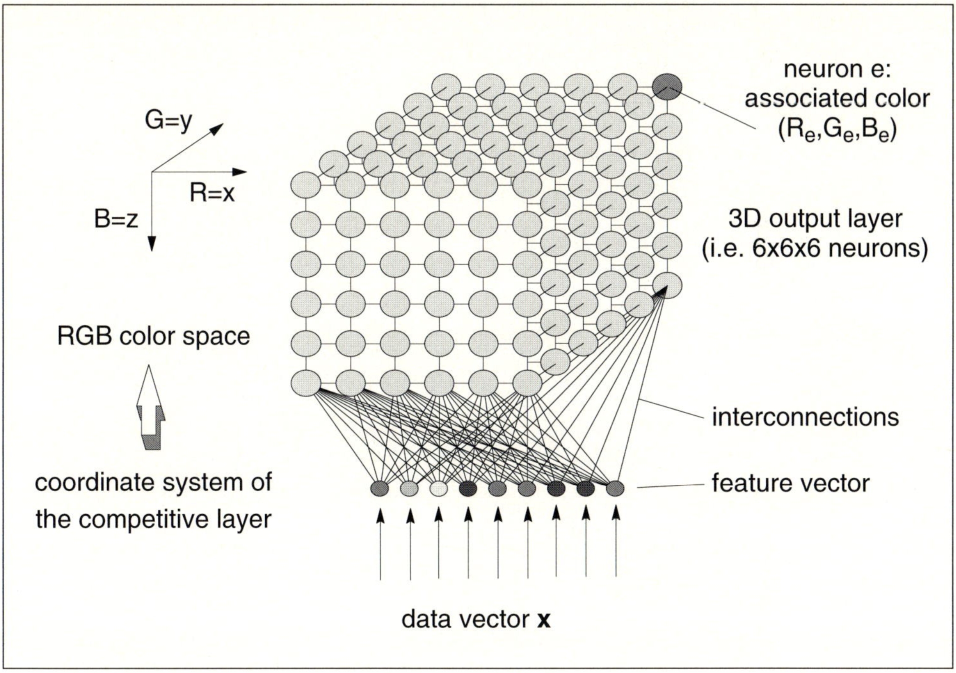

Figure 160:
3D extension of a Kohonen map for visualization purposes

Referencing the axes of the cube with the primaries R, G, and B, each neuron of the competitive layer represents a discrete entity in R, G, B space, i.e., it corresponds to a particular color triplet. The time-dependent neighborhood can easily be extended to 3D by Eq. (192). This is also illustrated in Fig. 160.

$$\begin{aligned} x_e - d(t) &< x < x_e + d(t) \\ y_e - d(t) &< y < y_e + d(t) \\ z_e - d(t) &< z < z_e + d(t) \end{aligned} \qquad (192)$$

Since the network now arranges the neurons during topological training, neighboring neurons with similar colors react to data neighbored in multidimensional space. Thus, the similarity of the color provided by the reacting neuron refers to a neighborhood in N-dimensional space.

The reader is invited to compare Figs. 183 and 104 in Chap. 7

Knowing well from the previous chapters that visual data analysis is always a perceptual task of human vision and that the R, G, B presentation is not a perceptual color space, postprocessing transforms might improve the results, for instance by referencing in CIE L^*,a^*,b^* or CIE L^*,u^*,v^* or others.

Clustering of Data Sets

The following example illustrates the dynamic behavior of the network during training and shows the results obtained from a presentation of data sets with different statistical distributions (see also [94]). Since only the dynamic ordering shall be demonstrated during training, we set $N = L = 3$.

In the first example (Fig. 161) the training data triplets are randomized and equally distributed in 3D space. Since the connection weight vectors $\boldsymbol{m}_i$ of the competitive neurons represent cluster centers of the input data they must also be equally distributed in 3D space in terms of codebook vectors. Figure 161 illustrates this process as a function of the learning time. The neurons are visualized as small spheres of the corresponding color as illustrated in Fig. 160. Their positions in (x, y, z) are given by the associated mean vectors $\boldsymbol{m}_i$. Where the $\boldsymbol{m}_i$ are initialized with small random values, at the beginning the network reveals a discrete representation of the 3D space with an increasing number of training cycles. Neighboring neurons in the 3D layer are connected by white lines.

The competitive layer of the network has 10 x 10 x 10 neurons. The network performs a clustering of the white noise data by equally distributed means. The topological ordering of the corresponding neurons is illustrated by colors of the 3D grid that accord with the R, G, B space.

The second example (Fig. 162) shows a mapping of a Gaussian distributed data set of zero mean, with

$$p(x) = e^{-\frac{x^2}{2\pi\sigma^2}} \qquad (193)$$

and $\sigma = 0.2$. The neurons arrange themselves according to the distribution of $p(\boldsymbol{x})$. In this case, the center of the Gaussian function $p(\boldsymbol{x})$ is located in the lower right corner of the cube. Thus the centroids to represent only 1/8 of a whole Gaussian. However, it is interesting to see that the network tries to preserve both the neighborhood of the colors and the distribution $p(\boldsymbol{x})$.

The above examples illustrate the two major properties of the Kohonen map, namely clustering and topological ordering.

Learning Vector Quantization

So far the Kohonen map has only been introduced for clustering, topological organization, and subspace mapping. For supervised classification, however, each neuron – and also each cluster centroid – has to be assigned to a certain class, depending on the definition of the user. This can be done by interactive selection of training areas and by a majority voting of each neuron stimulated by the training set. After this, each neuron has an associated class and the network is then able to classify. However, during the organization process the goal was to find a limited set of centroids representing the data in a *c*–means sense rather than to find optimal placements of the decision boundaries in a minimum error (Bayes) sense. For this reason, the network can be once again trained with a supervised postprocessing in order to move corresponding centroids towards the Bayes decision boundary and to improve the classification result.

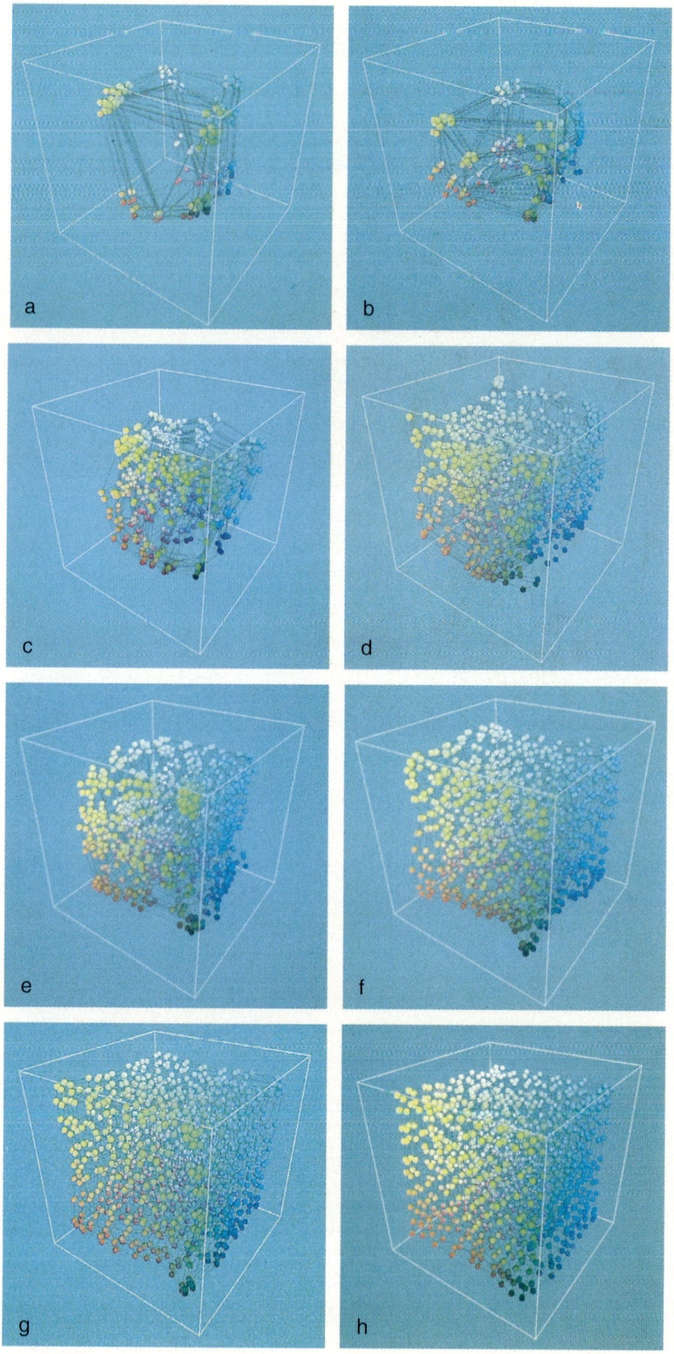

Figure 161: Organization process of a 3D Kohonen map with white noise data after 1000, 6000, 8500, 10500, 12500, 14500, 17000 and 20000 training cycles (from [94])

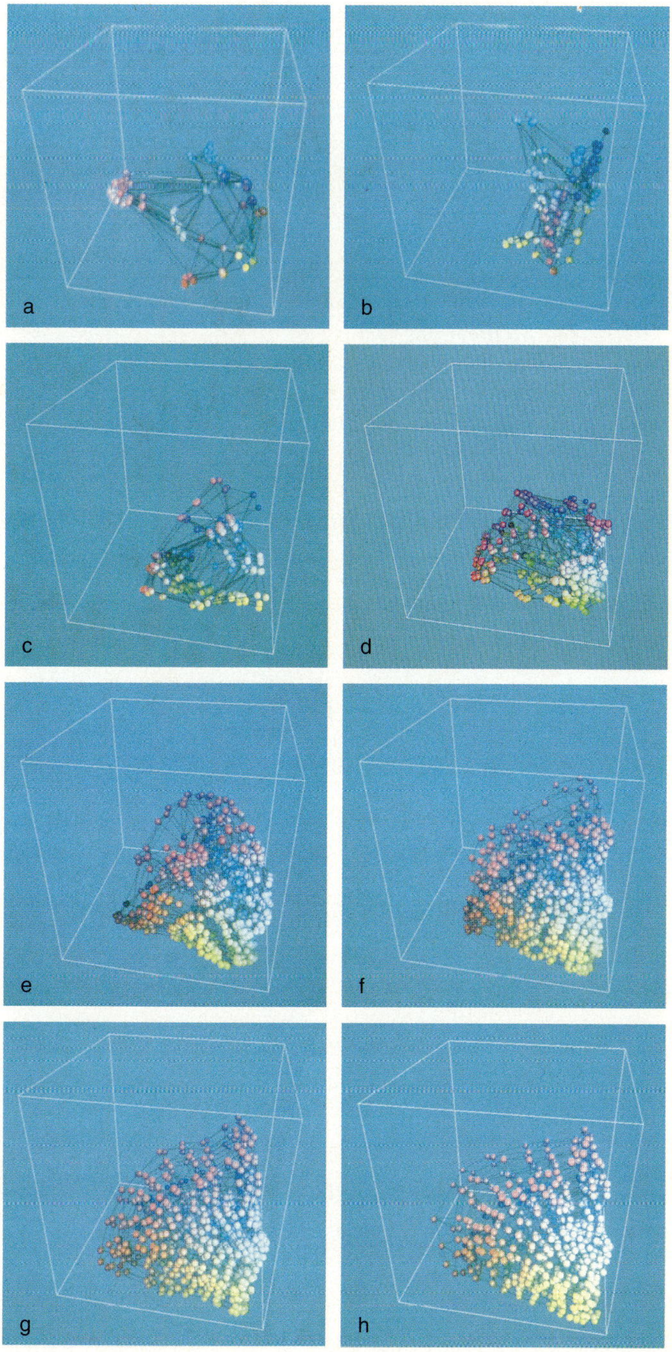

Figure 162: Organization process of a 3D Kohonen map with white Gaussian distributed data after 1000, 2000, 3500, 5000, 6500, 7500, 8500 and 10000 training cycles (from [94])

This postprocessing is well known as learning vector quantization (LVQ 1, 2, 3) [139] and type 3 can be described as follows:

For a given input pattern $\boldsymbol{x}$ let $\boldsymbol{m}_i$ and $\boldsymbol{m}_j$ be the closest centroids to $\boldsymbol{x}$. We modify these mean vectors according to

$$\boldsymbol{m}_i(t+1) = \boldsymbol{m}_i(t) - \alpha[\boldsymbol{x}(t) - \boldsymbol{m}_i(t)]$$

$$\boldsymbol{m}_j(t+1) = \boldsymbol{m}_j(t) + \alpha[\boldsymbol{x}(t) - \boldsymbol{m}_j(t)] \tag{194}$$

/* *if* *−$\boldsymbol{m}_i$ and $\boldsymbol{m}_j$ are the two closest weight vectors to the input vector $\boldsymbol{x}$,*
−$\boldsymbol{x}$ and $\boldsymbol{m}_j$ belong to the same class,
−$\boldsymbol{x}$ and $\boldsymbol{m}_i$ belong to different classes and
−$\boldsymbol{x}$ falls into the window */

$$\boldsymbol{m}_k(t+1) = \boldsymbol{m}_k(t) + \varepsilon\alpha[\boldsymbol{x}(t) - \boldsymbol{m}_k(t)] \tag{195}$$

/* *if* *$\boldsymbol{x}$, $\boldsymbol{m}_i$ and $\boldsymbol{m}_j$ belong to the same class*
($k \in \{i,j\}$)

where ε and α are small constants */

The window is defined as a symmetric area around the midplane of $\boldsymbol{m}_i$ and $\boldsymbol{m}_j$. Then $\boldsymbol{x}$ falls into the window if

$$\min\left(\frac{d_i}{d_j}, \frac{d_j}{d_i}\right) > \delta \tag{196}$$

$$\delta = \frac{1-w}{1+w} \tag{197}$$

Where d_i and d_j are the two distances of $\boldsymbol{x}$ to $\boldsymbol{m}_i$ and $\boldsymbol{m}_j$. The threshold δ is calculated according to Eq. (197) and the relative window size w is chosen to be about 20%.

A detailed study of LVQ and of related methods can be found in [62]. Further discussions of the capabilities and the efficiency of this visualization method appear in Chap. 7.

Topology and Training Rules

The backpropagation method, introduced by [223, 224] is a supervised gradient descent optimization for multilayer perceptrons that is based on mean square criteria. The classical perceptron that has already been introduced goes back to [220]; however, the training method was not suited for multilayered, feed-forward networks and thus the mathematical advantages of these systems could not be harvested. The topology of a multilayer perceptron is shown in Fig. 163. It consists of a number of processing units organized in layers, where the neurons of each layer can either be entirely interconnected (Fig. 163) or only with a spatially coherent section, their receptive field (Fig. 164) that is defined according to its biological origin. The connections have, like the Kohonen map, associated weights that are adjusted during training.

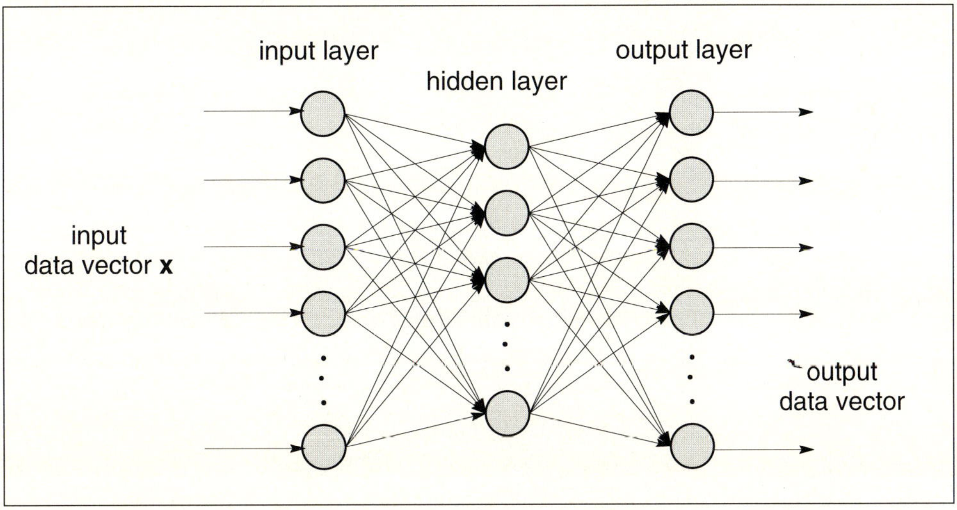

Figure 163: Fully interconnected multilayer percepton

The advantage of the network lies in the nonlinearity of the floating point activation function. As a single neuron j receives the activation values a_i from its predecessor neurons $V(j)$, they are weighed with the connection weight w_{ji} and summed up to calculate the overall activation net_j of the neuron j

$$net_j = \sum_{i \in V(j)} w_{ji}\, a_i + w_{j\Theta}\, 1 \qquad (198)$$

Θ_j: *Bias node*

that performs a sigmoidal transmission to the output a_j

$$a_j = \frac{1}{1 + e^{-net_j}} \qquad (199)$$

After initialization of the connection weights with random values, the learning process is performed via a gradient descent error optimization of the weights w_{ji}, where η is the learning rate and a_i the output of the predecessor.

$$w_{ji}(t + 1) = w_{ji}(t) + \Delta w_{ji} \qquad (200)$$

$$\Delta w_{ji} = \eta\, \delta_j\, a_i \qquad (201)$$

If a_j is the present activation of the neuron j and T_j the target value resulting from a training data set we receive according to [223]:

$$\delta_j = a_j(1 - a_j)(T_j - a_j) \qquad (202)$$

for the output layer and from there recursively

$$\delta_j = a_j(1 - a_j) \sum_{k \in N(j)} w_{kj}\, \delta_k \qquad (203)$$

for each neuron of the other layers. k stands for all successors $N(j)$ of neuron j. The quality of what is learnt is often measured by the root mean square E_{RMS}, where n_p is the number of training vectors and n_j the number of output neurons:

$$E_{RMS} = \sqrt{\frac{\sum_p \sum_j (T_j - a_j)^2}{n_p n_j}} \qquad (204)$$

It should be noted that gradient methods do not always lead to global minimum configurations. Moreover, for complex networks local minima might be a serious problem [82]. The deviation of the above equations follows simple mathematical rules (see [223]).

Topologies for Imaging Applications

During the last few years, back-propagation networks have been extensively used in the field of imaging [104].

Figure 164 shows a configuration of the network used for multidimensional satellite image classification. The network picks up the multidimensional data vector of each pixel and its environment and one of the output neurons has to be assigned to the respective class, for instance desert, sea, oil clouds, cities, etc. Texture based classification requires complex network topologies but may provide more reliable results. In these cases, receptive fields help to reduce the total number of weights to be updated and, therefore, accelerate the convergence of the network.

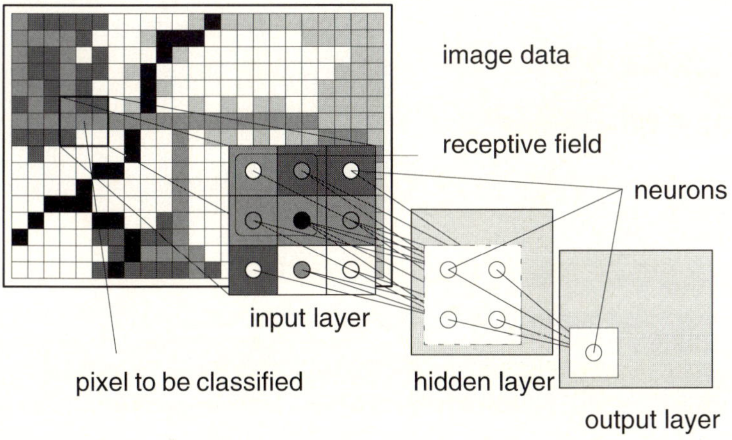

Figure 164: Back-propagation network for simple texture based approaches [104])

Another typical configuration is illustrated in Fig. 165 for character recognition [105]. All pixels of a character are passed to a hidden layer. The output layer consists of n_j neurons, where n_j is the number of different characters to be recognized.

It should be noted that the activity of a neuron in the output layer can be interpreted as the discriminant function $g_i(\boldsymbol{x})$ for the class that is represented by that neuron. After training the net, the neurons in the output layer respond selectively to feature vectors belonging

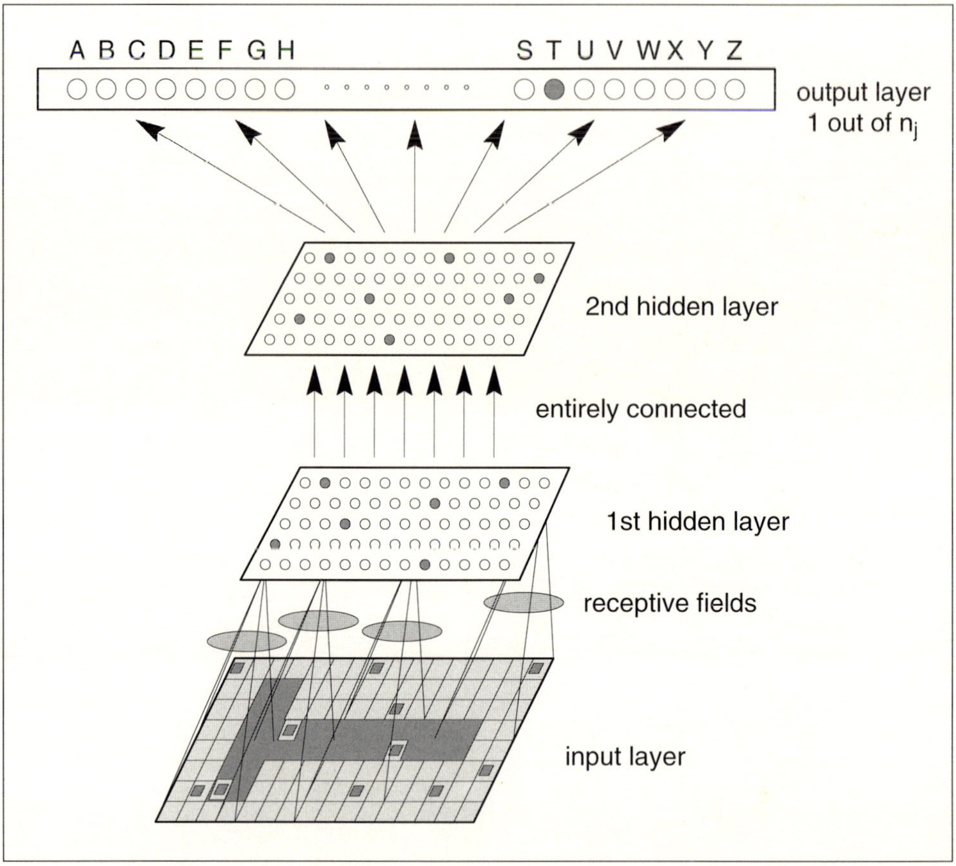

Figure 165: Topology for pixel oriented character recognition

to their class. If a distorted character is presented to the net, as in Fig. 165, the neuron representing that class has the strongest response out of all neurons in the output layer and a maximum decision gives the classification result. Since the output neurons have real output values, these types of networks can also be taken to solve approximation problems or scattered data interpolation. One of the biggest disadvantages of back-propagation networks is the appropriate selection of the number of hidden units. There are countless approaches to this problem, including genetic algorithms [78].

6.3.4. Other Neural Network Models

Competitive Learning Networks

The competitive learning method is in some sense a predecessor of the Kohonen map and is given non-supervised training for clustering. These types of self-organizing nets have for instance been used for recognition of handwritten characters [72, 73].

The neurons are preorganized in different non-overlapping sets, the inhibitory clusters, where each neuron inhibits all other neurons in that cluster. The connections to the neuron that responds strongest in each cluster are changed. Figure 166 shows the architecture of a competitive learning system.

The input to a competitive learning net is binary and is guaranteed by a threshold function in most models. In Fig. 166 adjacent layers are entirely connected and for all weights w_{ji} of connections to a neuron j:

$$\sum_i w_{ji} = 1 \qquad (205)$$

For training the net, the total activation S_j is calculated from the feature vector $\boldsymbol{x}$:

$$S_j = \sum_i w_{ji} x_i \qquad (206)$$

The winning neuron j, that responds strongest in an inhibitory cluster C_k, is activated with

$$a_j = \begin{cases} 1, \text{ if } S_j = \max_{i \in C_k} \{ S_i \} \\ 0, \text{ else} \end{cases} \qquad (207)$$

and its connection weights are changed iteratively with

$$w_{ji}^{\text{new}} = w_{ji}^{\text{old}} + \eta \left(\frac{x_i}{n_a} - w_{ji}^{\text{old}} \right) \qquad (208)$$

η: *learning rate*
n_a: *number of active neurons in the preceding layer.*

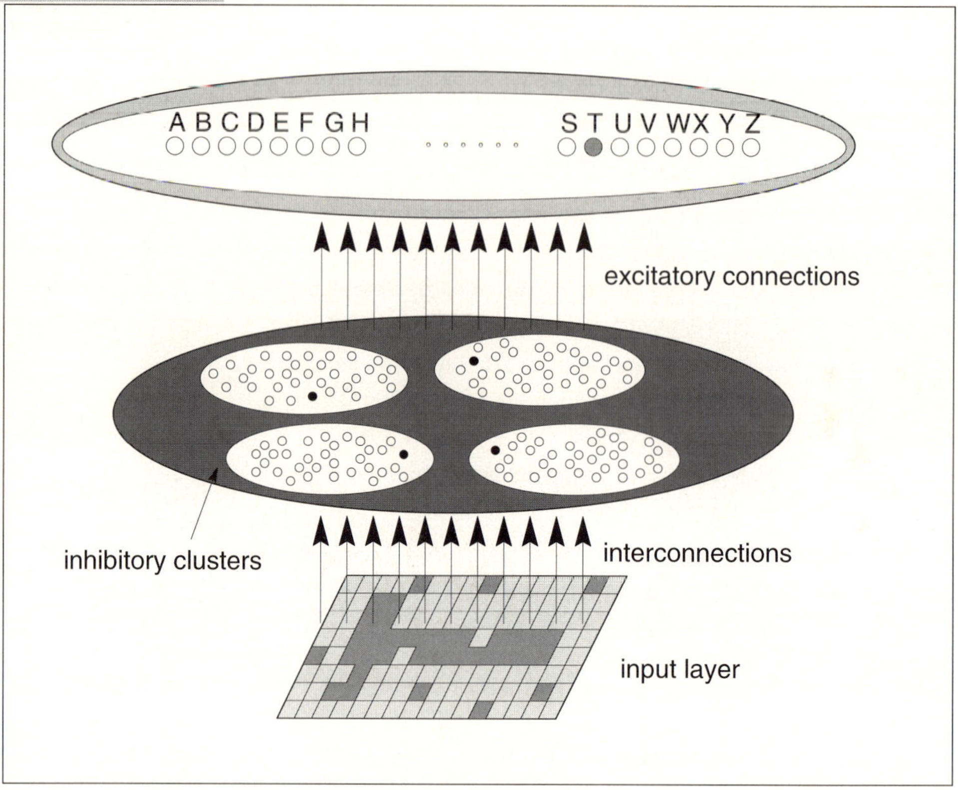

Figure 166: Topology of a competitive learning network for character recognition [2]

Since all other neurons in that cluster remain unchanged, the network can be thought as a simple implementation of the lateral inhibition principle of Chap. 3.

In this way it is possible to adapt the net to a continuously changing input. There is no difference between learning and working. But, of course, the net can also be trained supervised where the neurons in the output layer will be assigned to the classes they represent. During the classification mode, the connections have to stay unchanged. Only the neuron that represents the respective class will be activated for a particular feature vector (see Eq. (208)).

Boltzmann Machines

The Boltzmann machine [1] is another interesting type of neural network that is trained supervised. Contrary to the deterministic behavior of the gradient descent backpropagation rule, it is based on probabilistic simulated annealing [174], which we have already introduced in Chap. 5. The topology of the network is illustrated in Fig. 167.

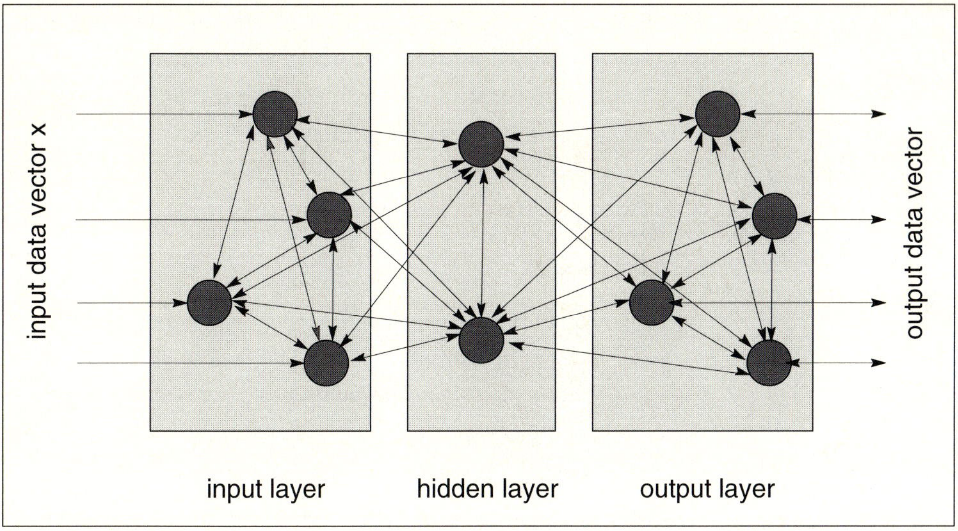

Figure 167: Topology of a Boltzmann machine type neural network

In contrast to the strict feed-forward architecture of back-propagation, the neurons of the Boltzman machine can be arbitrarily connected, where we simply distinguish between input, output, and hidden units. The units themselves are binary and the probability of state transition of the activity a_j of a neuron j is given by the Boltzmann distribution

$$P_j = \frac{1}{1 + e^{-\Delta E_j/T}} \qquad (209)$$

T: *temperature*

The energy difference ΔE_j corresponds to the sum of weighted activities of all neurons $A(j)$ connected with j:

$$\Delta E_j = \sum_{i \in A(j)} w_{ji}\, a_i \qquad (210)$$

The parameter T can be interpreted as temperature that anneals with increasing simulation time.

The equilibrium is forced by the relationship of two global state probabilities P_A and P_B of the Boltzmann machine as a function of their temperature T.

$$\frac{P_A}{P_B} = e^{-(E_A - E_B)/T} \qquad (211)$$

The idea is to escape from local minima in the configuration by using the state probabilities to escape from them.

The learning process can be divided into two phases that are repeated successively until a lower limit is reached.

Phase A:

I. The I/O patterns of the training data set are presented and restrict the activities of the input and output neurons.

II. An equilibrium is reached by annealing the temperature, and the mean state probabilities P^+_{ji} for both unit i and unit j being in state "On" are computed and stored in terms of expectation values.

Phase B:

I. Only the input patterns are presented to the network and the output is open.

II. An equilibrium is also reached by annealing the temperature and the state probabilities P^-_{ji} are computed

III. The modification of a weight w_{ji} follows the rule.

$$\Delta w_{ji} = \eta \; (P^+_{ji} \quad P^-_{ji}) \qquad (212)$$

η: *learning rate*

This procedure is repeated until an error limit is reached. It should be noted that the units of the Boltzmann machine are binary and thus any float vectors have to be presented in that way. The Boltzmann machine has been successfully applied by [136] to solve user interface constraints in computer graphics.

RCE Networks

The restricted coulomb energy network (RCE) was introduced by [49] and adapts the number of neurons to the classification problem to be solved using very simple rules. Figure 168 illustrates the algorithm for a 2-dimensional feature vector solving a two-class problem with complex class boundaries.

The network itself is usually a three-layered, entirely connected, feed-forward version. It is constructed during training as follows.

Suppose we have a 2D feature vector $\boldsymbol{x_1} = (x_{11}, x_{12})$ and a first training sample that belongs to class A. The algorithm constructs one neuron that connects the input $\boldsymbol{x}$ with the output A. The neuron is characterized by the weights $w_{11} = x_{11}$ and $w_{12} = x_{12}$ and a parameter λ_1 that stands for a radius. For any other $\boldsymbol{x}$ presented to the network that does not fall into that radius, a new neuron is implemented and connected either to output A or to B depending on the class assignment of $\boldsymbol{x}$ (see also Fig. 168b).

Usually, the circles given by λ_1 and λ_2 are overlapping and ambiguties may arise for $\boldsymbol{x}$ falling both into λ_1 and λ_2 (Fig. 168c, d). In these cases the class for $\boldsymbol{x}$ cannot be determined and therefore first a reduction of the respective λ has to be performed based on the distances to $\boldsymbol{w}_1$ and $\boldsymbol{w}_2$.

This algorithm finally approximates the decision boundaries by means of circles or hyperglobes that are superimposed. The neurons of the network can be interpreted as local centers in which the single classes are decomposed. Although the basic principle is very primitive and straightforward, this type of neural network has proved to be very reliable for classification.

Oja's Principal Component Analyzer

Aside from the classical approach in solving the previously introduced eigenvector problem, there have been numerous approaches for approximating eigenvectors with neural networks. In particular, the mathematical analysis of [11] or [195] proved a correspondence between internal neural data representation and principal components of the data set to be trained with. Oja was the first to introduce a simple neuron model as a principal component analyzer

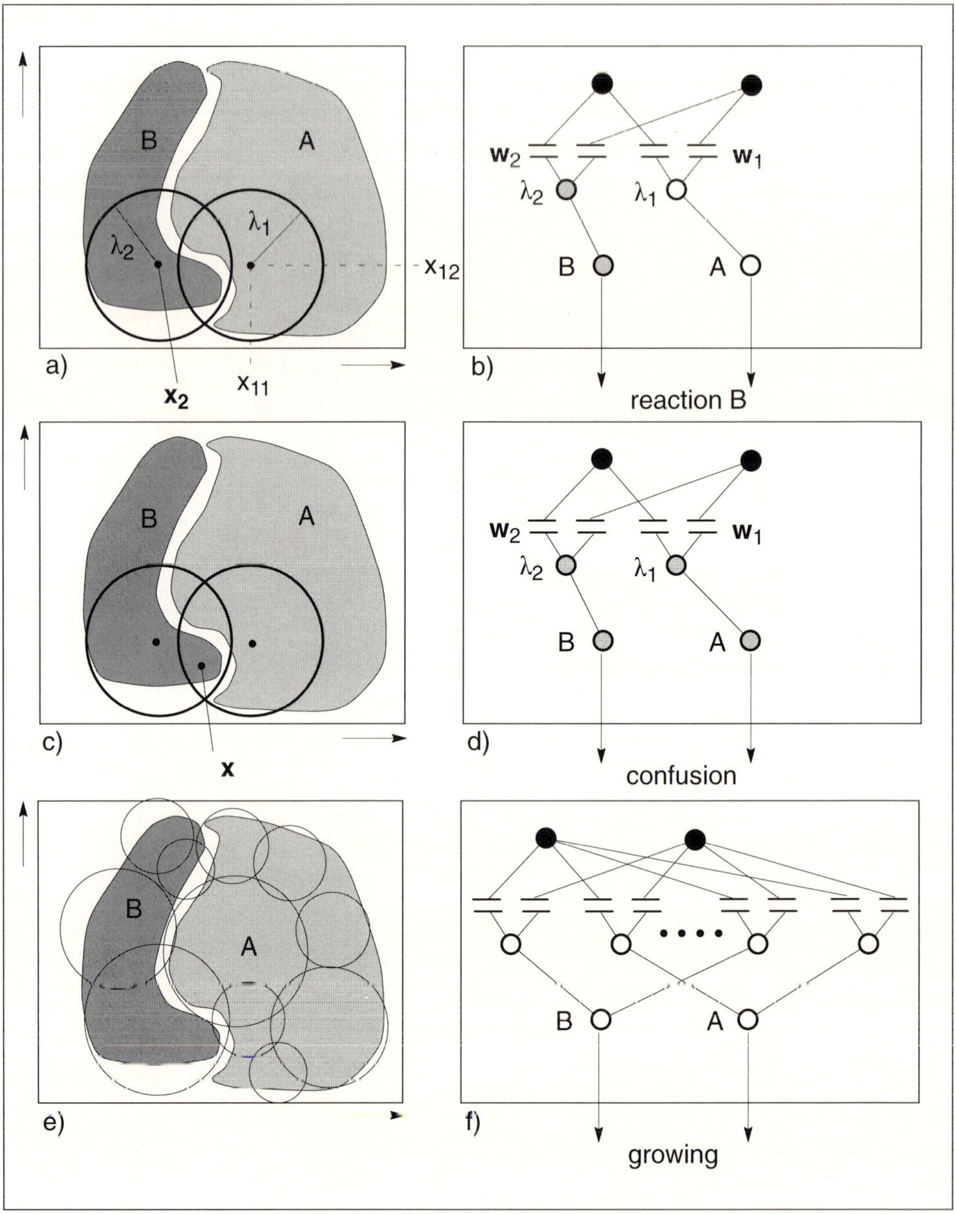

Figure 168: Basic principle of an RCE network

and proposed a one-layered backcoupled neural network [196] to learn the first K principal components of a data set presented to that network. This model can be used to implement the PCA. Introducing a neural network as in Fig. 169 with a general output function

a, the connection weight matrix $\boldsymbol{W}$ will be updated during training according to:

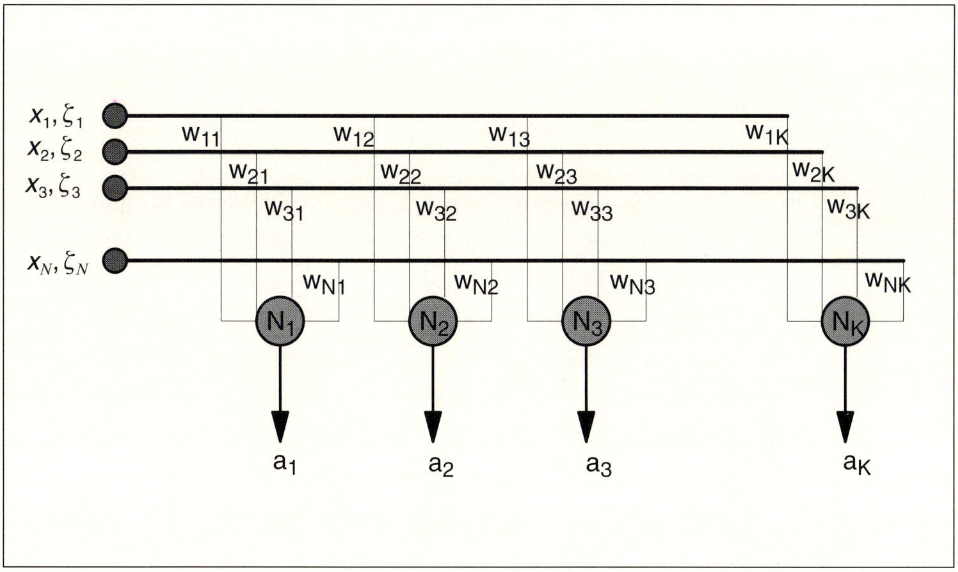

Figure 169: Oja's neural network model that approximates principle components (see [196])

$$\frac{d\boldsymbol{W}}{dt} = \eta(\boldsymbol{x} - \boldsymbol{z})\boldsymbol{a}^T = \eta\left[\boldsymbol{CW} - \boldsymbol{W}[\boldsymbol{W}^T\boldsymbol{CW}]\right] \qquad (213)$$

$$\boldsymbol{W} = [w_{ji}]$$

$$\boldsymbol{C} = \boldsymbol{x}\,\boldsymbol{x}^T$$

$$\boldsymbol{a} = (a_1, .., a_K)^T$$

$$\boldsymbol{z} = (\zeta_1, .., \zeta_N)^T \qquad \textit{(internal feedback term)}$$

We calculate

$$a_j = \sum_{i=1}^{N} w_{ji}\, x_i \qquad (214)$$

and the internal feedback as

$$\zeta_i = \sum_{k=1}^{K} w_{ki} a_k \qquad (215)$$

for a single weight w_{ji} we obtain according to Eq. (215)

$$\frac{dw_{ji}}{dt} = \eta a_j(x_i - \zeta_i) \tag{216}$$

$$= \eta \sum_{g=1}^{N} w_{jg}x_g \left(x_i - \sum_{k=1}^{K} w_{ki}\left(\sum_{l=1}^{N} w_{kl}x_l\right) \right)$$

η: *learning rate*

Due to the difficulties in analytically solving the third-degree matrix polynomial of Eq. (213), Oja studied the iterative learning scheme provided in Eq. (213) – (216) and found that for long iteration times $(t \rightarrow \infty)$ $\boldsymbol{W}=(\boldsymbol{w}_1,..,\boldsymbol{w}_K)$ tends to have orthonormal columns that approximate the eigenvectors of the covariance matrix of the data set $\boldsymbol{C}$.

7. Neural Networks for Graphics and Imaging

7.1. Introduction

This chapter illustrates the capabilities of the artificial neural models introduced in Chap. 6, by means of real world examples. All of them have been developed by the author and by others during the last few years at the Computer Graphics Center in Germany. Most of them are in the scope of this book since they touch *both graphics and imaging* and make use of certain models for decision making and clustering. In order to give a deeper insight into the advantages of the previously explained methods, the application background has also been illustrated for each example.

The first example [105] derives from the field of telecommunication and data transmission over noisy channels. A transmission model for the pixel-based recognition of characters is set up and analyzed mathematically. The receiver of the modeled system is characterized by a multidimensional classifier. This paradigm was selected to give the reader an overview of the advantages and disadvantages of neural versus classical classifiers.

The second example [104, 94] illustrates the capabilities of subspace mapping and clustering with a Kohohen map. This method has already been introduced in Chap. 6 and is now applied to the visualization of multispectral Landsat-TM images. Thus a 7-dimensional feature space was mapped down to the 3D RGB space. Furthermore, the performance of supervised classification was compared to maximum likelihood estimation using extensive true ground areas [237].

The third example [38] derives from the field of medical imaging and can be taken as a prototype application of *Visual Computing* methods. In order to render volumes from MR image slices or to reconstruct isosurfaces in 3D, the images have first to be segmented. Simple linear thresholding is not sufficient and therefore we employ the Kohonen map for a texture-based segmentation of the data, where we primarily focus on brain tumors. The underlying physics of MR is highlighted in a brief subsection.

The last example [87] selected for this chapter deals with the automatic recognition of human faces. An algorithm based on principal component analysis and neural classifiers is analyzed. This section has to be understood as a case study for human-computer interaction that shows not only the capabilities but also the limits of the algorithm. In particular, a comparison of the distances of face images in eigenspace is given for the results of a psychological experiment. In this case, different test persons performed pairwise evaluations.

7.2. Recognition of Distorted Characters

7.2.1. General Remarks

Pixel-oriented binary transmission of alphanumeric characters has proved to be of fundamental importance in communication technology. In particular, recognition systems for text require robust classification methods in order to discriminate the original character from the binary image. Where standard transmission systems use codec that are specific to the problem (e.g., fax), the automatic methods for character recognition work in general on the decompressed image [35, 36, 73]. Within the transmission pipeline, the signal is affected by noise and distortions with different statistical properties. Aside from correlated distortions, such as missing lines, additive, meanfree Gaussian white noise is specially interesting. For this purpose, classic information theory offers methods, such as matched filtering, that take into optimal account the respective properties of the noise signal. The decision rule then statistically minimizes the error probability in the sense of Bayesian estimation theory [198].

In contrast to this one-dimensional case of binary recognition and decisions between true and false, automatic text recognition has to work on a bitmap and thus becomes a multidimensional classification problem [264]. The final step in this task is to discriminate the character; this is usually performed by mathematical techniques [58].

The following section describes a computational study on the advantages and shortcomings of neural networks and classic classification methods for a fundamental task in information theory: the discrimination of distorted characters, represented by bitmaps. The attention has been directed to the error probability of the recognition depending on the signal–noise ratio. First of all, an introduction to the statistical signal description of matched filter systems is given and the corresponding transmission model is introduced. Furthermore, the classification techniques of Chap. 6 have been investigated and a detailed analysis evaluating learning and discrimination behavior is given.

7.2.2. Matched Filtering

Matched filters play a fundamental role in information technology when dealing with signals distorted by noise [159]. First introduced by [193], they optimally take into account the noise characteristics in order to maximize the signal-noise ratio of a given signal source. Using methods of statistical signal description [80, 112, 222], we are able to derive the matched filter from a simple optimization procedure. The following model is based on Fig. 170, where we introduce a pipeline consisting of a transmitter, a channel distorted by an additive noise signal, and a linear time-invariant (LTI) filter reconstructing the transmitted signal. If binary information is assumed, it is

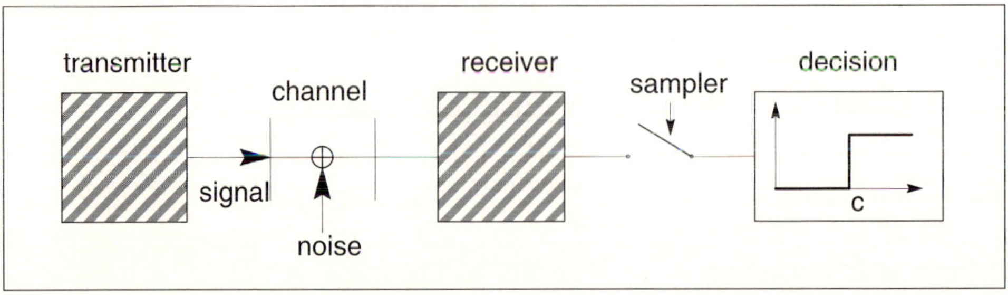

Figure 170: Model for the detection of distorted binary signals

necessary to decide on the value of the output after sampling. This can be performed by a threshold function. If the time-dependent signal amplitude is described with $s(t)$ and the noise with $n(t)$ the linear filter with the impulse response function $h(t)$ yields $y(t)$ as an output, where

$$y(t) = [s(t) + n(t)] * h(t) \tag{217}$$

The output function $y(t)$ can be decomposed into a signal $g(t)$ and a noise amplitude $n_e(t)$. The sampler detects at the time T a value

$$y(T) = g(T) + n_e(T) \tag{218}$$

Introducing the methods of statistical signal description, we obtain the signal power S_a at T with

$$S_a = < g^2(T) > \tag{219}$$

and the noise power N with

$$N = < n_e^2(T) > \tag{220}$$

Supposing a deterministic signal $g(t)$ with $S_a = g^2(T)$ and white noise with

$$\overline{n_e^2(t)} = N_0 \int_{-\infty}^{\infty} h^2(t)dt \tag{221}$$

N_0: *power spectrum of the noise signal*

and using the convolution integral, we have

$$\frac{S_a}{N} = \frac{\left[\int_{-\infty}^{\infty} h(\tau)s(T-\tau)d\tau\right]^2}{N_0 \int_{-\infty}^{\infty} h^2(\tau)d\tau} \tag{222}$$

Introducing the signal energy $E = \sigma^2$ yields:

$$\frac{S_a}{N} = \frac{E}{N_0} \frac{\left[\int_{-\infty}^{\infty} h(\tau)s(T-\tau)d\tau\right]^2}{\int_{-\infty}^{\infty} h^2(\tau)d\tau \int_{-\infty}^{\infty} s^2(T-\tau)d\tau} \tag{223}$$

The right-hand side term in Eq. (223) represents the sequence of the normalized cross correlation coefficient p_{sh}^E between $h(t)$ and $s(T-t)$.The response function $\bar{h}(t)$ that maximizes the signal-noise ratio in

$$\left.\frac{S_a}{N}\right|_{\max} = \frac{E}{N_0} \; with \; \left(\bar{p}_{sh}^E\right)^2 = 1 \tag{224}$$

represents then the matched filter that is optimally adapted on the signal

$$\bar{h}(t) = const \; s(T-t) \tag{225}$$

where *const* is a small constant.

The output $g(t)$ of the matched filter is given by

$$g(t) = const \; \phi_{ss}^E(t-T) \tag{226}$$

where $\phi_{ss}^{E}(t - T)$ represents the autocorrelation function of the signal $s(t)$ shifted with T. Sampling the function in its maximum T yields

$$g(T) = const\ \phi_{ss}^{E}(0) \tag{227}$$

7.2.3. Error Probability for Binary Signals

Using the model of Fig. 170 for the transmission of binary signals, we have to decide whether the value of $y(t)$ is 'true' or 'false'. This is usually done by a threshold τ. A correctly detected '1' is obtained when $y_1(T) > \tau$, where

$$y_1(T) = g(T) + n_e(T) \tag{228}$$

is a random value with a distribution $p_{y_1}(x)$. The error probability of a false detection can be calculated with

$$P_{E_1} = prob\{y_1(T) \le \tau\} \tag{229}$$

If we suppose Gaussian noise, we obtain

$$p_{y_1}(x) = \frac{1}{\sqrt{2\pi N}} e^{-(x-\sqrt{S_a})^2/2N} \tag{230}$$

and for the error probability

$$P_{E_1} = \frac{1}{\sqrt{2\pi N}} \int_{-\infty}^{\tau} e^{-(x-\sqrt{S_a})^2/2N} dx \tag{231}$$

$$P_{E_1} = \frac{1}{2} erfc\left(\frac{\sqrt{S_a} - \tau}{\sqrt{2N}}\right) \tag{232}$$

where $erfc(x) = 1 - \frac{2}{\sqrt{\pi}} \int_0^x e^{-\xi^2} d\xi$ (233)

In the same way, we can easily describe the error probability P_{E_0}, based on

$$y_0(T) = n_e(T) \quad (234)$$

and

$$P_{E_0} = prob\{y_0(T) > \tau\} \quad (235)$$

$$P_{E_0} = \frac{1}{2} erfc\left(\frac{\tau}{\sqrt{2N}}\right) \quad (236)$$

Supposing our information source to deliver 'false' with probability π_0 and 'true' with $\pi_1 = (1 - \pi_0)$, we obtain the total error probability P_E as

$$P_E = \pi_0 P_{E_1} + \pi_1 P_{E_0} \quad (237)$$

The optimization is now to minimize the error probability with respect to the threshold τ.

$$\bar{P}_E = \min P_E|_{\tau} \quad (238)$$

For the case of $\pi_0 = \pi_1 = ½$ we obtain $\bar{P}_E$ as

$$\bar{P}_E = \frac{1}{2} erfc\left(\sqrt{\frac{E}{8N_0}}\right) \quad (239)$$

Equation (239) describes now the error probability of a false detection depending on the signal-noise ratio E/N_0.

It should be noted that this decision rule refers directly to a one-dimensional Bayesian maximum-likelihood classifier (see also Sect. 6.2.6).

7.2.4. Transmission and Discrimination of Characters

So far, the classification of the binary-valued signal *s(t)* has been reduced to a simple threshold operation. The recognition of characters, however, requires an extended model, as illustrated in Fig. 171.

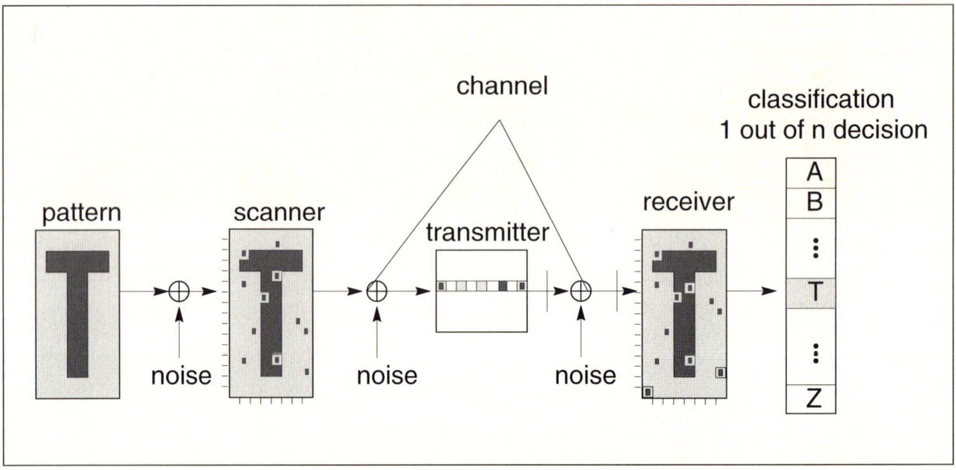

Figure 171: Model employed for the transmission and discrimination of alphanumeric characters

Assuming a pixel-oriented description and neglecting a transmission code, the original pattern is scanned, transmitted, received, and classified. The receiver has to recognize the corresponding character automatically in a classification step. For this purpose, it must initially sample the transmitted values in order to reconstruct the image. Distortions can emerge from the original, from the scanner, and from the channel as well. The following investigations only consider white noise. Nonlinear distortions that may arise from the scanning process are no longer considered. The normalized signal power S_a was set to:

$$\begin{aligned} S_a &= 1.0 \mapsto \textit{true} \\ S_a &= 0.0 \mapsto \textit{false} \end{aligned} \qquad (240)$$

The presented input characters only consist of binary pixel values; no grey levels are allowed.

The Gaussian distributed noise signal is completely described by its power spectrum N_0 or its variance σ^2, where

$$\sigma^2 = N_0 \quad (241)$$

Figure 172 for instance shows the character 'T' distorted with noise of variance $\sigma^2 = 0.04$ and signal-noise ratio of 14 dB (bottom) and $\sigma^2 = 1.0$ and 0 dB (top). The technique used for visualization represents the distortion by a variation of the pixel size. Amplitudes larger than 1.0 and less than 0.0 are cut for the presentation.

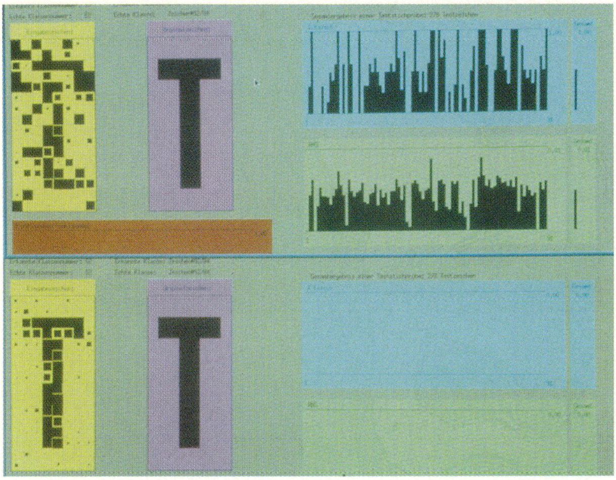

Figure 172: Distorted characters with 14 dB (bottom) and 0 dB (top) distortion distance. (Prototype including the X/Motif user interface)

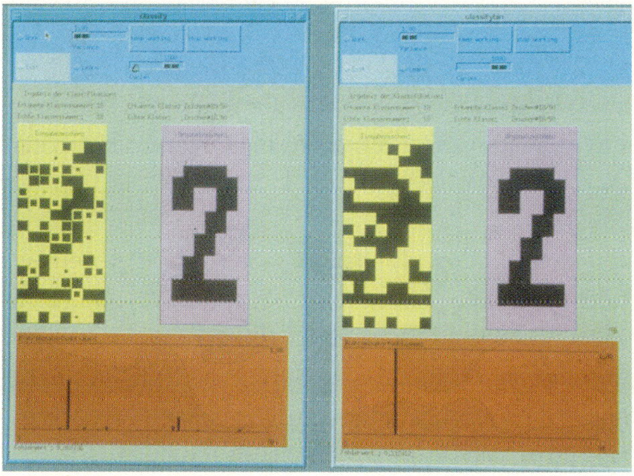

Figure 173: Distorted character before (left) and after (right) applying the threshold function

The task of the classifier as a part of the receiver is now to decide on the character that is presented by a set of distorted pixels. For this purpose, classic techniques are used as well as artificial neural networks. To prepare the pixel values of each character for classification, it is necessary to introduce an additional threshold function for some binary classifiers such as the competitive learning network. Figure 173 shows the difference between the original and the thresholded image for $\sigma^2 = 1.0$.

It is now the task of the classifier to map the scanned values of the pixel matrix which are interpreted as a feature vector $\boldsymbol{x}$, to a distinct character, i.e., to a class. With an average number of characters recognized to be false we can approximate the *error probability* P_E with its expectation value:

$$P_E \approx \frac{M_F}{M_{Ftot}} \tag{242}$$

M_F: *number of characters recognized to be false*
M_{Ftot}: *total number of transmitted characters.*

7.2.5. Results

Learning Behavior

For the simulations an ASCII character set with 91 characters of 8 x 16 pixels was employed. The size of the training set was limited to 30 000 characters distorted with noise of variance $\sigma^2 = 0.04$. The training data was presented randomly. The test sample consisted of 9100 characters, 100 derived from each class, with a noise of variance $\sigma^2 = 0.04$. The goal was to classify the test set with an error probability $P_E \leq 1$ %.

Four different back-propagation nets (bp) were evaluated as well as a next neighbor classifier (nn3), a regression analysis (ra) and a two-layered competitive learning network (cl). The competitive learning network has two layers and employs a threshold function. All back-propagation nets have at least three layers, since two layered perceptrons do not solve the problem. The first two networks use receptive fields of size 4 x 4. Only the first layer is divided into receptive fields; the second layer is entirely connected with the third layer. The first net has one connected unit for each possible receptive field (bp 513_1 with 5 x 13 hidden units). The second net is constructed with four connected units to each receptive field, but there are only 3 x 7 fields that are shifted with an offset of two neurons in each direction (bp 374_2 with 3 x 7 x 4 hidden units). All other nets are entirely interconnected. The third network has 8 x 4 neurons in the hidden layer (bp 84) and the fourth net has 8 x 8 neurons in the hidden layer (bp 88).

Figures 174 and 175 illustrate the learning behavior as a function of the learning cycles *Z*.

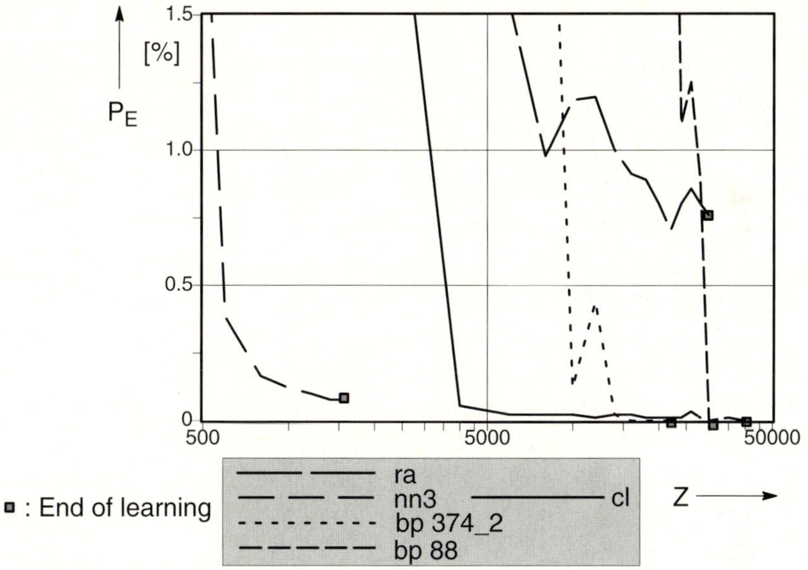

Figure 174:
Learning behavior as a function of learning cycles

We can see that back-propagation nets with receptive fields have almost double the learning speed of entirely connected nets. Figure 176 shows a comparison for two back-propagation networks for different signal-noise ratios. It is interesting to see that there are more errors on a test set disturbed with 20 dB ($\sigma = 0.1$) than on a test set even more strongly disturbed with 14 dB ($\sigma = 0.2$), after 24 000 learning cycles have been computed (see grey ellipse in Fig. 176). In all other cases, however, higher signal-noise ratios are recognized with higher rates. Furthermore, this illustrates that there is still the problem of specifying the number of hidden neurons.

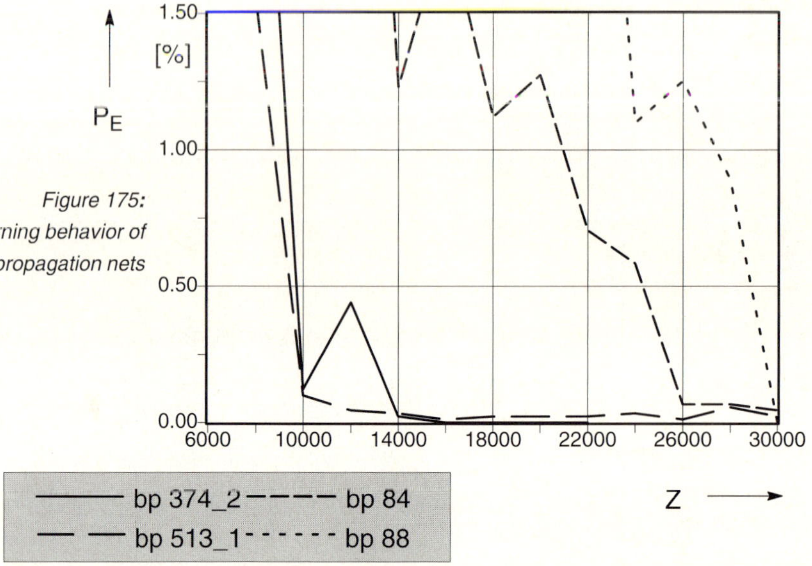

Figure 175: Learning behavior of back-propagation nets

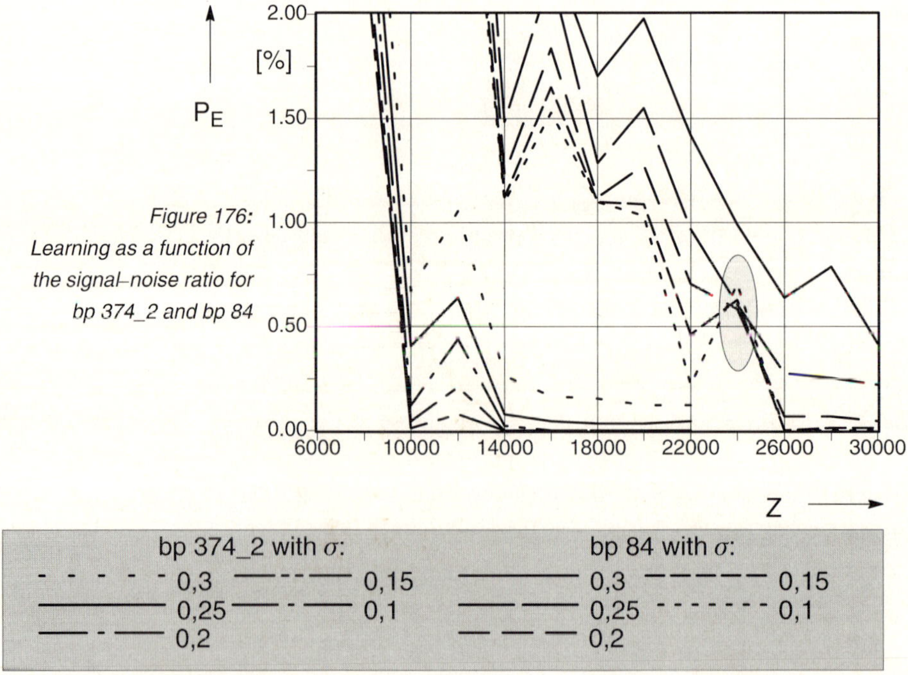

Figure 176: Learning as a function of the signal–noise ratio for bp 374_2 and bp 84

RMS Error Limit

The *RMS error* (root mean square) E_{RMS} has already been introduced to characterize the quality of neural networks (see also Eq. 177).

Figure 177 shows the course of the E_{RMS} during learning. It has to be noted that the errors for the different classification methods cannot be compared directly since the values for the discriminant functions are computed differently for each method. But even if only one method is taken into account, a smaller RMS error does not necessarily imply that there are fewer characters recognized to be erroneous. Therefore, the relation between RMS error and error probability can only be found empirically and not in a precise way.

The RMS error, however, can be used for determining the end of the learning phase. The RMS error curves are usually smoother than error probability curves, and learning can be stopped once its deviation crosses a lower threshold.

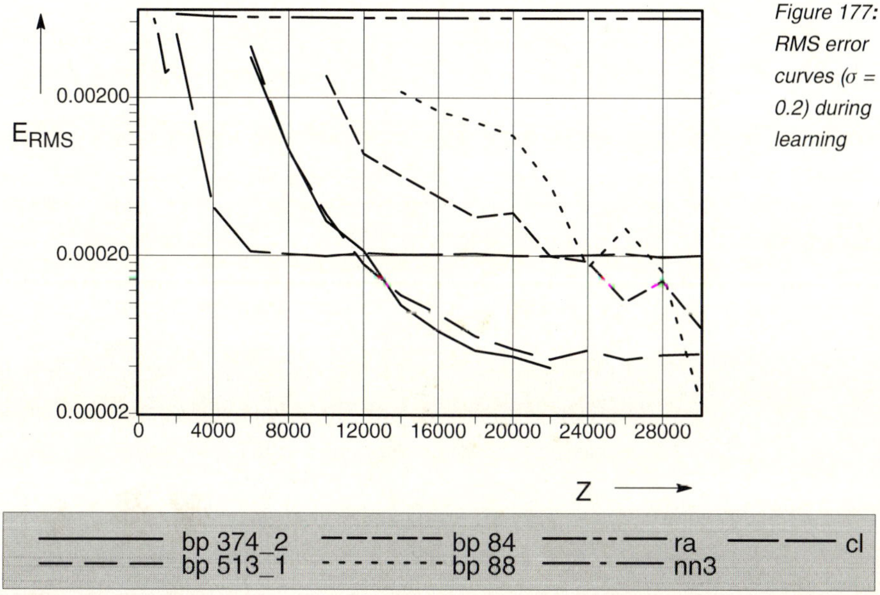

Figure 177: RMS error curves (σ = 0.2) during learning

Classification Behavior

Finally, the working phase of the networks have been analyzed. The error probability dependence on the signal-noise ratio is shown in Fig. 178. The classification method that best discriminates unknown characters from the training set is the next neighbor classifier. For applications in character recognition only the first part of the curves, i.e., the area for $\sigma = 0.1$ to 0.3 and $P_E \ll 1\%$ is of interest and zoomed in Fig. 179.

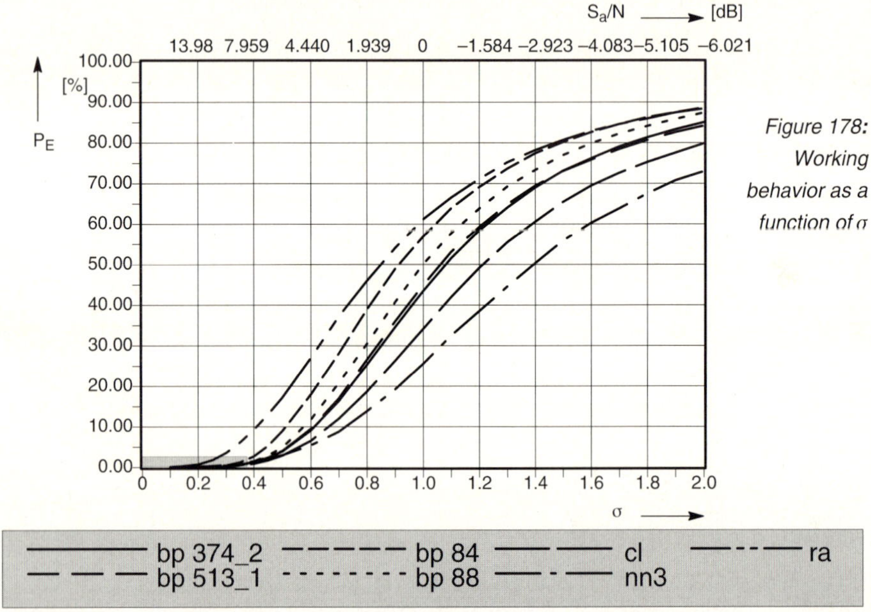

Figure 178: Working behavior as a function of σ

This property can be called selectivity. The only classifier that is not error-free at $\sigma = 0.1$ is the regression analysis, although it reaches the 0.1 % boundary. At $\sigma = 0.15$ the next neighbor classifier and bp 84 are not error-free and this shows that they do not separate the feature space very well. Both back-propagation networks and competitive learning yield good results.

This example has given a detailed insight into the behavior of neural classifiers compared to some standard methods using simple examples. The following application deals with a much more complex problem, specifically the cluster analysis, subspace mapping, visualization, and classification of multidimensional image data sets.

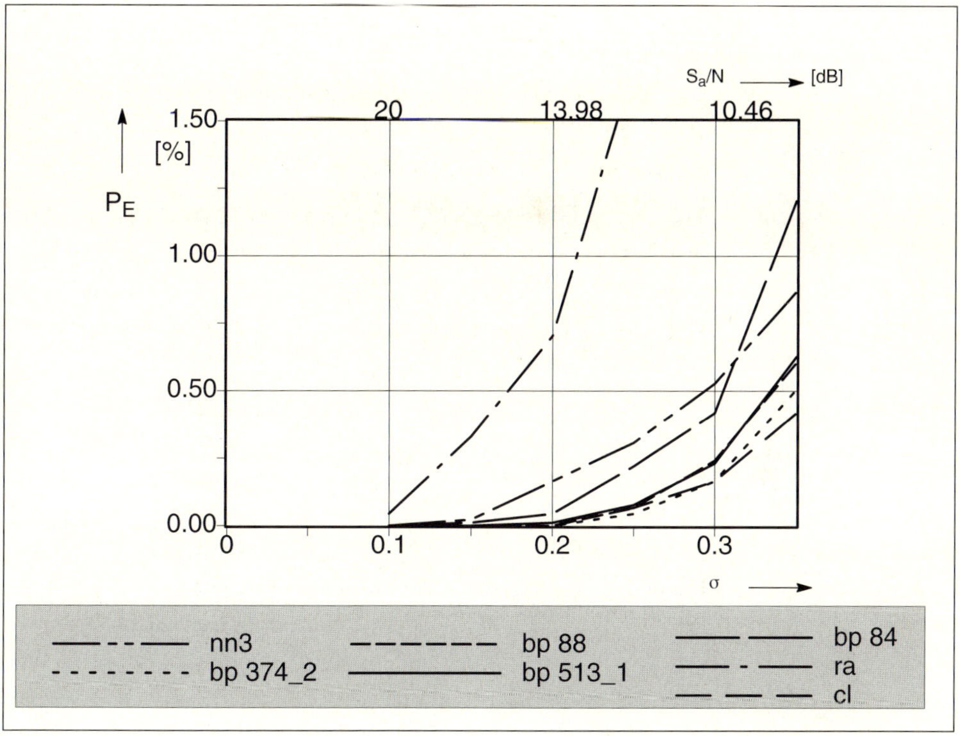

Figure 179:
Working behavior for low error probabilities

7.3. Analysis and Visualization of Mutidimensional Remotely Sensed Image Data Sets

7.3.1. Remote Sensing Techniques

The visual interpretation of high-dimensional data sets is an emerging subfield in scientific visualization and has become increasingly important. For this task, it is necessary to analyze the raw data sets with mathematical methods that find significant features and subspaces that can be visualized. Classical statistics [58, 71] offers a large variety of methods for this. Basically, these methods can be interpreted as optimizations, where the goal is on the one hand to reduce both the amount of data and its dimensionality and on the other hand to find a presentation that is as close as possible to the original data set (see also Sect. 6.2.3). There have been numerous applications of these mapping techniques for visualization, as in [51] or [263]. In particular, the most popular methods used are cluster anlysis, vector quantization, and principal component analysis. But there are also different approaches, such as iconic representations [23] or techniques adapted from computational geometry [207], such as Voronoi tessellation and scattered data modeling.

Basically, the problem of visualizing multidimensional data sets can be described as a two-pass optimization:

I. *Find an optimal representation of the density distribution of the data in a multidimensional space by means of codebook vectors or cluster centroids!*

II. *Find a low-dimensional presentation of these clusters that preserves their most important features in terms of distances or other criteria!*

However, if we remember Chap. 6 and recall the properties of the Kohonen map, it is easy to see how it may be employed for this purpose.

This section describes a visualization method for multidimensional data sets, based on Kohonen mapping, that was first introduced by [94].

The 3D extension of the model was analyzed (see also Chap. 6) where the neurons represent discrete entities in RGB space. Confronting the network with data sets of different statistical properties illustrated these two main properties referring to the problem: the clustering and the topological ordering of the neurons. We now consider the application of this method on multidimensional images, namely Landsat-TM remote sensing data of Kuwait and its burning oil fields, following [94]. This application from environmental sciences aims at extracting smoke and pollution densities and oil-water emulsions. But the method can be straightforwardly applied on any visualization problem.

In particular, referring to Chap. 4 where advanced environmental monitoring systems were introduced, we see that remote sensing techniques and satellite image classification are required for elegant input data acquisition. For this reason, all the investigations below were done in the context of the prototype TERRA and are examples in the spirit of the *integration of graphics and imaging techniques.*

Remote sensing itself has proved to be a very helpful and effective method for getting semantical ground information. For this reason several satellites have been launched and are used to scan the Earth's surface sequentially. Among the most well-known satellites are SPOT, ERS 1 and Landsat-TM. The latter has 7 different spectral channels taking into account atmospheric distortion from absorption, scattering, diffraction, and refraction, as in Fig. 180.

Figure 180: Intensity losses of reflected light by the atmosphere

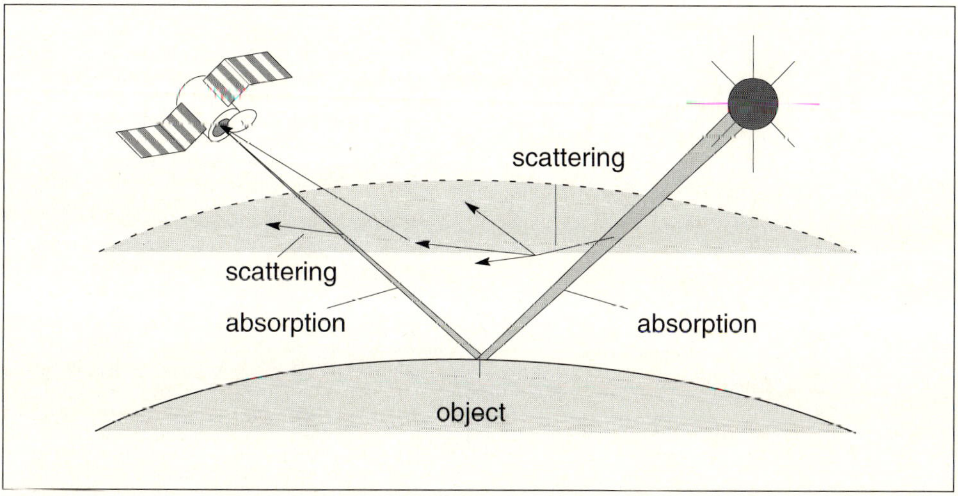

The atmospheric window is transparent to visible light and near- infrared radiance.

On the other hand, the characteristic signatures of vegetation are influenced by the spectral reflection distribution, by shadows of leaves, by the morphology of plants, etc. This is illustrated in Fig. 181 and is influenced by the pigments of leaves, the cell structure and the water content.

Figure 181: Spectral reflection of typical green leaves

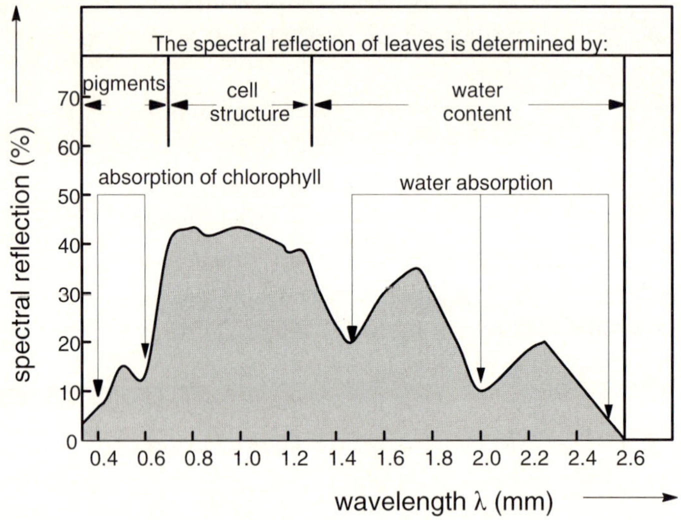

The spectral sensitivities of the Landsat-TM channels have been optimized with respect to the facts stated above and are explained in Table 11.

Table 11: Sensitivity of the different Landsat-TM spectral bands

band	wavelength	sensitivity to
1	0,45 – 0,52 µm	coastal cartography soil vegetation separability
2	0,52 – 0,60 µm	healthy vegetation/correlation of chlorophyll
3	0,63 – 0,69 µm	classification of plants absorption of chlorophyll
4	0,76 – 0,90 µm	humidity
5	1,55 – 1,75 µm	content of water/cloud – snow separation
6	10,4 – 21,5 µm	heat stress of plants
7	2,08 – 2,35 µm	water temperature

Thus, each Landsat-TM image consists of seven different channels. In order to obtain the essential ground information, a raw image has to be clustered and classified in a 7-dimensional feature space.

Towards this end a non-supervised cluster analysis is first performed in order to interactively optimize the training areas of a supervised method. Figure 182 shows the corresponding pipeline.

In spite of all the classical methods proposed in the past, however, the problem of how to visualize the cluster topologies identified in a multidimensional space still remains. This is crucial for a reliable interactive selection of the training areas since they have to represent the statistical data properties of the corresponding class.

7.3.2. Cluster Visualization and Subspace Mapping

The 3D Kohonen map of Chap. 6 and the proposed visualization method were both applied on multispectral remotely sensed image data, namely for the analysis of the burning oil fields in Kuwait. In this case, a 7-dimensional image of spectral responses of a Landsat-TM was given. Although there are many classic methods for clustering and classifying remote sensing data, there has been no useful method to visualize the relationship of the pixel data in 7-dimensional space.

The result of the method is pseudocolored images, where due to the topological mapping the similarity of color represents a similarity in the original multidimensional data set. Figure 184a shows channel 1 of the raw image. Figures 183a–h show the results obtained by the Kohonen maps where 3 x 3 x 3, 4 x 4 x 4, 5 x 5 x 5 and 6 x 6 x 6 competitive neurons were respectively chosen. Each cluster analysis is based on a different weight initialization and produces a result where the colors produced are different. The upper left parts of the images show Kuwait Bay, and lower left we recognize the smoke of the burning oil fields.

The images in Fig. 183a–d can be used for ground interpretation. For instance, the smoke of the clouds has a decreasing density referring to similar features in the 7D space. Thus, our method has visualized the cloud in similar colors. Other similarities can be obtained for water regions which also yield corresponding color bands.

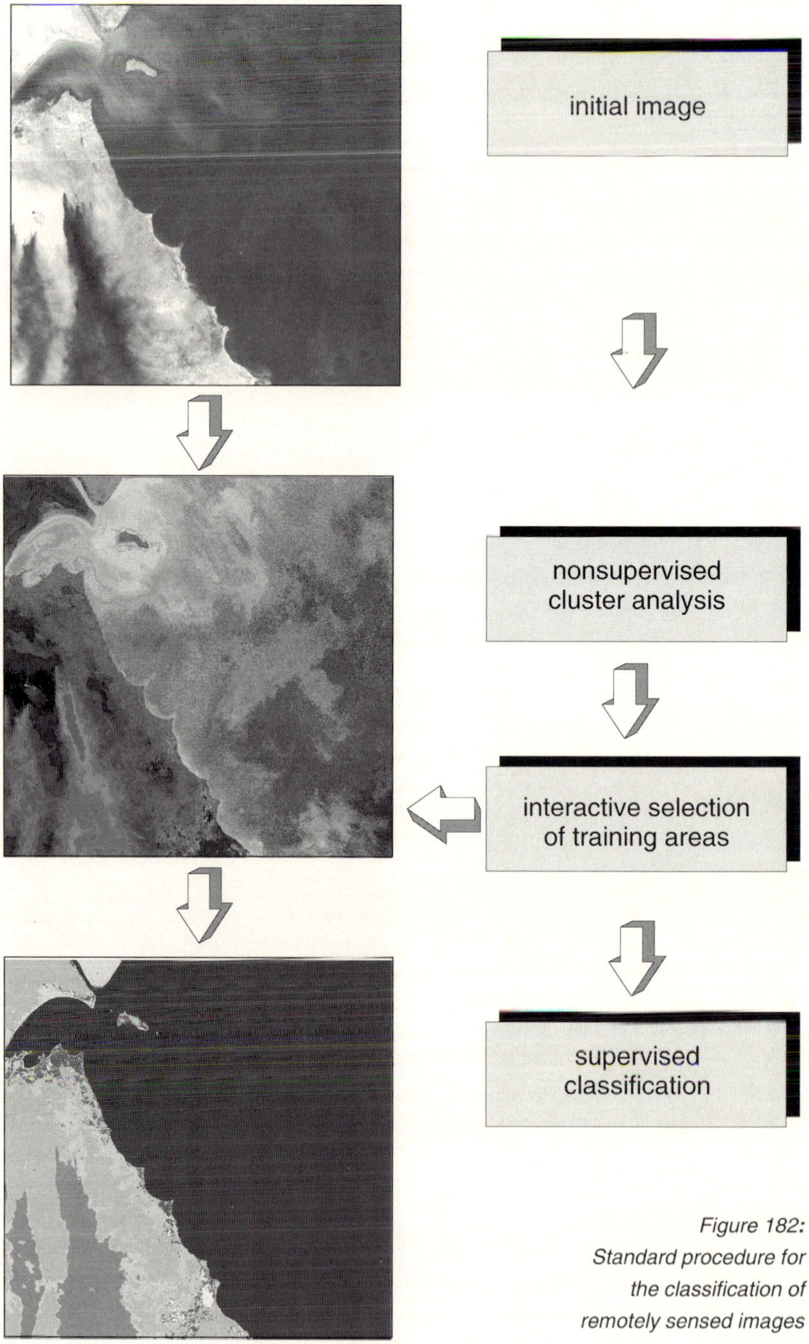

Figure 182: Standard procedure for the classification of remotely sensed images

Furthermore, it is possible to compare the colors of the smoke area with those of the water since we know that the water was polluted by oil. Liquid oil and burned oil have some physical properties in common.

The maps were learned with 100 000 randomly selected pixels from the raw image. The color itself is set up during the dynamical organization of the network because the weights are initialized with small random numbers. The clustered images of Fig. 183 are particularly important as a preprocessing for supervised trained classification methods. Selecting training areas on the basis of these clustered images (Fig. 184b), we were able to classify the image with a back-propagation network, either pixel-based (Fig. 184c) or including a texture analysis (Fig. 184d).

The classification was done with a prototype system called ICAN including numerous X/Motif widgets for zooming, panning, interactive picking, etc.

The following classes of the Table 12 refer to the colors in Figs. 184c and 184d.

number	**color**	**ground class**
I.	yellow	desert
II.	blue	water
III.	red	buildings
IV.	gray	burning oil
V.	white	salt morass

Table 12: Colors used to represent the different ground classes in Fig. 184

7.3.3. Studies on Satellite Image Classification

Other interesting investigations on satellite image classification have been reported for instance in [157, 237, 95]. For example, a Landsat-TM image of a storm-damaged region of about 400 x 400 pixels in Bavaria was considered. The goal was to examine primarily the applicability of the satellite image classification based on neural networks for the differentiation of forest types from storm damaged areas. The true ground information was available. In this study pixel-oriented and texture-oriented classification schemes by back-propagation networks, as well as Kohonen feature maps with LVQ training were employed. For the verification of the results and for

Figure 183:

a, b) Topological clustering with a 3x3x3 Kohonen map; c, d) with a 4x4x4 Kohonen map
e, f) Topological clustering with a 5x5x5 Kohonen map; g, h) with a 6x6x6 Kohonen map
(source: EOSAT, raw image courtesy provided by GAF, Munich, Germany); all from [94]

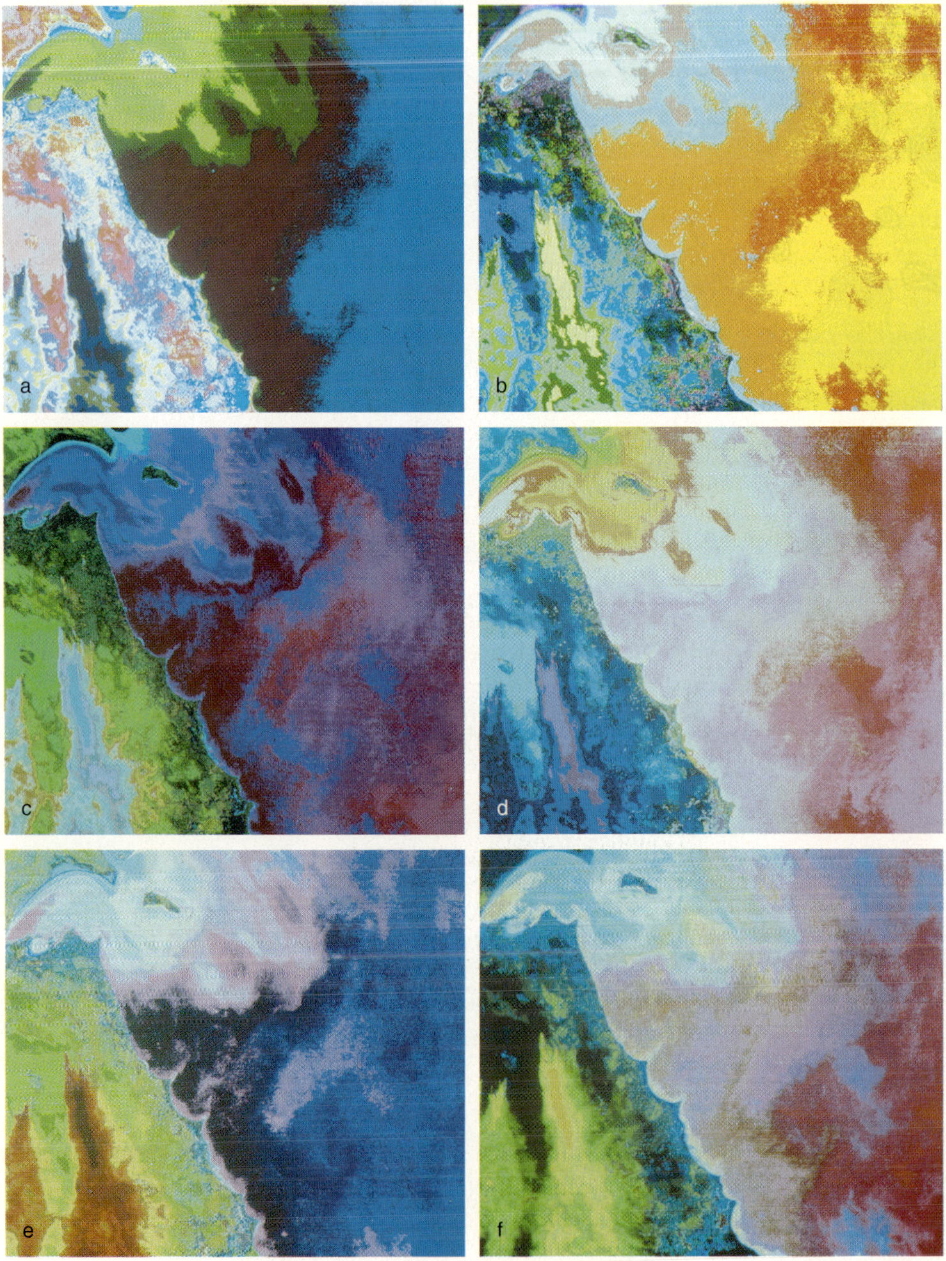

Figure 184:

a) Infrared channel of a Landsat-TM image of Kuwait (15.02.91)

b) Training areas for a supervised classification with back-propagation networks

c) Pixel based classification; d) Texture based classification

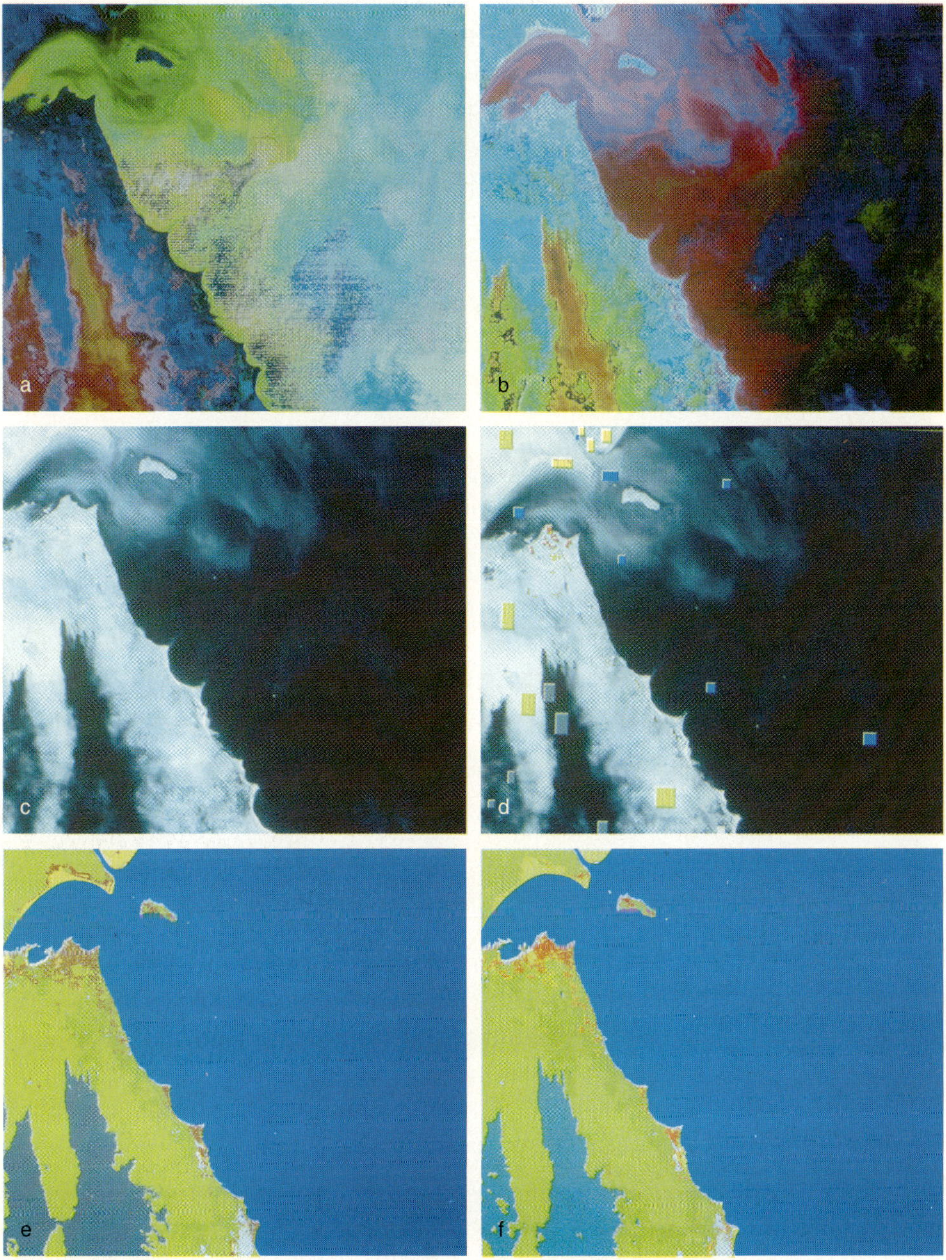

the evaluation of the classification quality, a confusion matrix is often used, which can be obtained by reclassifying the training areas. However, these matrices only evaluate the quality of what is learnt, not the generalizing behavior.

It finally turned out that the average recognition rate for pixel-oriented back-propagation networks provided worse results (82.7%) than the texture-oriented one (88.1%). In this application the LVQ yields the best results (94.9%). The details of this examination can be found in [104].

Finally, Table 13 illustrates the confusion matrix for the LVQ classifier for 9 different classes. The bold-typed classes represent the different types of forests to be discriminated.

Table 13: Confusion matrix for the LVQ classifier

	AKB	AK	SIE	STE	WAS	**NA**	**LAU**	**MIS**	**DEF**
AKB	98.9	–.–	1.1	–.–	–.–	–.–	–.–	–.–	–.–
AK	–.–	99.3	0.8	–.–	–.–	–.–	–.–	–.–	–.–
SIE	9.0	–.–	90.3	–.–	–.–	–.–	–.–	–.–	0.7
STE	–.–	–.–	–.–	100	–.–	–.–	–.–	–.–	–.–
WAS	–.–	–.–	–.–	–.–	100	–.–	–.–	–.–	–.–
NA	–.–	–.–	–.–	–.–	–.–	**87.8**	**1.0**	**10.2**	**1.0**
LAU	–.–	–.–	–.–	–.–	–.–	**–.–**	**92.9**	**7.1**	**–.–**
MIS	–.–	–.–	–.–	–.–	–.–	**3.3**	**9.9**	**86.8**	**–.–**
DEF	0.5	–.–	2.7	–.–	–.–	**1.1**	**–.–**	**–.–**	**95.6**

total quality: 94,9

Other interesting results are provided by the investigations of [237]. Classification tests were performed on two Landsat-TM images covering a district of Niederbayern in southeast Germany. The images were recorded in the summer of 1990 and ground truth was available for 1% (410 segments at 700 m x 700 m) of the whole region.

Only bands 2, 3, 4, 5, and 7 were considered for differentiation of landcover and vegetation, as well as an edge-preserving smoothing filter together with a stratification was performed.

In this study a maximum likelihood classifier (MLC, see Chap. 6) was compared with a backpropagation network (BP) (5 x 104 x 13 neurons, 200 000 training cycles). For the MLC a careful extensive preprocessing was necessary, which included clustering, cleaning and subclass definitions. These time-consuming interactive tasks were not necessary for the backpropagation.

Table 14 shows the confusion matrix for the MLC and can be compared to Table 15 representing the results of the BP for stratum 1.

We see that the average accuracy of the BP is even higher than the MLC, although there was no need for subclustering and other extensive preprocessing

Table 14: Confusion matrix of the MLC for stratum 1 in [%]

	WW	WR	SB	RY	OA	MA	PO	SU	PG	HO	WO	WA	OL	portion
WW	67,3	8,4	1,1	0,9	4,6	4,6	0,5	0,7	4,8	0,6	2,6	0,5	3,0	20,1
WR	6,9	78,6	0,5	0,3	1,5	2,8	0,1	0,4	2,7	0,5	1,5	0,0	4,1	8,3
SB	36,1	8,3	33,3	5,6	2,8	5,6	2,8	0,0	2,8	0,0	0,0	0,0	2,8	0,4
RY	14,7	1,6	1,6	77,1	1,6	1,6	0,0	0,0	1,6	0,0	0,0	0,0	0,0	0,6
OA	42,4	5,3	0,5	0,0	21,5	9,8	0,5	0,5	6,3	1,9	6,8	1,5	2,4	2,1
MA	5,4	3,0	0,1	0,1	1,9	72,2	2,3	3,7	6,5	0,4	2,7	0,5	1,3	11,6
PO	13,1	3,6	0,0	0,0	1,2	22,6	30,1	17,9	6,0	0,0	2,4	0,0	2,4	0,1
SU	4,8	1,2	0,0	0,0	0,0	6,7	1,2	83,5	0,6	0,0	0,6	0,0	1,2	1,8
PG	6,9	13,1	0,3	0,1	2,6	11,2	1,1	0,5	44,3	1,3	8,8	0,7	8,8	10,3
HO	5,5	6,0	0,0	0,0	1,2	7,2	0,4	0,4	7,6	45,0	11,2	0,8	14,7	2,7
WO	1,1	1,3	0,0	0,1	0,4	2,0	0,1	0,1	3,5	1,3	87,7	0,7	1,8	33,1
WA	0,0	0,0	0,0	0,0	0,0	0,0	0,0	0,0	0,0	0,0	6,9	92,5	1,4	1,6
OL	3,6	15,0	0,3	0,3	1,3	4,0	0,3	0,3	11,8	4,1	2,0	0,7	56,3	6,5

total quality: 71,18

WW = winter wheat	WR = winter barley + rape
SB = spring barley	RY = rye
OA = oats	MA = maize
PO = potatoes	SU = sugar beets
PG = permanent grassland	HO = hop
WO = wood	WA = water
OL = other land use	

The generalization behavior is illustrated in Tables 16 and 17. The data set was subdivided into two parts, where the first one was employed for training and the second one for testing the generalization.

Table 15: Confusion matrix of the BP-net for stratum 1 in [%]

	WW	WR	SB	RY	OA	MA	PO	SU	PG	HO	WO	WA	OL	portion
WW	52,2	3,7	15,4	3,0	4,7	2,7	5,3	0,8	2,6	0,1	3,4	0,0	5,3	21,2
WR	2,3	79,4	5,1	0,6	0,5	1,2	1,3	0,1	0,9	0,6	0,4	0,0	7,7	9,0
SB	2,0	0,0	85,7	4,1	0,0	0,0	0,0	0,0	2,0	4,1	0,0	0,0	2,0	0,1
RY	16,1	1,2	8,5	68,2	0,0	0,7	0,9	0,0	1,2	0,0	0,0	0,0	3,2	1,0
OA	37,0	2,2	8,0	0,0	15,8	14,2	3,7	0,0	0,8	14,0	0,4	0,0	4,0	1,2
MA	0,8	1,1	0,6	0,1	0,4	79,0	9,7	2,4	4,0	0,8	0,2	0,0	0,8	9,0
PO	0,7	0,0	9,6	0,0	2,9	22,8	42,7	11,0	4,4	5,2	0,0	0,0	0,7	0,3
SU	2,5	1,1	0,1	0,0	0,0	15,0	4,6	75,2	0,8	0,1	0,0	0,0	0,4	1,7
PG	0,3	0,2	1,4	0,0	0,7	8,9	2,1	0,0	74,8	8,3	0,5	0,0	2,8	3,3
HO	0,7	0,5	2,8	0,0	0,1	0,7	1,0	0,0	1,9	82,7	0,5	0,0	9,1	1,8
WO	0,1	0,1	0,1	0,0	0,1	1,9	0,04	0,0	1,0	6,1	39,9	0,1	0,5	43,8
WA	1,5	0,0	0,5	0,0	2,4	3,4	0,0	0,0	0,0	5,0	6,6	77,8	2,8	2,7
OL	0,3	6,7	6,2	0,0	0,6	0,1	0,5	0,0	4,0	8,1	0,4	1,4	71,6	4,8

total quality: 76,63

The total qualities that were computed show that the BP provides good generalization behavior. Due to the extensive true grounds that were available for this investigation, the results obtained here should be taken seriously.

Table 16: Confusion matrix for the training areas (BP-net)

	WW	WR	SB	RY	OA	MA	PO	SU	PG	HO	WO	WA	OL	portion
WW	19,1	4,9	15,3	2,1	23,4	9,0	6,7	1,5	7,0	1,5	6,2	0,0	3,3	10,6
WR	2,0	78,2	8,3	0,7	1,5	0,5	0,9	0,0	1,3	0,5	0,4	0,0	5,7	4,5
SB	4,2	0,0	87,5	8,3	0,0	0,0	0,0	0,0	0,0	0,0	0,0	0,0	0,0	0,1
RY	0,0	2,3	13,4	80,2	0,0	1,8	1,4	0,0	1,0	0,0	0,0	0,0	0,0	0,5
OA	4,8	3,6	12,0	0,0	62,4	3,2	0,4	0,0	4,0	9,6	0,0	0,0	0,0	0,6
MA	0,3	0,5	0,7	0,3	1,5	85,7	5,6	0,2	3,7	1,0	0,2	0,0	0,5	4,5
PO	0,0	0,0	4,4	0,0	0,0	64,7	20,6	4,4	4,4	0,0	0,0	0,0	1,5	0,2
SU	0,6	1,4	0,0	0,3	0,6	25,3	5,9	65,5	0,3	0,3	0,0	0,0	0,0	0,9
PG	0,4	0,6	1,8	0,0	0,3	7,2	1,3	0,0	80,1	7,5	0,8	0,0	0,2	1,6
HO	0,8	0,3	3,2	0,0	0,5	0,3	0,0	0,0	8,4	85,1	0,3	0,0	1,1	0,9
WO	0,1	0,1	0,7	0,0	0,2	0,5	0,0	0,0	0,6	6,9	91,1	0,0	0,2	22,0
WA	0,7	0,0	0,0	0,0	0,2	0,0	0,0	0,0	0,0	1,2	2,6	92,7	2,6	1,4
OL	0,7	3,8	2,7	0,0	0,5	0,5	0,1	0,0	8,6	15,7	0,1	1,2	66,2	2,4

total quality: 71,45

	WW	WR	SB	RY	OA	MA	PO	SU	PG	HO	WO	WA	OL	portion
WW	54,5	1,7	11,7	4,7	22,2	0,4	1,0	0,02	1,4	1,4	0,5	0,0	0,4	10,6
WR	1,8	76,8	2,4	0,3	1,1	2,8	0,7	0,0	5,7	1,0	0,4	0,0	6,9	4,5
SB	0,0	0,0	84,0	0,0	0,0	0,0	0,0	0,0	4,0	12,0	0,0	0,0	0,0	0,06
RY	1,4	0,0	24,9	33,6	38,7	0,0	0,0	0,0	1,4	0,0	0,0	0,0	0,0	0,5
OA	21,2	0,8	4,0	0,0	21,6	24,4	3,2	0,0	0,4	21,6	2,8	0,0	0,0	0,6
MA	0,9	1,6	0,05	0,0	0,4	84,0	4,4	0,9	5,8	1,8	0,2	0,0	0,1	4,5
PO	0,0	0,0	10,3	0,0	3,0	20,6	38,2	2,9	3,0	22,1	0,0	0,0	0,0	0,2
SU	1,7	0,8	0,0	0,3	1,9	37,2	0,6	55,3	2,2	0,0	0,0	0,0	0,0	0,9
PG	0,0	0,0	0,3	0,0	0,4	12,9	1,5	0,0	73,9	9,2	0,0	0,0	1,8	1,6
HO	0,3	0,8	1,6	0,0	0,0	1,9	0,0	0,0	4,9	88,3	0,0	0,0	2,4	0,9
WO	0,02	0,04	0,1	0,0	0,04	1,2	0,04	0,0	1,3	12,3	84,1	0,1	0,6	21,9
WA	0,0	0,0	1,1	0,0	11,7	6,6	0,0	0,0	0,0	8,4	9,9	62,4	0,0	1,4
OL	0,1	8,4	9,0	0,0	0,8	0,0	0,0	0,0	10,1	4,8	0,6	0,0	66,3	2,4

Table 17: Confusion matrix for the test areas (BP net)

total quality: 73,58

This application has illustrated the advantages of neural classifiers for a complex image classification problem. In particular, the capabilities of the Kohonen map as a method for visualizing subspaces have been shown. Moreover, it represents both a *graphics and an imaging technique that derives from the basic principles of human information processing.*

The following application explains another variant of this algorithm for volume visualization and analysis in medical imaging.

7.4. Interactive Identification and Reconstruction of Brain Tumors in MR-Images

7.4.1. Segmentation of Volume Data

Volume rendering has become increasingly important during the last few years, particularly in the field of medical imaging. Advanced volume renderers, [121, 151, 173] have been developed as well as 3D surface reconstruction methods like marching cubes [158] or Delaunay triangulation [207]. However, to provide reliable and high-quality images, both 3D reconstruction algorithms and volume renderers require a robust pre-segmentation of the initial 3D data sets to be analyzed. Most methods presented are based either on a linear separation of the grey values [186] or on interactive treatment of the voxels to be rendered [121].

A robust segmentation, however, refers to a cluster analysis of the volume data and there are several ways to it. Magnetic resonance imaging allows the generation of multiparameter images that can be clustered and segmented pixelwise with standard statistical methods such as [58, 71] or with fuzzy approaches as in [109]. In practice, however, multiparameter scans are both too expensive and too stressful for the patients. Thus, one promising way to extract features from grey-level images is texture analysis, as introduced in Chap. 5, which describes the local pattern to be discriminated in a texture feature space. In addition to classical methods stemming from image processing [80], neural networks as introduced in Chap. 6 have prove to be a promising alternative for many applications. The problem that arises, however, is the internal presentation of the texture features in neural networks and thus the evaluation of its capability as a texture analyzer. For this reason, the most reliable method for texture analysis is based on the concepts of Chap. 5 using a standard feature extractor (for instance wavelets), a nonlinear operator, a dimensionality reduction, and a neural network for classification only. But due to the promising results obtained by texture-based approaches with back-propagation networks on multiparameter images in the previous section, [38] proposes an easy-to-use, interactive, fast method for the segmentation of pre- and post-contrasted MR images. It is based on a Kohonen map which performs a visualization, subspace mapping, segmentation, and classification of a texture feature space. In this example the texture space immediately derives from the image set, each consisting of a pre- and postcontrasted picture. However, this idea can be easily extended with an additional preprocessing, such as in Chap. 5. The subspace mapping and visual data analysis are here helpful in analyzing a given high-dimensional texture feature space, and it once again *integrates visualization and imaging* in order to get reliable results on a complex problem. In particular, the determining role of interactivity in segmentation and classification is illustrated.

To give an insight into MR technology, a brief overview of the underlying physics is provided, taken from [38] and [155].

7.4.2. Magnetic Resonance Technology

Magnetic resonance imaging is one of the most effective methods developed so far to give an *in vivo* insight into the human body. Providing 3D volume data sets, MR images have often been used to illustrate the capabilities of rendering and reconstruction techniques. However, in contrast to standard computer X-ray tomography, where the data set always presents the density of the analyzed volume, MR images demand a much more complex underlying understanding of quantum mechanics. Moreover, the interpretation of MR images strongly depends on the parameter sequences used for the recording process. In order to develop a reliable automatic segmentation method, it is of crucial importance that the physics of the MR method be understood. The following section will briefly introduce the basic physics using a simplified mechanical model and explaining the meaning of the three main parameters that can be measured, namely the longitudinal relaxation time T_1, the transversal relaxation time T_2, and the numerical density of protons. A good introduction to MR imaging can be found in [155] or [201].

The Larmor Equation

Magnetic resonance is a phenomenon that was discovered in the 1940s. It is based on the interaction of atomic nuclei, located in a constant magnetic field, with an electromagnetic high-frequency (HF) field. From the point of view of classical physics, this interaction can be explained as a precession of the nuclear spin with an isotope dependent frequency, the so-called Larmor frequency. The precession itself is stimulated by means of the HF field. This is illustrated in Fig. 185.

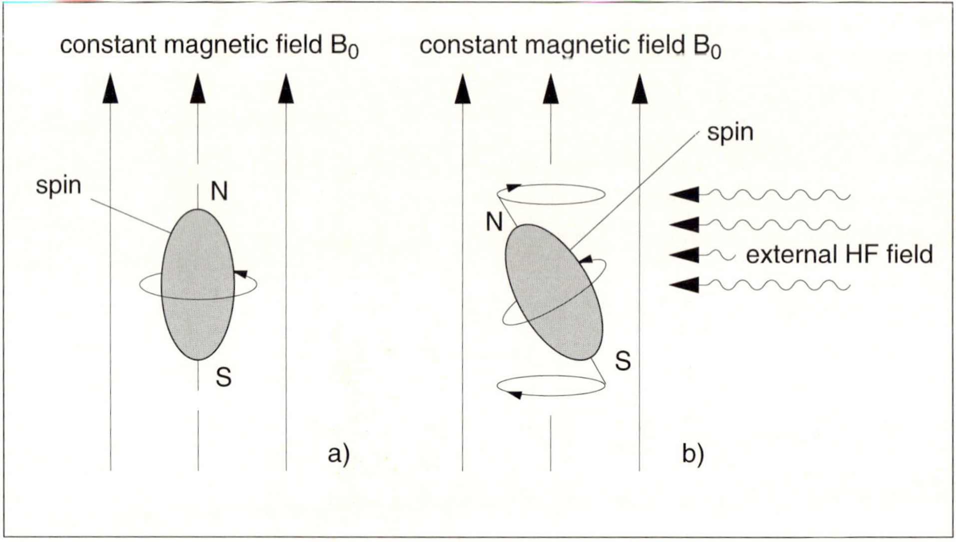

Figure 185: Simplified model for magnetic resonance of a nucleus stimulated by an external HF field (see [201]):
a) spin oriented in a constant magnetic field B_0
b) precession of the spin stimulated by a transient HF impulse

Any atomic nucleus that consists of an odd number of protons and neutrons is characterized by an angular momentum or spin. In a classical physics interpretation, the spin gives rise to a circular current, due to the positive charge of the nucleus, and thus to a magnetic momentum. In this way, the nucleus can be interpreted as a tiny magnet. If we expose it to an external magnetic field the direction of the spin will change according to the external force (see also Fig. 185). During the relaxation process of the nucleus, the spin will describe a precession movement for a short time with a characteristic frequency, the so-called Larmor frequency ω_L. According to Eq. (243) the Larmor frequency depends on the strength B_0 of the external field and on a constant *const*.

$$\omega_L = const\ B_0 \qquad (243)$$

After being oriented towards the direction of this external field, nuclear relaxation can be stimulated again by additional transient HF impulses. To achieve resonance and in-phase precession, the frequency of the transient field has to correspond to the Larmor frequency of the nucleus.

In most practical applications, H^+ nuclei (i.e., single protons) are measured because of their sensitivity and their numerical density in organic matter. The temporal behavior of the relaxation strongly depends on how big the nucleus is (i.e., how many nucleons it contains).

Relaxation Times

The magnetic momentum **M** will result from a superposition of the momentums of all nuclei of the corresponding volume. During relaxation, the vector **M** of the magnetic momentum can be decomposed into components in the direction of the external constant field *(z)* and of those perpendicular *(x,y)*. This is illustrated in Fig. 186a, which shows the vector components of **M**. After relaxation into the equilibrium, the $\mathbf{M}_{xy}$ components of **M** will be decreased to zero and **M** will be equal to $\mathbf{M}_z$ again. The temporal behavior of $\mathbf{M}_z$ and of $\mathbf{M}_{xy}$ components is described by two time constants T_1 and T_2, also shown in Fig. 186.

T_1 describes the relaxation process in the z-direction (longitudinal relaxation) and the growth of the $\mathbf{M}_z$ component by exchange of energy with the environment, whereas T_2 stands for the decrease of the $\mathbf{M}_{xy}$ component (transversal relaxation). The two constants are only weakly correlated, since statistical phase shifting of single spins accelerate the reduction of the sum $\mathbf{M}_{xy}$.

Finally, it can be stated that the echo measured depends on numerous parameters, such as:

I. Spin density
II. Relaxation T_1
III. Relaxation T_2
IV. Chemical shifts
V. Flux (blood)

The following paragraph briefly describes one of the pulse sequences of the stimulating HF field to measure T_1 and to generate T_1-weighted images.

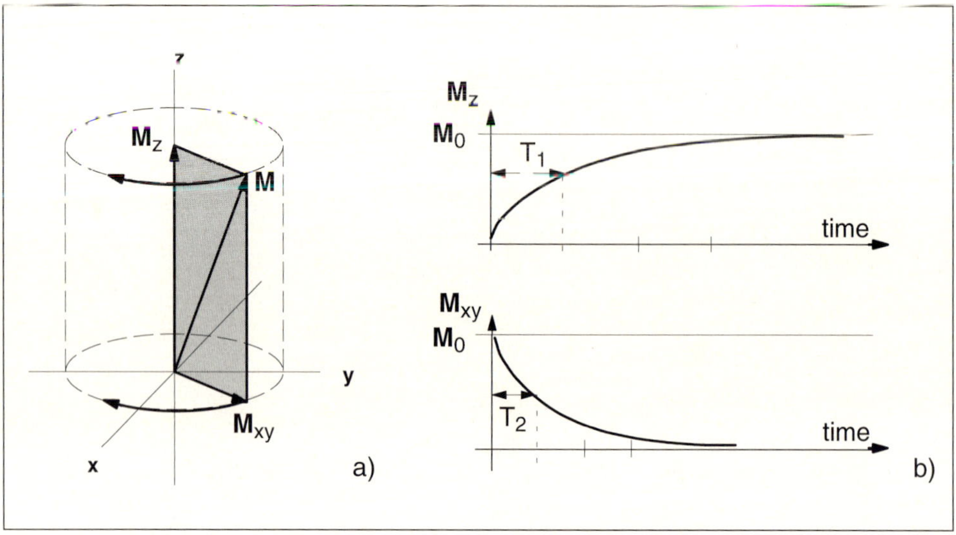

Figure 186:
a) Magnetic momentum ***M*** *and its components*
b) Temporal relaxation behavior of the components of ***M*** *(see [201])*

The Spin-Echo Sequence

In addition to saturation recovery and inversion recovery, the spin-echo sequence (see Fig. 187) is one of the three most important impulse sequences used for measuring the parameters stated above. To measure a signal which depends mainly on T_1, the $\mathbf{M}_z$ component has to be tipped into the *xy*-plane, where the signal can be detected. This is performed by a first 90° pulse. The coherence of the single spins, however, will rapidly get lost and the resulting response will decrease with time. This is shown in Fig. 188. To create an echo, a second 180° impulse will invert the phase drifts and will again generate coherence for a short time interval. The maximum response resulting from this can be measured as the echo-time T_e.

After this second 180° pulse the relaxation process will turn the magnetic momentum back to its equilibrium. If we repeat the pulse sequence described above with a time rate T_R that is much shorter than T_1, the actual strength of the measured response will strongly depend on the T_1 of the nucleus. If, however, T_R is longer than T_1 the resulting echo will mainly depend on T_2 and on the density of the spins.

Choosing successive short repetition times, a value that represents T_1 and characterizes the nucleus will be received for each volume element.

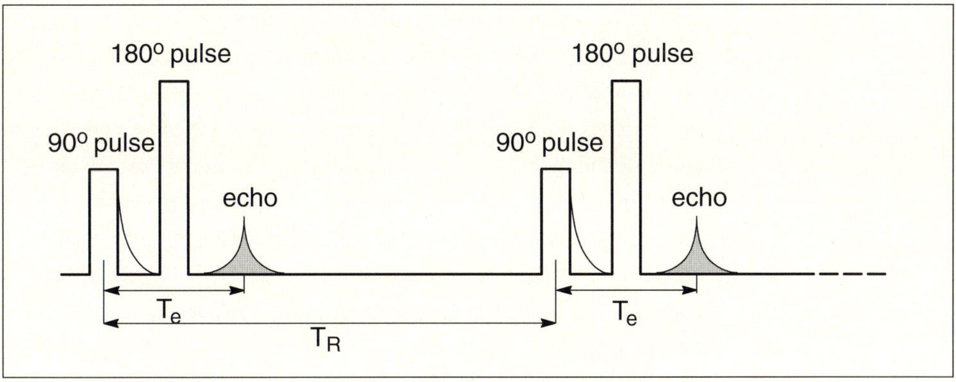

Figure 187:
Spin-echo sequence characterized by echo time T_e and pulse repetition time T_R

Finally, the question arises of how to code the spatial position of the volume elements in 3D and how to look inside the volume. If we look back to the Larmor equation (243) we recall that the resonance frequency depends on the strength of the magnetic field. Using this relationship, additional gradient magnetic fields in x, y and z directions can be superimposed to code the spatial position in terms of different Larmor frequencies for one type of nucleus. The 3D volume image itself can then be obtained by methods such as an inverse 3D Fourier transform of the data set measured. This will not be described here in detail but can be found in [155] or [201].

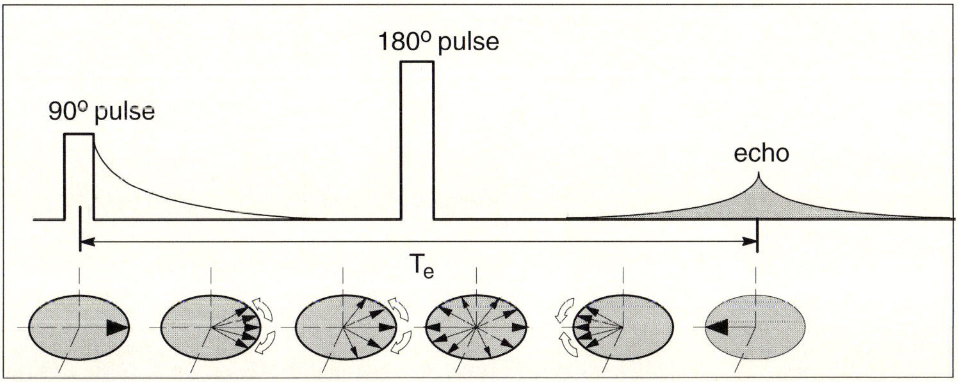

Figure 188:
Temporary loss of phase coherence in the $\mathbf{M}_{xy}$ component of the momentum

7.4.3. Clustering High-Dimensional Texture Feature Spaces

Chap. 6 has shown that the standard Kohonen map can be used for dimensionality reduction of data sets. To do so, the number of input neurons has to be equal to the dimension of the input data, where the components of each data vector are simultaneously presented to the net. Since the neurons in the competitive layer are ordered topologically, i.e., neighboring neurons react to data vectors that are similar in the input space, the mapping can be interpreted as a reduction of any N-dimensional space into K dimensions preserving the topology of the data as much as possible. The resolution of this discrete K-space is given by the number of competitive neurons, corresponding to clusters.

The visualization of cluster topologies in high-dimensional spaces is very important for the interactive process in the selection of training areas for a supervised classification step (see also Sect. 7.2). For this purpose a 3D version of the Kohonen map was already introduced. Figure 189 shows a slight modification of this method using an 18-dimensional input space for texture-based analysis of MR image slices. It is derived from the local neighborhoods of one pixel each in the precontrasted and postcontrasted image.

Since the network now arranges the neurons topologically during random training on the image, neighboring neurons with similar colors react to texture features that are neighbors in multidimensional space. Thus, the similarity of the color provided by the reacting neurons refers to an adjacency in 18-dimensional space, rather like the examples given in the remote sensing application.

7.4.4. Some Results

Image Data Used

The following examples present some of the results obtained with the Kohonen map, explained in detail in [38]. The image shown in Fig. 191 presents a typical T_1-weighted MR image slice of a brain cancer patient affected by two meningiomas. It was recorded with a spin-echo sequence of $T_R = 600$ ms and $T_e = 15$ ms. The spatial res-

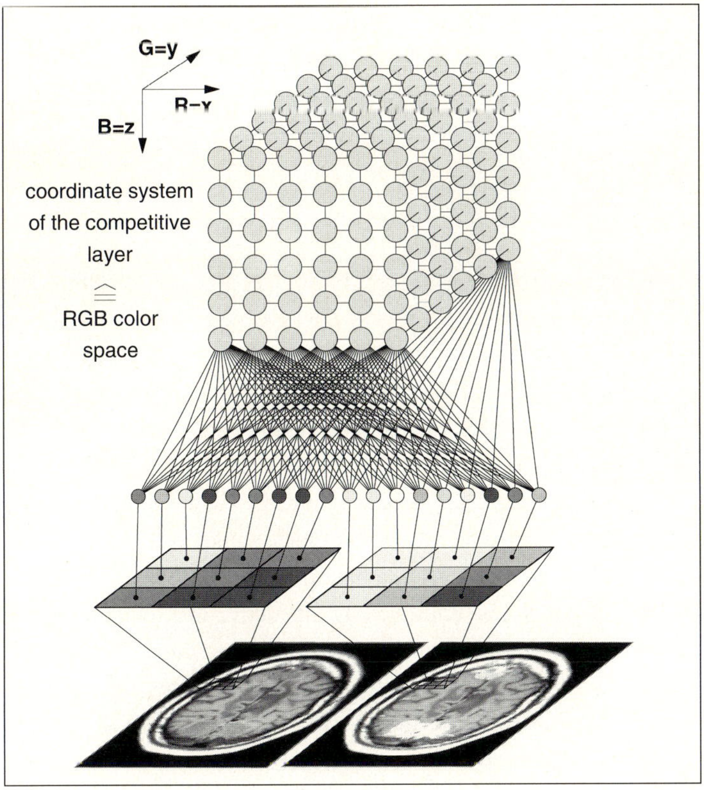

Figure 189:
3D extension of the Kohonen map with a 2x3x3 input layer for texture segmentation

olution is approx. 1 mm in the image plane and the signal is coded with 12 bits. Figure 190 shows the same image after contrasting where the echo of the tumor appears much brighter. This image set illustrates that a standard linear separation of the grey values as proposed in [186] will never lead to reliable segmentation since the fat tissue surrounding the skull has a similar intensity. Bones do not appear in MR images.

Clustering and Visualization of Texture Features

This section shows the application of a Kohonen map of size 6 x 6 x 6 neurons on the two image data sets (Figs. 191 and 190). It was trained on one slice by randomly selecting center pixels and a 3 x 3 environment in the pre- and postcontrasted images according to Fig. 189. Figure 192 shows the result of the cluster analysis and dimensionality reduction from 18 to 3, namely R,G,B. The similarity of the colors stands for adjacent neurons responding to a similarity of the local texture elements. We see that the larger tumor appears yellow and can be separated from the smaller one (blue) and from other tissue types in all slices of the data set. The network was trained for 20 000 cycles.

Supervised Classification

Using the clustering results as a base, it is possible to define and evaluate polygonal training areas for a supervised method, as shown in Fig. 193. For each of the 7 anatomical classes defined, pixels within the polygons representing that class were used to train the network with LVQ postprocessing in 50 000 cycles. The result of the supervised method for one selected slice is shown in Fig. 194.

Although the clustering results indicate the possibility of separating the tumors from other tissue types, some errors still remain, stemming either from inadequate training areas or from local minima. This result can be improved by interactive manipulation of the class assignments of the neurons in the Kohonen cube. For this purpose an interactive X/Motif tool was built on top of the software prototype ICAN, as presented in Fig. 195. This leads to an optimizing shift of the decision boundaries for the classification. The improved result in Fig. 195 is based on this additional information, which was not included in the training areas.

The optimized classifier was applied on the entire image data set (see Fig. 195) and can serve as an input for 3D reconstruction techniques.

Generalization

The reliability of this scheme was evaluated by generalizing the classification to data sets stemming from different persons. With the constraint of using similar parameters for data acquisition it is possible to apply the Kohonen map that was previously trained.

In this case the interpretation is much more difficult for the physician. The contrast medium increases the signal behind the left eye of the patient as well as in the rear right part of the cortex. A determination of the tumor boundaries is very difficult due to the fact that the boundaries between the healthy tissue and the pathological tissue are not well defined.

Applying the Kohonen map (trained on the image data shown in Fig. 196) for clustering we achieve a result as in Fig. 197a which reveals the characteristics of the pathological tissue. Since the image contains the same tumor type (meningioma) the network indicates these regions with yellow colors (the reader should compare the colors with the result presented in Fig. 192). The classified image is shown in Fig. 197b. The red color indicates the tumor.

The results of this experiment are very promising. Since the network has been trained on only one pathological data set, it is capable of generalizing the clustering and classification results to other comparable data sets. Using a statistically representative database of brain cancer victims, we could interactively optimize one large scale network and apply it to further new data stemming from everyday clinical requests for diagnosis.

The generic capability of the Kohonen feature map used for clustering or classification tasks is not dependent on the network topology in terms of the size of the competitive layer. This is illustrated in Fig. 198, which shows clustering results on the data of Fig. 196, using a Kohonen feature map with 10 x 10 x 10 neurons. Due to the different size of the map and to the random initialization of the network, the colors in the clustering results associated with the tissue types are not the same. Although the colors are different, the similarity of colors in corresponding regions is preserved.

Surface Reconstruction

The classified image slices from Fig. 195 can serve as an input for any kind of surface reconstruction or volume rendering method. For surgery and radiotherapy we need a fast and reliable method to achieve a 3D shape from our sparse data slices that offers more than photorealistic ray traced images from slices of extreme density.

One problem arises when applying algorithms like *marching cubes* on a classified data set with a low number of slices: we have to solve the task of interpolating in between, i.e., of classifying image slices instead of using simple grey-value slices.

A fast approach to this problem is a modified weighted interpolation scheme [38] as illustrated in Fig. 200.

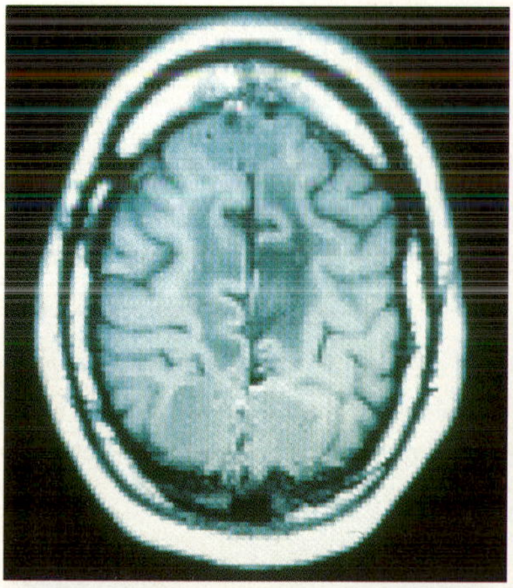

Figure 190: T_1 weighed MR image (precontrasted) (Raw image data courtesy of the German Cancer Research Institute, Heidelberg)

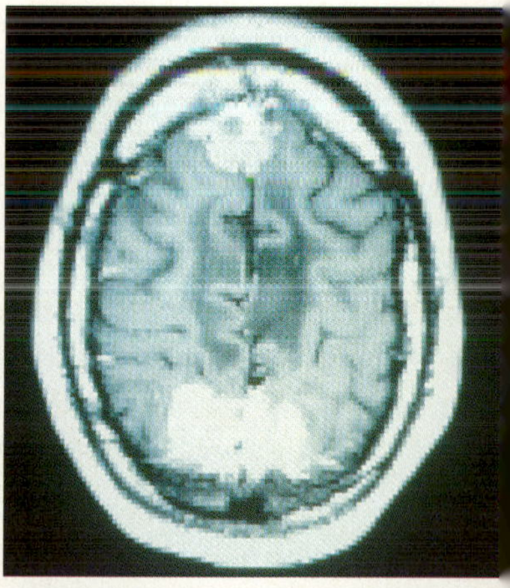

Figure 191: T_1 weighed MR image (postcontrasted)

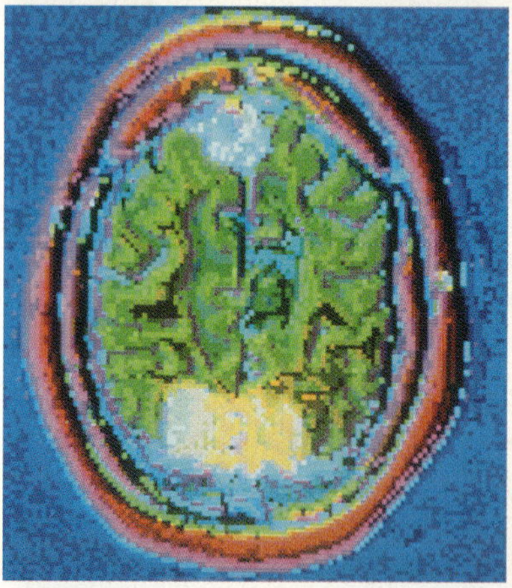

Figure 192: Cluster analysis, dimensionality reduction and visualization of the local texture properties of one slice (see also [38])

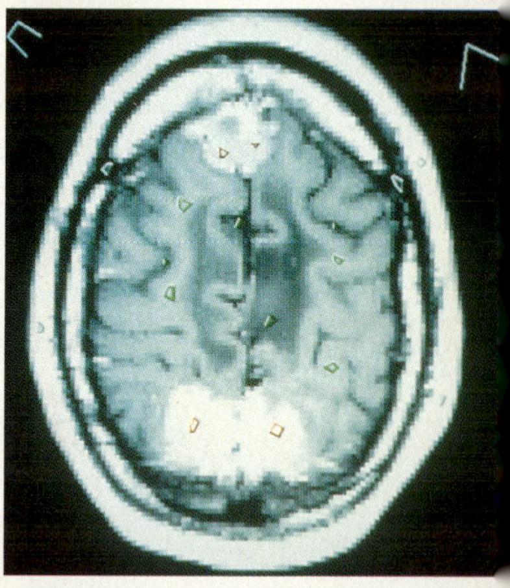

Figure 193: Example for setting the polygonial training areas

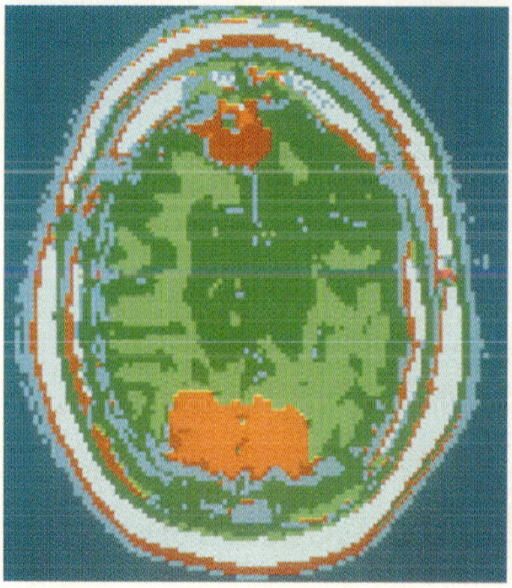

Figure 194: Supervised classification of a selected slice

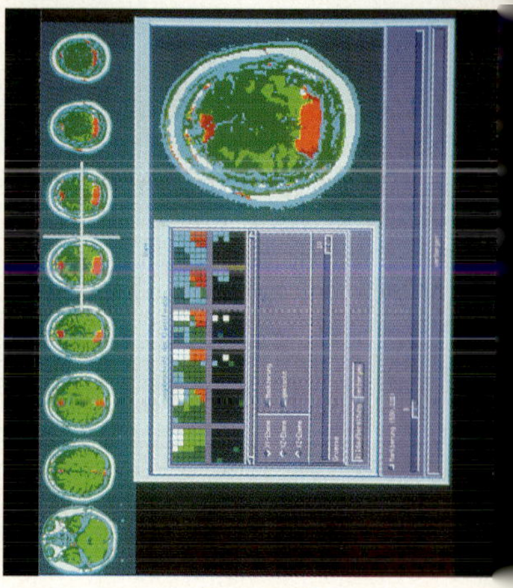

Figure 195: Changes of the class assignments of single neurons in the Kohonen cube and result after interactive optimization (prototype system: ICAN)

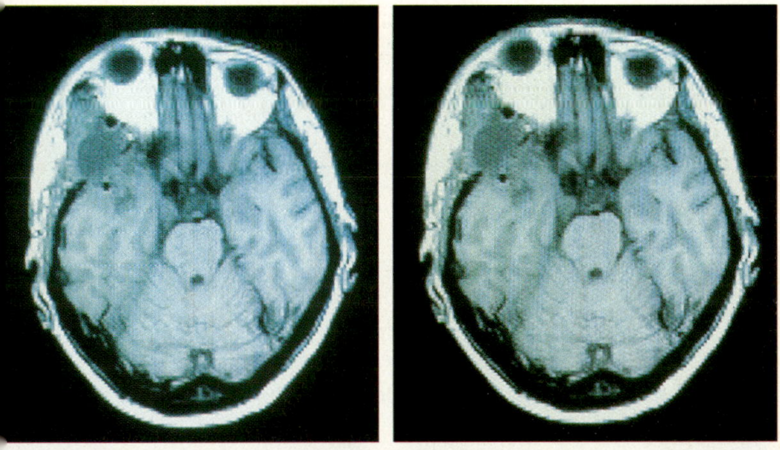

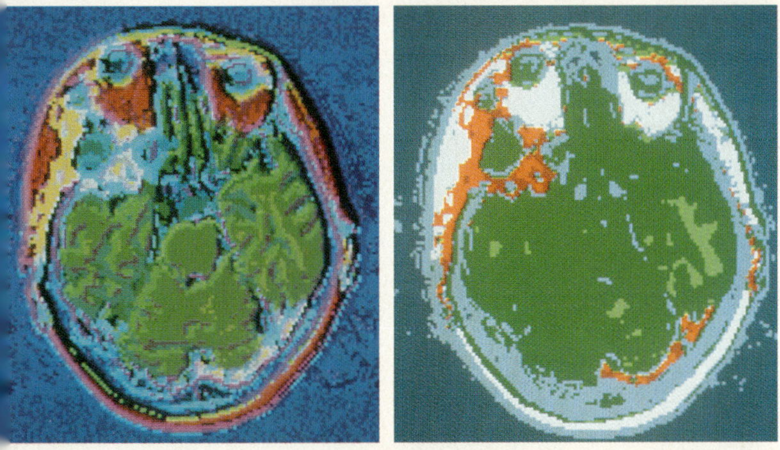

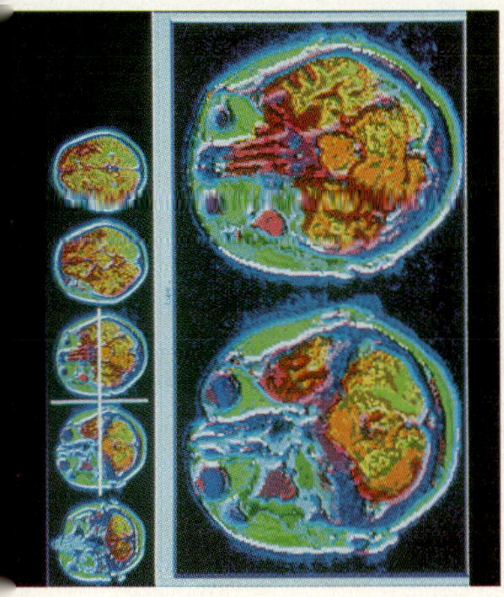

Figure 196:
Raw images for testing the generalization capabilities (T_1-weighted image affected by a meningnioma)
a) precontrasted image
b) postcontrasted image

Figure 197:
Generalization with the Kohonen feature map
a) clustering result
b) classification result

Figure 198:
Clustering of the image with a different 10x10x10 Kohonen map

Figure 199:
Tumor location in a transparent skull

The scheme is based on a distance weighted maximum decision for the class assignment of the respective voxel to be interpolated. This can be expressed by Eqs. (244) and (245):

$$class(x_v, y_v, z_v) = n \;\mid\; w(n) = \max_i[w(i)] \qquad (244)$$

$$w(i) = \sum_{j=1}^{8} \frac{1}{s_j} \;\mid\; class(j) = i \qquad (245)$$

i:	*index for the classes (i = 1,..,7)*
j:	*index for the vertices of the cuboid (j = 1,..,8)*
s_j:	*distance of voxel coordinate* (x_v, y_v, z_v) *from the coordinate of vertex j*
class (j):	*class assignment of vertex j*
n:	*specific class index* $\in \{1,..,7\}$

This scheme for class assignments takes into account both the distances and the frequency of the labels on the vertices.

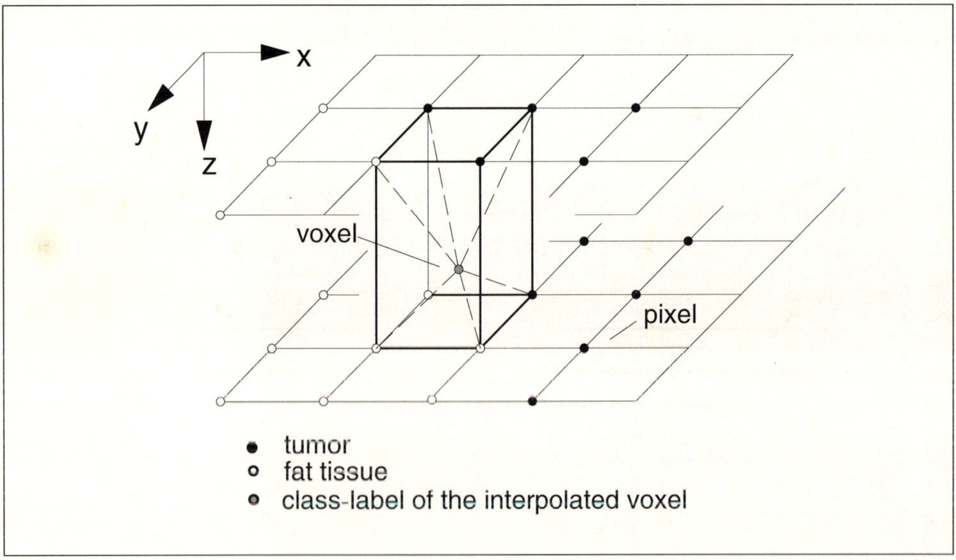

Figure 200: Distance weighted interpolation and class assignment of voxels

The generation of surface polygons can be performed by a marching cubes algorithm [158] acting on the classified and on the interpolated image slices. With a simple modification, the two possible states of a vertex, namely inside or outside the surface, can be obtained by considering the actual classes to be reconstructed. According to the combination of inside and outside states in one cube consisting of 8 vertices, it is possible to build up a lookup -table of precalculated triangles. To provide the surface normal for the shading algorithm, standard surface normals were computed from the triangle geometry and stored in the look-up table. This accelerates the rendering process. However, only a limited set of different triangles and normals are reached which leads to a more boxlike appearance of the image. In this sense the method is very fast but does not lead to smooth surfaces. However, in surgery it is often necessary to keep the original appearance of the data. Another way would be to compute the normals out of the grey level gradients from the raw image. But this would give rise to artefacts stemming from the difference between the density of a voxel and its class assignment. Thus the most reliable method for surface reconstruction would be a direct triangulation of the object boundaries in each slice as in [179].

An illustration of the localization of the tumor is given in Fig. 199, showing the tumor in a transparent skull, illuminated from the left side.

The above example has shown that complex medical imaging tasks require hybrid methods including both *computer graphics and image processing* algorithms. Furthermore, the important role of interactivity has been illustrated, since fully automatic decision making will usually not provide more reliable results than those obtained by human beings. In this case, due to the pre- and postcontrasted images, it was possible to perform the texture analysis simply and fast by feeding the 2D image data directly into the network. In more complex cases, for instance when using only the precontrasted voxel set, more expensive preprocessing has to be included and a texture analysis pipeline has to be built up as in Chap. 5. Feature based recognition techniques [42] could also be employed.

7.5. Automatic Face Recognition

7.5.1. Face Recognition Methods

The automatic identification of human faces, described below, is one of the most attractive and challenging problems in the field of computer vision and recognition. Reliable and robust methods can be used in a broad range of applications, for instance when checking the security of persons in companies or airports or as a part of the man-machine interface of the future. Otherwise, these algorithms could help to match and identify human faces for rendering and animation [147]. As a special case of the general recognition problem, face recognition can be divided into two parts. First, we have to find a set of features invariant against size, rotation, translation, illumination, facial expressions, disguise, etc. Once this is done, the second part of face recognition requires a minimum error classifier to compare the features derived from an unknown face image with internal knowledge stemming from a database.

Due to the enormous importance of the face for human recognition and due to the sophistication of our visual system mechanism for performing this task in real time, numerous approaches have been introduced so far. The early approaches [79, 115] derived characteristic geometric features from human identification studies and used face profiles to describe them. Other approaches use deformable template matching of symbolic features such as eyes [265, 233] and neural network approaches use elastic labeled graphs including local image features [34] as well as self-organizing structures [164]. Another very basic iconic approach is presented in [75], where the subsampled image is fed directly into a multilayered perceptron. Also multiresolutional approaches, as image pyramids have been introduced in [37].

One of the most popular approaches to the face recognition problem is to apply a principal component analysis (Karhunen–Loeve expansion (see also Chap. 6) on the initial face image data set and expand it by means of the eigenvectors obtained. The features are derived from projecting the images into a subspace defined by a limited set of eigenvectors. Given an optimal representation of the face in feature space, a Euclidian distance classifier is applied to discriminate unknown images. Generally, the concept of PCA (see Chap. 6) is very popular with statistical data analysis [71, 58] and is often used for image coding [128], since it removes the correlation of the data and represents an optimal coding scheme. It was first introduced for faces by Sirovich and Kirby [236, 137] and was adapted and modified by several other authors [244, 5, 87].

On the other hand, the relationship between the internal representation of knowledge in neural networks and the eigenvector decomposition has a long tradition. Several authors [11, 195, 196] have proved that neural network learning can approximate an eigenvector description of the data presented.

This section presents an evaluation and extension of the concepts of [5, 236, 244] by combining the standard procedure with a more complex nonlinear neural classifier. The goal of the investigation reported in [87] was to examine whether this global iconic approach can always provide optimal representations of feature clusters in feature space. In this case the use of complex classifiers may improve the accuracy of the method significantly. For this purpose, an evaluation of the method for the recognition of a limited set of people based on a systematically built-up image data base has been provided, the classification and generalization behavior investigated, and the results obtained compared with those using Euclidian distance mappings. Furthermore, a comparison between the computed distances of the face images and those obtained by several test persons is given. In this sense, the study that was primarily done for human-computer interaction compares *human visual analysis to machine vision techniques.*

7.5.2. Eigenfaces and Neural Networks

The general idea of using the principal component analysis for finding facial features is illustrated in Fig. 201. In the initial step, a set of face images stemming from the database of faces to be included is projected into the subspace defined by their most important eigenvectors. The feature vectors derived from this procedure serve as a training basis for any supervised classification scheme. For reasons of robustness, usually different face images from one person are taken. Once the classifier is trained, we are able to discriminate any new and unknown image during the working phase by projection and classification.

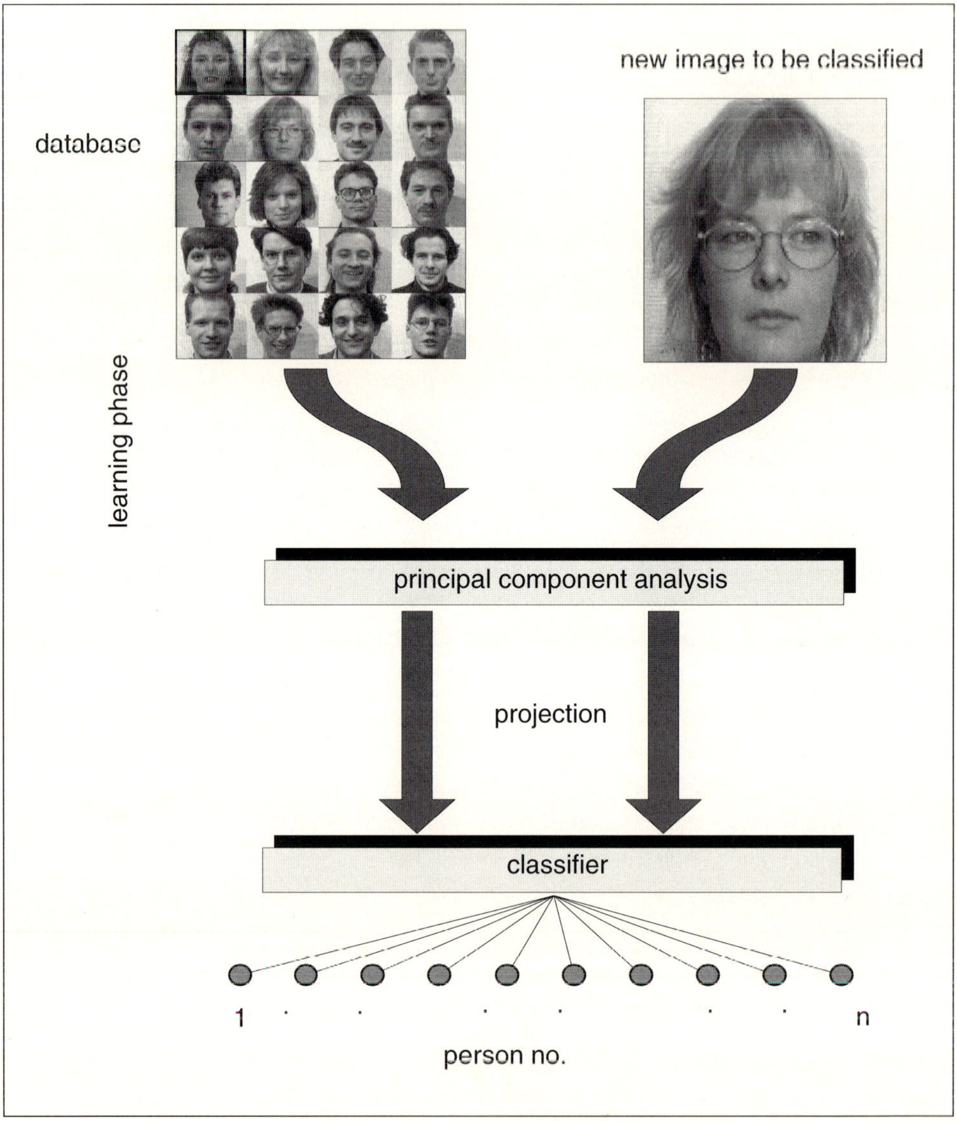

Figure 201: *General scheme for face recognition using PCA (see [87])*

If we suppose this method will provide an optimal representation of the facial features of different persons, i.e., if the clusters in feature space and their corresponding decision boundaries are non-overlapping lower-order hypersurfaces, a simple Euclidian distance classifier should be sufficient. This concept can briefly be described as follows.

According to the concepts of the PCA in Chap. 6 we compute for each person i $(i = 1,..,Q)$ the projection $\Omega_{ij} = (\omega_{ij}^{(1)},..,\omega_{ij}^{(K)})$, $j = 1,..,P$ and their mean overall face pictures

$$\overline{\Omega}_i = \frac{1}{P}\sum_{j=1}^{P}\Omega_{ij} \qquad (246)$$

Projecting a new face image in eigenspace yields

$$\Rightarrow \quad \Omega_{\text{new}}$$

We now compute the Euclidian distances ε_i with

$$\varepsilon_i = \| \Omega_{\text{new}} - \overline{\Omega}_i \| \qquad (247)$$

and find the minimum

$$\bar{\varepsilon} = \min_i[\varepsilon_i] \qquad (248)$$

and define a threshold τ to reject unknown faces, if $\bar{\varepsilon} \geq \tau$.

However, extensions of [5] using FFT preprocessing and increasing the robustness of the method have shown that the representation of facial features with a PCA is not optimal, and for this reason more complex classifiers have to be used to improve the accuracy.

For instance, [87] proposed a back-propagation network and investigated its behavior against the standard Euclidian distance. The results of this investigation are reported below.

7.5.3. Results

The database used for this study contains 12 different representations for each of the 20 persons to be recognized. The idea was to obtain a sample of several situations and facial expressions where the illumination was kept constant. Figure 202 shows the 12 situations generated for each person.

The goal was to investigate the influence of the percentage of eigenfaces used to define the subspace as well as the number of training pictures for each person. For this purpose the data set was divided into two parts: a training set of 1–6 pictures per person and a data set for generalization with all other pictures from the database used to calculate the accuracy.

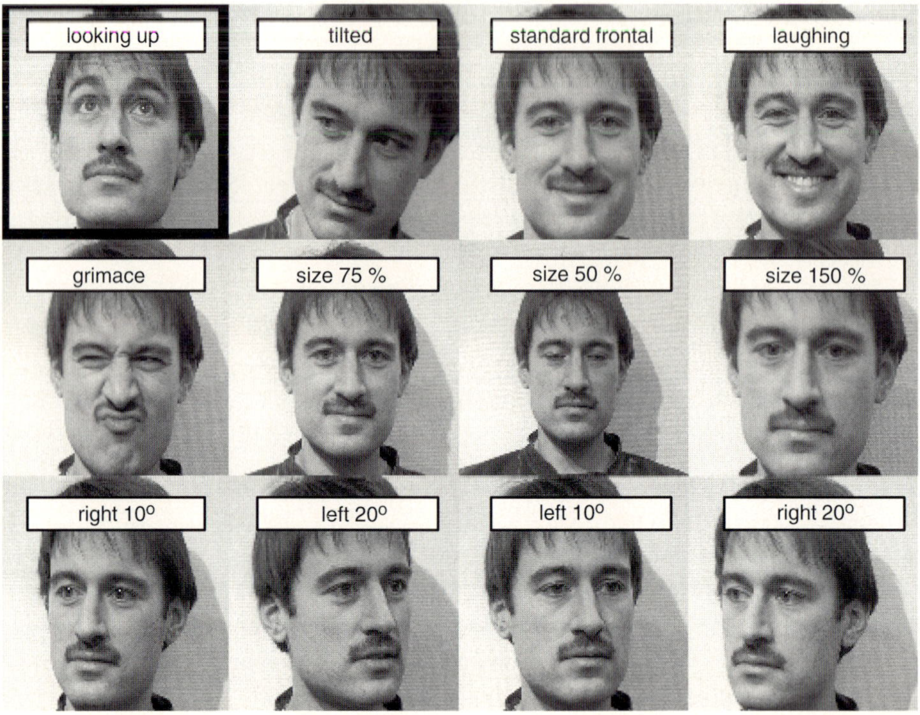

Figure 202: Different face images used for the data base

The different neural classifiers used were trained to 100% recognition of the training set.

To give an overview, the diagrams in Figs. 203 and 204 show only the bandwidth of accuracy achieved with the neural classifiers (grey bands). The corresponding accuracy achieved by the Euclidian distance classifier (EDC) is represented by a bold line in the diagrams.

Figure 203 shows 6 diagrams illustrating the quality of generalization behavior depending on the number of eigenfaces used (for training sets of 20–120 images, respectively 1–6 images/person). We can see that the neural classifiers constantly perform better than the EDC. This is also expressed in a different way in Fig. 204.

The maximum accuracy achieved in this study was about 85% (generalization!) using a 5 images/person training set.

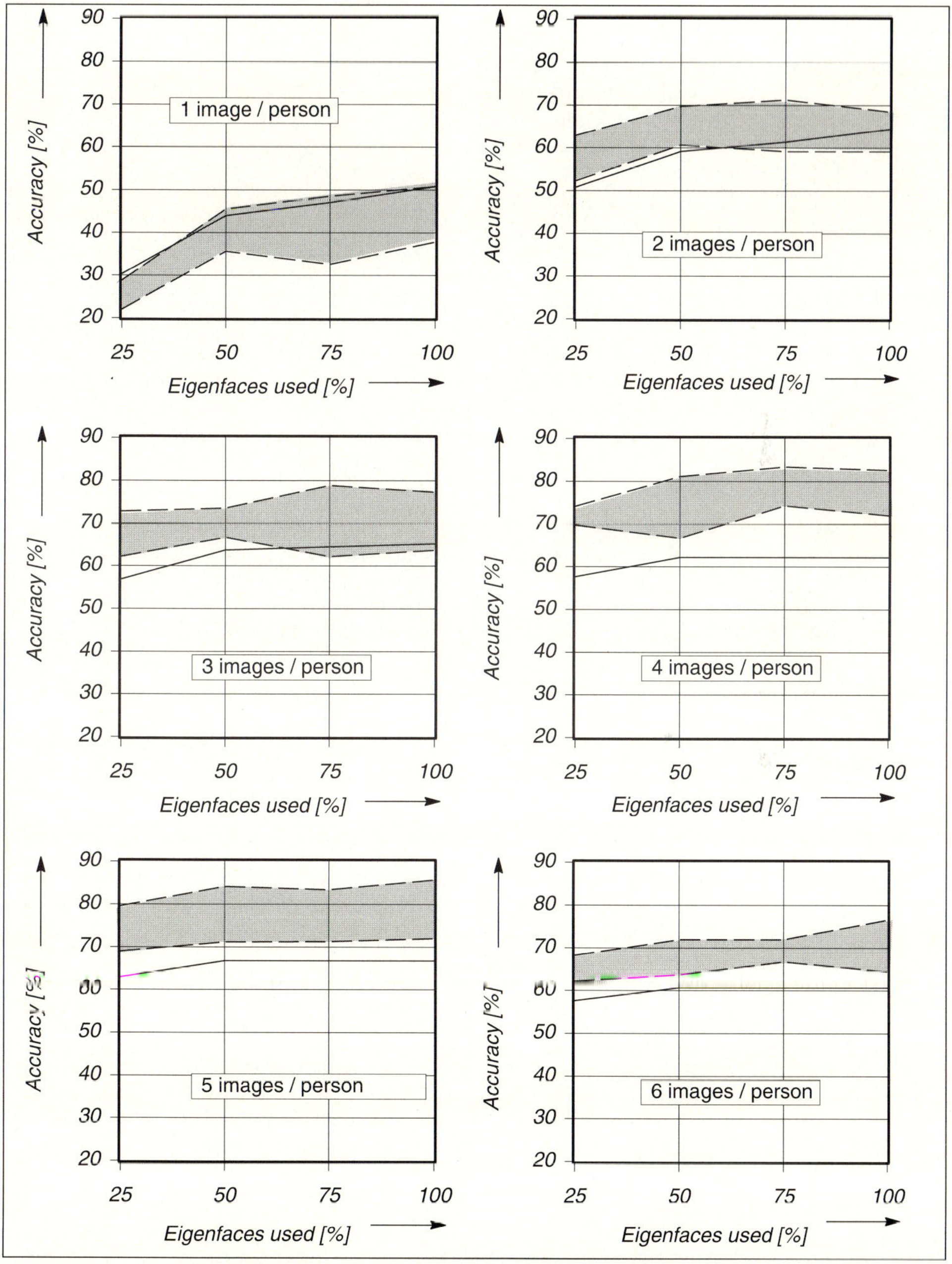

Figure 203:
Generalization accuracy for training sets of 1–6 images/person (from [87])

Finally, Fig. 205 illustrates the single accuracy achieved by our neural classifier for the best (5 images/person) training data set. The numbers along the abscissa denote the number of neurons for each layer of the classifier. "-20-20" means a 20-neuron hidden layer and a 20-neuron output layer.

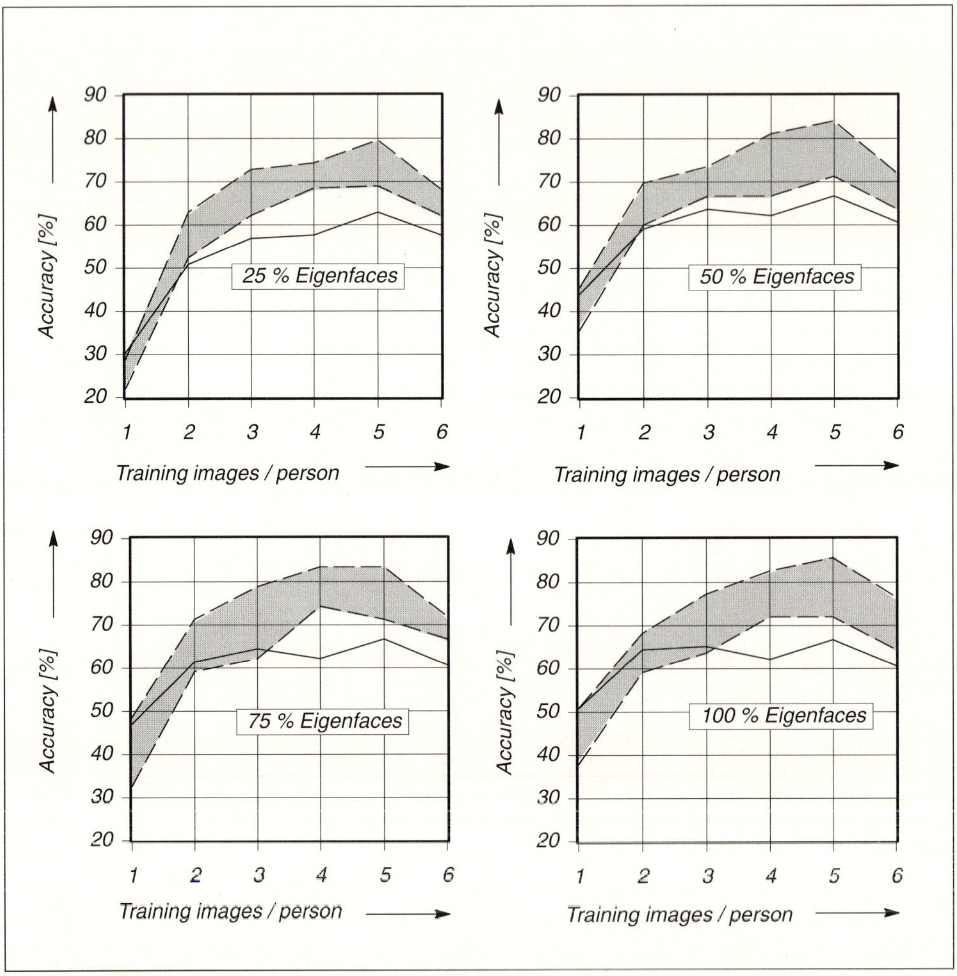

Figure 204:
Generic accuracy depending on the number of eigenfaces used (from [87])

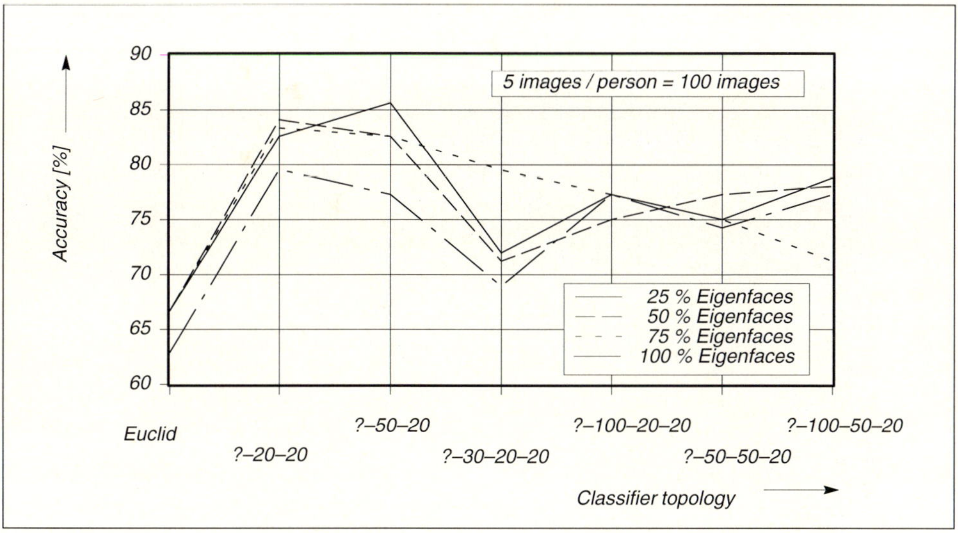

Figure 205: Accuracies achieved by different back-propagation networks for the best training data set (from [87])

7.5.4. Psychophysical Evidence

In order to compare the results obtained by the PCA algorithm with those based on the individual visual perception capabilities of human beings, the following psychological experiment was done according to the work of [74]. First, the distances between the centroids of the faces of all the persons were computed for our data set in eigenspace. This was done for the best match with 5 images/person and 100% eigenfaces. Let $\overline{\Omega}_i = (\overline{\omega}_i^{(1)},..,\overline{\omega}_j^{(K)})$ be the coordinates of a person i and $\overline{\Omega}_n = (\overline{\omega}_n^{(1)},..,\overline{\omega}_n^{(K)})$ these of a person n, then we obtain the distance ε_{in} in eigenspace as:

$$\varepsilon_{in} = \sqrt{\sum_{m=1}^{K}(\bar{\omega}_i^{(m)} - \bar{\omega}_n^{(m)})^2} \qquad (249)$$

Table 18 shows these distances computed according to Eq. (249) and normalized in the range [0,..,9]. The respective persons are illustrated by their frontal view pictures.

In a psychological experiment 6 different test persons were asked to evaluate the individually perceived similarities of the faces

i →

n ↓

.	4.0	7.0	8.0	6.0	5.0	6.0	8.0	0.0	6.0	7.0	7.0	7.0	9.0	5.0	8.0	7.0	6.0	0.0	7.0
.	*.*	6.0	6.0	5.0	4.0	5.0	6.0	7.0	5.0	7.0	5.0	5.0	6.0	3.0	7.0	4.0	6.0	7.0	6.0
.	*.*	*.*	2.0	4.0	6.0	1.0	3.0	7.0	6.0	3.0	4.0	6.0	8.0	6.0	6.0	5.0	5.0	8.0	4.0
.	*.*	*.*	*.*	5.0	6.0	3.0	2.0	7.0	8.0	2.0	5.0	7.0	8.0	6.0	7.0	4.0	6.0	9.0	4.0
.	*.*	*.*	*.*	*.*	6.0	4.0	3.0	8.0	6.0	5.0	3.0	5.0	7.0	4.0	6.0	3.0	4.0	7.0	5.0
.	*.*	*.*	*.*	*.*	*.*	6.0	8.0	7.0	5.0	7.0	8.0	8.0	0.0	5.0	8.0	7.0	5.0	9.0	8.0
.	*.*	*.*	*.*	*.*	*.*	*.*	3.0	8.0	6.0	4.0	3.0	6.0	8.0	6.0	6.0	4.0	5.0	8.0	3.0
.	*.*	*.*	*.*	*.*	*.*	*.*	*.*	8.0	8.0	3.0	2.0	6.0	7.0	5.0	6.0	3.0	6.0	8.0	2.0
.	*.*	*.*	*.*	*.*	*.*	*.*	*.*	*.*	8.0	8.0	8.0	8.0	9.0	8.0	0.0	8.0	7.0	8.0	8.0
.	*.*	*.*	*.*	*.*	*.*	*.*	*.*	*.*	*.*	8.0	6.0	7.0	0.0	7.0	9.0	7.0	6.0	9.0	8.0
.	*.*	*.*	*.*	*.*	*.*	*.*	*.*	*.*	*.*	*.*	5.0	7.0	9.0	6.0	7.0	5.0	6.0	0.0	4.0
.	*.*	*.*	*.*	*.*	*.*	*.*	*.*	*.*	*.*	*.*	*.*	4.0	5.0	4.0	5.0	1.0	5.0	6.0	4.0
.	*.*	*.*	*.*	*.*	*.*	*.*	*.*	*.*	*.*	*.*	*.*	*.*	6.0	6.0	6.0	5.0	6.0	6.0	5.0
.	*.*	*.*	*.*	*.*	*.*	*.*	*.*	*.*	*.*	*.*	*.*	*.*	*.*	7.0	6.0	6.0	9.0	5.0	7.0
.	*.*	*.*	*.*	*.*	*.*	*.*	*.*	*.*	*.*	*.*	*.*	*.*	*.*	*.*	6.0	4.0	6.0	7.0	7.0
.	*.*	*.*	*.*	*.*	*.*	*.*	*.*	*.*	*.*	*.*	*.*	*.*	*.*	*.*	*.*	6.0	9.0	8.0	6.0
.	*.*	*.*	*.*	*.*	*.*	*.*	*.*	*.*	*.*	*.*	*.*	*.*	*.*	*.*	*.*	*.*	6.0	6.0	4.0
.	*.*	*.*	*.*	*.*	*.*	*.*	*.*	*.*	*.*	*.*	*.*	*.*	*.*	*.*	*.*	*.*	*.*	8.0	6.0
.	*.*	*.*	*.*	*.*	*.*	*.*	*.*	*.*	*.*	*.*	*.*	*.*	*.*	*.*	*.*	*.*	*.*	*.*	9.0
.	*.*	*.*	*.*	*.*	*.*	*.*	*.*	*.*	*.*	*.*	*.*	*.*	*.*	*.*	*.*	*.*	*.*	*.*	*.*

Table 18: Distances ε_{in} between different persons computed and normalized in eigenspace

by numbers. For this reason, all possible frontal views have been presented pairwise and in a random order. The persons were asked to rate the similarity for each pair, where 0 represents the most similar ones and 9 the most dissimilar ones. During a practice session, the persons became familiar with the faces and the procedure and could establish freelines for the most similar and dissimilar pairs.

We obtain the mean ratings m_{in} and the standard deviations σ_{in} by Eqs. (250) and (251) respectively:

i →

n ↓

.	4.3	6.8	4.5	5.3	4.7	5.5	6.5	5.5	4.3	5.2	6.8	6.3	5.8	4.8	7.2	6.0	6.0	6.7	4.0
.	*.*	6.2	4.3	5.7	2.8	6.8	6.3	7.2	4.2	5.7	6.2	3.8	6.0	3.5	6.0	4.7	6.8	6.3	6.3
.	*.*	*.*	2.8	5.2	5.5	3.7	5.3	5.0	4.3	4.5	5.2	6.7	5.7	6.3	3.5	6.7	3.0	5.7	4.7
.	*.*	*.*	*.*	3.8	6.7	4.5	6.7	5.5	4.7	5.2	4.8	7.3	4.3	7.0	5.2	4.0	3.8	6.2	5.3
.	*.*	*.*	*.*	*.*	4.2	5.2	4.3	5.3	4.3	7.0	6.3	6.2	6.8	6.0	7.3	5.5	6.5	4.7	5.2
.	*.*	*.*	*.*	*.*	*.*	4.7	7.5	5.5	3.5	6.0	6.7	5.7	5.0	7.0	6.2	5.5	6.2	6.5	3.2
.	*.*	*.*	*.*	*.*	*.*	*.*	4.8	6.2	3.2	5.8	3.5	4.2	5.3	5.7	6.3	4.8	8.2	4.5	5.3
.	*.*	*.*	*.*	*.*	*.*	*.*	*.*	4.8	7.0	6.5	3.8	4.3	6.3	5.8	7.3	3.7	5.5	5.2	4.0
.	*.*	*.*	*.*	*.*	*.*	*.*	*.*	*.*	5.2	5.3	5.3	6.2	5.5	7.2	6.0	6.8	6.8	6.7	4.5
.	*.*	*.*	*.*	*.*	*.*	*.*	*.*	*.*	*.*	5.7	4.8	5.7	4.2	7.2	5.7	5.2	5.3	5.0	5.7
.	*.*	*.*	*.*	*.*	*.*	*.*	*.*	*.*	*.*	*.*	5.5	5.7	3.3	6.2	7.0	4.7	6.0	7.0	4.3
.	*.*	*.*	*.*	*.*	*.*	*.*	*.*	*.*	*.*	*.*	*.*	7.5	4.8	5.5	6.7	3.2	5.3	6.3	4.0
.	*.*	*.*	*.*	*.*	*.*	*.*	*.*	*.*	*.*	*.*	*.*	*.*	5.8	3.7	6.3	5.2	7.2	3.8	5.8
.	*.*	*.*	*.*	*.*	*.*	*.*	*.*	*.*	*.*	*.*	*.*	*.*	*.*	6.3	4.5	5.2	4.8	5.0	3.2
.	*.*	*.*	*.*	*.*	*.*	*.*	*.*	*.*	*.*	*.*	*.*	*.*	*.*	*.*	6.5	4.2	7.0	6.0	6.0
.	*.*	*.*	*.*	*.*	*.*	*.*	*.*	*.*	*.*	*.*	*.*	*.*	*.*	*.*	*.*	5.7	4.7	4.7	6.7
.	*.*	*.*	*.*	*.*	*.*	*.*	*.*	*.*	*.*	*.*	*.*	*.*	*.*	*.*	*.*	*.*	6.0	5.0	5.3
.	*.*	*.*	*.*	*.*	*.*	*.*	*.*	*.*	*.*	*.*	*.*	*.*	*.*	*.*	*.*	*.*	*.*	7.7	6.3
.	*.*	*.*	*.*	*.*	*.*	*.*	*.*	*.*	*.*	*.*	*.*	*.*	*.*	*.*	*.*	*.*	*.*	*.*	5.8
.	*.*	*.*	*.*	*.*	*.*	*.*	*.*	*.*	*.*	*.*	*.*	*.*	*.*	*.*	*.*	*.*	*.*	*.*	*.*

Table 19: Mean values m_{in} of the pairwise dissimilarities averaged over the rating of 6 test persons

$$m_{in} = \frac{1}{6}\sum_{k=1}^{6} x_{ink} \qquad (250)$$

x_{ink}: *pairwise dissimilarity between face i and face n rated by test person k*

$$\sigma_{in} = \sqrt{\frac{1}{6}\sum_{k=1}^{6}(x_{ink} - m_{in})^2} \qquad (251)$$

Table 19 shows the mean values m_{in} given for the pairwise similarities and Table 20 shows its standard deviation σ_{in}. In this sense

Table 20 can be interpreted as expressing the covariance matrix of the study.

i →

n ↓

.	1.2	0.7	2.6	1.7	1.4	2.2	1.4	1.4	1.8	2.8	1.5	1.8	1.5	1.1	1.1	1.5	3.3	1.5	2.5
.	*.*	1.6	2.3	2.4	1.1	2.4	1.6	2.0	1.6	3.1	1.6	1.1	1.6	1.4	2.9	2.4	2.0	1.5	1.6
.	*.*	*.*	0.9	1.5	1.9	1.4	2.1	1.3	0.9	2.6	1.3	0.9	1.4	1.8	2.1	0.9	1.9	2.2	1.5
.	*.*	*.*	*.*	1.1	1.8	2.1	1.1	1.1	1.5	1.5	2.1	2.0	2.6	1.2	1.2	2.3	1.7	2.0	1.4
.	*.*	*.*	*.*	*.*	0.9	1.8	1.4	1.6	2.1	1.5	1.4	2.4	1.6	1.7	0.7	1.5	1.3	2.8	1.3
.	*.*	*.*	*.*	*.*	*.*	2.7	1.4	2.4	1.3	2.1	1.2	0.7	2.7	1.5	3.3	2.8	2.0	3.0	2.5
.	*.*	*.*	*.*	*.*	*.*	*.*	2.3	1.9	1.8	2.2	2.1	1.2	2.5	1.1	1.9	1.3	0.9	1.9	1.5
.	*.*	*.*	*.*	*.*	*.*	*.*	*.*	1.7	1.3	2.0	2.2	3.0	0.9	1.3	1.5	1.7	3.9	2.1	1.0
.	*.*	*.*	*.*	*.*	*.*	*.*	*.*	*.*	1.6	1.4	1.8	3.3	1.8	1.3	3.1	1.3	1.6	0.9	1.3
.	*.*	*.*	*.*	*.*	*.*	*.*	*.*	*.*	*.*	2.1	2.3	1.8	0.9	1.6	1.2	1.2	2.8	2.2	1.4
.	*.*	*.*	*.*	*.*	*.*	*.*	*.*	*.*	*.*	*.*	2.3	2.6	1.4	1.1	1.7	1.6	1.5	1.4	2.2
.	*.*	*.*	*.*	*.*	*.*	*.*	*.*	*.*	*.*	*.*	*.*	1.0	2.3	1.6	1.7	2.2	0.9	1.2	1.3
.	*.*	*.*	*.*	*.*	*.*	*.*	*.*	*.*	*.*	*.*	*.*	*.*	2.2	0.7	3.0	1.9	1.1	1.6	1.6
.	*.*	*.*	*.*	*.*	*.*	*.*	*.*	*.*	*.*	*.*	*.*	*.*	*.*	1.2	1.3	1.6	1.6	2.1	1.8
.	*.*	*.*	*.*	*.*	*.*	*.*	*.*	*.*	*.*	*.*	*.*	*.*	*.*	*.*	2.2	2.1	2.4	1.9	1.9
.	*.*	*.*	*.*	*.*	*.*	*.*	*.*	*.*	*.*	*.*	*.*	*.*	*.*	*.*	*.*	2.2	2.7	2.3	1.4
.	*.*	*.*	*.*	*.*	*.*	*.*	*.*	*.*	*.*	*.*	*.*	*.*	*.*	*.*	*.*	*.*	2.2	1.5	2.0
.	*.*	*.*	*.*	*.*	*.*	*.*	*.*	*.*	*.*	*.*	*.*	*.*	*.*	*.*	*.*	*.*	*.*	1.1	1.4
.	*.*	*.*	*.*	*.*	*.*	*.*	*.*	*.*	*.*	*.*	*.*	*.*	*.*	*.*	*.*	*.*	*.*	*.*	2.1
.	*.*	*.*	*.*	*.*	*.*	*.*	*.*	*.*	*.*	*.*	*.*	*.*	*.*	*.*	*.*	*.*	*.*	*.*	*.*

Table 20: Standard deviation σ_{in} of the experiment

$$\sigma_{inPCA} = \sqrt{\frac{1}{6}\sum_{k=1}^{6}(x_{ink} - \varepsilon_{in})^2} \tag{252}$$

It is easy to see that the local variances differ sometimes very much for the test persons. A detailed comparison of the computational and of the psychological results is presented in Table 21, where the standard deviation σ_{inPCA} between the PCA distances ε_{in} (Table 18) and the single ratings of the test persons x_{ink} are shown according to Eq. (252). We can easily see that for some face pairs the distances correspond well, but for others not.

i →

n ↓

.	1.3	0.7	4.4	1.8	1.4	2.3	2.0	5.7	2.4	3.3	1.5	1.9	3.5	1.1	1.4	1.8	3.3	6.8	3.9
.	*.*	1.6	2.8	2.4	1.6	3.0	1.6	2.0	1.8	3.4	2.0	1.6	1.6	1.5	3.1	2.5	2.1	1.6	1.6
.	*.*	*.*	1.2	1.9	2.0	3.0	3.1	2.4	1.9	3.0	1.8	1.2	2.7	1.8	3.3	1.9	2.8	3.2	1.6
.	*.*	*.*	*.*	1.6	1.9	2.6	4.8	1.9	3.7	3.5	2.1	2.0	4.5	1.5	2.2	2.3	2.7	3.4	1.9
.	*.*	*.*	*.*	*.*	2.0	2.1	1.9	3.1	2.7	2.5	3.6	2.7	1.6	2.6	1.5	2.9	2.8	3.7	1.4
.	*.*	*.*	*.*	*.*	*.*	3.0	1.5	2.8	2.0	2.3	1.8	2.4	5.7	2.5	3.8	3.1	2.3	3.9	5.4
.	*.*	*.*	*.*	*.*	*.*	*.*	2.9	2.6	3.3	2.9	2.1	2.2	3.7	1.2	1.9	1.6	3.3	4.0	2.8
.	*.*	*.*	*.*	*.*	*.*	*.*	*.*	3.6	1.6	4.0	2.9	3.4	1.2	1.6	2.0	1.8	4.0	3.5	2.2
.	*.*	*.*	*.*	*.*	*.*	*.*	*.*	*.*	3.2	3.0	3.2	3.8	3.9	1.6	6.7	1.8	1.6	1.6	3.7
.	*.*	*.*	*.*	*.*	*.*	*.*	*.*	*.*	*.*	3.1	2.5	2.2	4.3	1.6	3.6	2.2	2.9	4.6	2.7
.	*.*	*.*	*.*	*.*	*.*	*.*	*.*	*.*	*.*	*.*	2.3	2.9	5.8	1.1	1.7	1.6	1.5	7.1	2.2
.	*.*	*.*	*.*	*.*	*.*	*.*	*.*	*.*	*.*	*.*	*.*	3.6	2.3	2.2	2.4	3.1	1.0	1.3	1.3
.	*.*	*.*	*.*	*.*	*.*	*.*	*.*	*.*	*.*	*.*	*.*	*.*	2.2	2.4	3.0	1.9	1.6	2.7	1.8
.	*.*	*.*	*.*	*.*	*.*	*.*	*.*	*.*	*.*	*.*	*.*	*.*	*.*	1.4	2.0	1.8	4.5	2.1	4.2
.	*.*	*.*	*.*	*.*	*.*	*.*	*.*	*.*	*.*	*.*	*.*	*.*	*.*	*.*	2.3	2.1	2.6	2.2	2.2
.	*.*	*.*	*.*	*.*	*.*	*.*	*.*	*.*	*.*	*.*	*.*	*.*	*.*	*.*	*.*	2.2	5.1	4.0	1.5
.	*.*	*.*	*.*	*.*	*.*	*.*	*.*	*.*	*.*	*.*	*.*	*.*	*.*	*.*	*.*	*.*	2.2	1.8	2.4
.	*.*	*.*	*.*	*.*	*.*	*.*	*.*	*.*	*.*	*.*	*.*	*.*	*.*	*.*	*.*	*.*	*.*	1.2	1.4
.	*.*	*.*	*.*	*.*	*.*	*.*	*.*	*.*	*.*	*.*	*.*	*.*	*.*	*.*	*.*	*.*	*.*	*.*	3.8
.	*.*	*.*	*.*	*.*	*.*	*.*	*.*	*.*	*.*	*.*	*.*	*.*	*.*	*.*	*.*	*.*	*.*	*.*	*.*

Table 21: Standard deviation σ_{inPCA} of the single ratings to the PCA distances ε_{in}

Comparing carefully the results obtained in Tables 18–21 we can divide them into 4 categories exemplified in Fig. 206. In some cases (fourth pair) both PCA (ε_{in}) and mean value m_{in} are similar and the standard deviation σ_{in} is low. Thus, all the test persons agreed more or less with their ratings. In other cases (third pair) we receive a good correspondence between the ratings and the PCA but the standard deviation between the ratings is very high. This means that the test persons disagreed and the respective means do not provide much information. In other cases (second pair) PCA distances do not correspond at all to the average ratings of the test persons although the corresponding standard deviations are small enough to ensure the reliability of the ratings. Finally (first pair) in some cases the results were just in between a 10%–20% error margin. This implies that the feature space set up by the PCA is appropriate at some locations only. This also proposes a kind of postprocessing warping of this space according to the results obtained by the psychophysical experiment.

face picture pairs

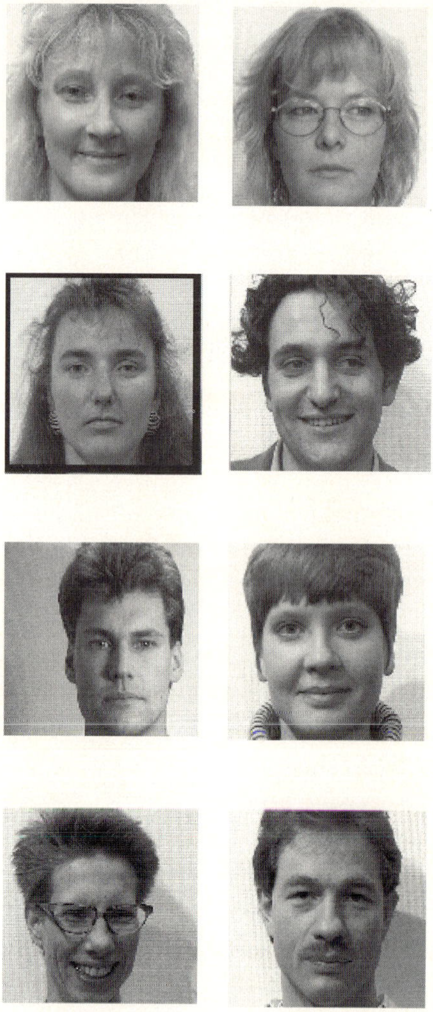

ε_{inPCA}	m_{in}	σ_{in}	σ_{inPCA}
4.0	2.8	1.1	1.6
0.0	6.7	1.5	6.8
8.0	6.2	3.3	3.8
5.0	5.3	0.9	1.0

Figure 206:
4 categories of cases that occurred in the psychological study

Generally, future work on this method will be focused in the following directions:

I. *A warping post-processing transform of the eigenspace including the results of psychophysical experiments*

II. *A geometric analysis of the trajectories generated by the face feature coordinates when applying any transform on the initial face, such as rotation, disguise, illumination, etc. (see [182]).*

III. *The application of multidimensional scaling techniques (see [74]) on the results of the experiment in order to derive interesting psychological features to recognize human faces.*

The study has shown that the evaluation of the similarity of human faces by means of test persons is strongly dependent on subjective criteria and on the individual knowledge of the person. Furthermore, a comparison with the PCA method illustrates also the limitations of this purely iconic and statistical approach for recognition. All in all, we see that it is possible to combine both human and artificial recognition features to approach very complex computer vision problems in the spirit of what we call *visual computing*. But still a lot of work remains to be done to build a robust face recognition machine.

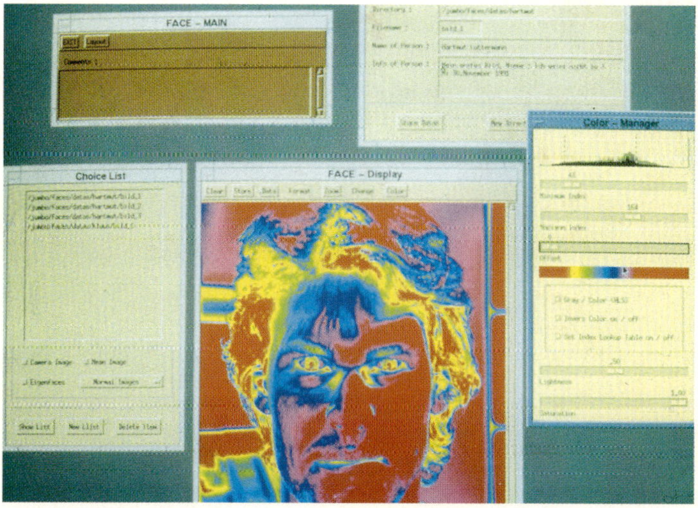

Figure 207: User interface of the prototype system FACEMAN [160]

8. The Way Ahead

This book has introduced the reader to the ideas of *visual computing* as a common framework for *computer graphics, imaging, and visual perception*. A collection of foundations that the author considers important in this field have been introduced. The applications that are included exemplify how to make use of *graphics and imaging techniques* to satisfy the demands of complex real world problems. From the basics of human vision to artificial neural networks all the algorithms that are illuminated can be used successfully in various fields. Since the book never claimed to be complete, the author is well aware that there might be readers who feel some aspects neglected, thus overemphasizing others. Moreover, when carefully analyzing the rich variety of research activities in the fields of graphics, image processing, artificial intelligence, neurobiology, experimental psychology, or human engineering we will find thousands of interesting methods and applications that will fit into our understanding of *visual computing*. A detailed analysis of these topics would be enough to fill numerous books, and yet still be a step behind.

In this way the book is the author's contribution to this very important topic and together with the work of others that has already been done or is still in progress we will move step by step in the right direction. The author hopes that the book will help motivate researchers and developers to support this integration actively and to increasingly think both of graphics and imaging as parts of an overall concept. Our goal of integration will not only depend on algorithms and data structures, but also on future hardware systems. Once we have found specific methods that can be be adapted to our problems they then have to be cast into VLSI structures that will be built into the next generation of workstations. This new generation will have to support *both graphics and imaging* and to provide the appropriate periphery.

In particular, some of the applications presented here have illustrated that the increasing complexity of the problems we face in industrial applications requires that we overcome the limitations of our own working areas and look over the border onto related research fields. Finally, the concept of *visual computing* introduced here serves only as a paradigm to exemplify one mainstream of future research activities: namely *interdisciplinary approaches.*

Literature

[1] Aarts, E.; Korst, J.: Simulated Annealing and Boltzmann Machines. Chichester: John Wiley & Sons, 1989

[2] Abel, V.: Untersuchung des Einsatzes neuronaler Netze und klassischer Verfahren bei der Zeichenerkennung. Diplom-thesis, Computer Science Department, Technische Hochschule Darmstadt, 1991

[3] Aggarwall, J.K.; Chien C.H.: 3-D Structures from 2-D Images. Advances in Machine Vision, Jorge L.C. Sanz. Y(Eds.), New York: Springer, pp. 64–121,1989

[4] Ahlmann, D.: Einsatz von Modellen des menschlichen visuellen Systems in der Werbung. Diplom–thesis, Computer Science Department, Technische Hochschule Darmstadt, 1990

[5] Akamatsu, S.; Sasaki, T.; Fukamachi, H.; Suenaga, Y.: A Robust Face Identification Scheme - KL Expansion of an Invariant Feature Space. Boston: Proceedings of the SPIE-conference, Intelligent Robots and Computer Vision, 1991

[6] Akansu, A.; Haddad, R.: Multiresolution Signal Decomposition. Transforms, Subbands, Wavelets. Telecommunications Series, Boston: Academic Press, 1992

[7] Akimoto, T.; Suenaga, Y.; Wallace, R. S.: Automatic Creation of 3D Facial Models. IEEE Computer Graphics and Applications, Vol. 13, No. 5, pp. 16–22, 1993

[8] Aloimonos, J.; Shulman, D.: Integration of Visual Modules. An Extension of the Marr Paradigm. New York: Academic Press, 1989

[9] Amkun, P.; Grant, E.; Whitted, T.: Managing Geometric Complexity with Enhanced Procedural Models. ACM Computer Graphics (Siggraph '86), Vol. 20, No. 4, pp. 189–195, 1986

[10] Anderson, J. A.; Rosenfeld, E. (Eds): Neurocomputing - Foundations of Research. Cambridge, MA: MIT Press, 1988

[11] Amari, S.: A Neural Theory of Association and Concept-Formation. Biological Cybernetics Vol. 26, pp. 175–185, 1977

[12] Amari, S.–L.: Field theory of Self-Organizing Neural Nets. IEEE Transactions on Systems, Man and Cybernetics, Vol. 13, pp. 741–748, 1983

[13] Amari, S.–L.:Mathematical Foundations of Neurocomputing. Proceedings of the IEEE, Vol. 78, No. 9, pp. 1443–1463, September 1990

[14] Arditi, A.: Binocular Vision. In Handbook of Perception and Human Performance, Vol. 1, New York: John Wiley and Sons, 1986

[15] Arnold, D.: Local Context in Matching Edges for Stereo Vision. In Proceedings Image Understanding Workshop Cambridge, MA, pp. 65–72, May 1978

[16] Auerbach, S.; Schaeben, H.: Surface Representations Reproducing Given Digitized Contour Lines. Mathematical Geology, Vol. 22, No. 6, pp. 723–742, 1990.

[17] Baker, H.: Edge–based Stereo Correlation. Proceedings Image Understanding Workshop, College Park, Md., pp.168–175,1980

[18] Balde, P.; Hornik, K.: Neural Networks and Principal Component Analysis. Learning from Examples Without Local Minima. Neural Networks, Vol. 2, pp. 53 58, 1989

[19] Banard, S. T.; Fishler, M. A.: Computational Stereo. ACM Computation Survey, Vol. 14, No. 4, pp. 553–572, 1982

[20] Banard, S. T.: A Stochastic Approach to Stereo Vision. Proceedings National Conference on AI (AAAI-86). Philadelphia, PA, Los Altos, CA: Kaufmann, pp. 676 – 680, 1986

[21] Barnard S. T.; Thompson, W.B.: Disparity Analysis of Images. IEEE Transactions on Pattern Analysis and Machine Intelligence, Vol. 2, No. 4, pp. 333 – 340,1980

[22] Berg, A.: Untersuchungen zur realitätsgetreuen Darstellung von Leuchtdichteverteilungen im Straßenraum. Diplom-thesis, Computer Science Department, Technische Hochschule Darmstadt, 1990

[23] Bergeron, D.; Grinstein, G.: A Reference Model for the Visualization of Multi-dimensional Data. Proceedings of the EUROGRAPHICS '89 Elsevier (North–Holland), pp. 393–399, 1989

[24] Bibel, W.: Constraint Satisfaction from a Deductive Viewpoint. Artificial Intelligence, Vol. 35, No. 3, pp. 401–413, 1988

[25] Bibel, W.: Towards a Connection Machine for Logical Inference. Future Generation of Computer Systems, Vol. 1, No. 3, pp. 177–188, 1985

[26] Blair, T. A.; Fite, R. C.: Weather Elements. New York: Prentice Hall, 1967

[27] Blake, A.; Zisserman, A.: Visual Reconstruction. Cambridge, MA, MIT Press, 1987

[28] Boff, K.; Kaufman, L.; Thomas, J. (Eds.): Handbook of Perception and Human Performance. Vol. 1 and 2, New York: John Wiley and Sons, 1986

[29] Böhm, K.: Konzeption und Entwicklung von 3D–Interaktions– und Editingtechniken für das Gelände- und Umweltvisualisierungssystem TERRA. Diplom–thesis, Computer Science Department, Technische Hochschule Darmstadt, 1991

[30] Böhm, W.; Farin, G.; Kahmann, J.: A Survey of Curve and Surface Methods in CAGD. Computer Aided Geometric Design, Vol. 1, pp. 1–59, 1984

[31] Bovik, A. C.; Clark, M.; Geisler, W.: Multichannel Texture Analysis Using Localized Spatial Filters. IEEE Transactions on Pattern Analysis and Machine Intelligence, Vol. 12, No. 1, pp. 55–73, 1990

[32] Braddick, O.; Sleigh, A. (Eds.): Physical and Biological Processing of Images. London: Springer, 1982

[33] Buhmann, B.: Beispielanalysen und Wirkungsgraduntersuchungen zur Bestimmung der Sichtbarkeit von Freileitungsmasten, -seilen, und -isolatoren. Studienarbeit, Department of Electrical Engineering, Universität des Saarlandes, 1989

[34] Buhmann, J.; Lange, J.; van der Malsburg, C.: Distortion Invariant Object Recognition by Matching Hierarchically Labeled Graphs. Proceedings of the IJCNN International Joint Conference on Neural Networks, Washington: IEEE, pp. 155–159, 1989

[35] Burr, D. J.: Designing a Handwriting Reader. IEEE Transactions on Pattern Analysis and Machine Intelligence, Vol. 5, No. 9, pp. 554–559, 1983

[36] Burr, D. J.: A Neural Network Digit Recognizer. Proceedings of the IEEE Conference on Systems, Man and Cybernetics, Atlanta, GA: IEEE, pp. 1621–1625, 1986

[37] Burt, P.: Smart Sensing within a Pyramid Vision System. Proceedings of the IEEE, Vol. 76, No. 8, pp. 1006–1015, 1988

[38] Busch, Ch.; Groß, M.: Interactive Neural Network Texture Analysis and Visualization for Surface Reconstruction in Medical Imaging. Computer Graphics Forum, Vol. 12, No. 3, (EUROGRAPHICS '93), pp. C49–C60, 1993

[39] Cadle, R. D.: Particles in The Atmosphere and Space. New York: Reinhold Publishing Corporation, 1966.

[40] Campbell, F. W.; Maffei, L.: Kontrast und Raumfrequenz. In Wahrnehmung und visuelles System, 2nd. Edition, Spektrum der Wissenschaft, Sonderband, pp. 132–139, 1987

[41] Canny, J.: A Computational Approach to Edge Detection. IEEE Transactions on Pattern Analysis and Machine Intelligence, Vol. 8, No. X, pp. 679–698, 1987

[42] Carlbom, I.; Terzopoulos, D.; Harris, K. M.: Reconstructing and Visualizing Models of Neuronal Dendrites. Proceedings of the CGI 91, Tokyo: Springer pp. 623–638, 1991

[43] Carpenter, G. A.; Grossberg, S.: The ART of Adaptive Pattern Recognition by a Self-Organizing Neural Network. IEEE Computer, Vol. 21, No. 3, pp. 77–88, 1988

[44] Chui, C.: An Introduction to Wavelets. Boston: Academic Press, 1992

[45] Chui, C. (Edt.): Wavelets: A Tutorial in Theory and Applications. Boston: Academic Pess, 1992

[46] Clavé, S.; Groß, M.: A Rendering Pipeline for Street Lighting Simulation. Proceedings of the 2nd Eurographics Workshop on Rendering, Barcelona, Spain, 1991

[47] Cohen, M.F.; Greenberg, D.P.: The Hemi-Cube. A Radiosity Solution for Complex Environments. ACM Computer Graphics (SIGGRAPH '85), Vol. 19, No. 3, pp. 31–40, 1985

[48] Cohen, M.F.; Greenberg, D.P.; Immel, D.S.; Brock, P.J.: An Efficient Radiosity Approach for Realistic Image Synthesis. IEEE Computer Graphics & Applications, Vol. 6, No. 2, pp. 26 – 35, 1986

[49] Cooper, L. N.; Elbaum, C.; Reilly, D. L.; Scofield, C. L.: Parallel, Multi-Unit, Adaptive, Nonlinear Pattern Class Separator and Identifier. U.S. Patent 4 760 604

[50] Cowan, W.B.: An Inexpensive Scheme for Calibration of a Color Monitor in Terms of CIE Standard Coordinates. ACM Computer Graphics (SIGGRAPH '83), Vol. 17, No. 3, pp. 315–321, 1983

[51] Crawford, S.; Fall, T.: Projection Pursuit Techniques for Visualizing High-Dimensional Data Sets. In Nielson, Shriver (Eds.) Visualization in Scientific Computing. Los Alamitos, CA: IEEE Computer Society Press, pp. 94–108, 1990

[52] Daubechies, I.: Orthonormal Bases of Compactly Supported Wavelets. Communications on Pure and Applied Mathematics, Vol. 41, pp. 909–996, 1988

[53] Daubechies, I.: The Wavelet Transform, Time-Frequency Localization and Signal Analysis. IEEE Transactions on Information Theory, Vol. 36, pp. 961–1005, 1990

[54] Dayhoff, J.: Neural Network Architectures. An Introduction. New York: Van Nostrand Reinhold, 1990

[55] Dietze, G.: Einführung in die Optik der Atmosphäre. Leipzig: Akademische Verlagsgesellschaft, 1957

[56] Drebin, R.A.; Carpenter, L.; Hanrahan P.: Volume Rendering. ACM Computer Graphics, Vol.22, No.4, pp.51–58, 1988

[57] Dreger, A.: Mathematische Formulierung und Implementierung eines Volumen-Ray-Tracingverfahrens im Waveletraum. Diplom-thesis, Computer Science Department, Technische Hochschule Darmstadt, 1994

[58] Duda, R.; Hart, P: Pattern Classification and Scene Analysis. New York: John Wiley and Sons, 1973

[59] Dyer, S.: apE - Providing Visualization Tools for a Statewide Supercomputing Network. Proceedings of the GI-workshop on Visualization of Volume Data, Darmstadt, 1990

[60] Encarnação, J.; Strasser, W.: Computer Graphics. 2nd Edition, München, Wien: Oldenburg, 1986

[61] Encarnação, J.L.; Groß, M.; Hofmann, R.; Hübner, W.: Integrating Computer Graphics and Computer Vision for Industrial Applications. Invited Tutorial paper, Proceedings of the CGI '92 conference, Tokyo: Springer, pp. 869–881, 1992

[62] Encarnação, M.L.; Groß, M.: An Adaptive Classification Scheme to Approximate Decision Boundaries Using Local Bayes Criteria - The 'Melting Octree' Network. Berkeley: CA, International Computer Science Institute (ICSI), Technical Report TR-92-047, 1992

[63] Fano, R. M.: Transmission of Information - A Statistical Theory of Communications. New York: MIT Press and John Wiley & Sons, 1961

[64] Farin, G.: Curves and Surfaces for Computer Aided Geometric Design - A Practical Guide. 2nd Edition, Boston, New York: Academic Press, 1990

[65] Feldman, J. A.: Time, Space and Form in Vision. Berkeley, CA: ICSI Technical Report, TR-88-011, International Computer Science Institute, 1988

[66] Fels, S.; Hinton, G.: Building Adaptive Interfaces with Neural Networks: The Glove-Talk Pilot Study. Proceedings of Interact 90, pp. 683–688, 1990

[67] Finke, R.; Shepard, R.: Visual Functions of Mental Imagery. In Handbook of Perception and Human Performance, Vol. II, New York: John Wiley and Sons, 1986

[68] Foley, J.; van Dam, A.; Feiner, S.; Hughes, J.: Computer Graphics, Principles and Practice. 2nd Edition, London: Addison Wesley, 1990

[69] Franke, R.; Nielson, G.: Scattered Data Interpolation and Applications: A Tutorial and Survey. In H. Hagen and D. Roller (Eds.), Geometric Modelling: Methods and Their Applications, pp. 131–160, Berlin: Springer, 1990

[70] Frisby, J: Seeing, Illusion, Brain and Mind. Oxford: Oxford University Press, 1979

[71] Fukunaga, K.: Introduction to Statistical Pattern Recognition. 2nd Ed., New York: Academic Press, 1990

[72] Fukushima, K.; Miyake, S.: Neocognitron: A New Algorithm for Pattern Recognition Tolerant of Deformations and Shifts in Position. Pattern Recognition, Vol. 15, No. 6, pp. 455–469, 1982

[73] Fukushima, K., Neural Network Models for Visual Pattern Recognition. In R. Eckmiller, G. Hartmann and G. Hanske. (Eds.), Parallel Processing in Neural Systems and Computers, Amsterdam: Elsevier pp. 351–356, 1990

[74] Getty, D. J.; Pickett, R.; Chylack, L. T.; McCarthy, D. F.; Huggins, A. W. F.: An Enriched Set of Nuclear Cataracts Identified by Multidimensional Scaling. Current Eye Research, Vol. 8, No. 1, pp. 1–8, 1989

[75] Ghezal, A.: Automated Human Face Recognition Using an Artificial Neural Network. Proceedings of the DAGM-Symposium, Berlin: Springer, pp. 75–81, 1991

[76] Giefing, G.; Mallot, H.: Ortsvariante Sensoradaptation durch Kohonen-Mapping. Proceedings of the DAGM–Symposium, Berlin: Springer, pp. 340–347, 1990

[77] Glassner, A. S.: How to Derive a Spectrum From an RGB Triplet. IEEE Computer Graphics and Applications, Vol. 9, No. 4, pp. 95–99, 1989

[78] Goldberg, D. E.: Genetic Algorithms in Search, Optimization and Machine Learning. New York: Addison Wesley, 1989

[79] Goldstein, J.; Harmon, L.; Lesk, A,: Identification of Human Faces. Proceedings of the IEEE, Vol. 59, No. 5, pp. 748–760, 1971

[80] Gonzales, R.G. Woods: Digital Image Processing. New York: Addison Wesley, 1992

[81] Goral, C.; Torrance, K.; Greenberg, D.; Battaille, B.: Modelling the Interaction of Light Between Diffuse Surfaces. ACM Computer Graphics (SIGGRAPH '84), Vol. 18, No. 3, pp. 213–222, 1984

[82] Gori, M.; Tesi,A.: On the Problem of Local Minima in Backpropagation. IEEE Transactions on Pattern Analysis and Machine Intelligence, Vol.14, No. 1, pp. 76–86, 1992

[83] Grimson, W.E.L.: A Computer Implementation of a Theory of Human Stereo Vision. Philosophical Transactions of the Royal Society, London, B292, pp. 217–253

[84] Groß, M.; Koglin, H.-J.: Representation of planned Overhead Lines - The Optical Impression on the Landscape. London: IEE Conference Publication No. 297, pp. 151–155, 1988

[85] Groß, M.; Koglin, H.-J.: Computer-Aided Overhead Line Design - New Methods and Algorithms. Proceedings of the 10th PSCC, London: Butterworths, pp. 9–15, 1990

[86] Groß, M.: Graphische Datenverarbeitung in der Freileitungsplanung -Innovative Methoden mittels Sichtbarkeitsanalyse. Elektrizitätswirtschaft, Vol. 6, pp. 260–268, 1990

[87] Groß, M.; Luttermann, H.: Combining Principal Component Analysis and Neural Networks for the Recognition of Human Faces - A Case Study for Man-Machine-Communication. Singapore: World Scientific, Proceedings of Pacific Graphics, pp. 176–192, 1993

[88] Groß, M.: Subspace Methods for the Visualization of Multidimensional Data Sets. Proceedings of the ONR Workshop on Scientific Visualization, to appear, Academic Press, 1994

[89] Groß, M.: The Analysis of Visibility-Environmental Interactions between Computer Graphics, Physics and Physiology. Computers & Graphics, Vol. 15, No. 3, pp. 407–415, 1991

[90] Groß, M.: Visibility and Camouflage - How to Combine Computer Graphics and Physiology. Bordeaux: Proceedings of the Image Com, pp. 256–261, 1990

[91] Groß, M.: Advanced Visualization Systems. Proceedings of the ISPRS Conference on Digital Photogrammetric Systems, pp. 295–310, München: Wichmann,1991

[92] Groß, M.: An Integrated Simulation and Visualization System for Environmental Protection. Proceedings 5th Symposium on Computer Science for Environmental Problems, pp. 808 – 817, Berlin: Springer, 1990

[93] Groß, M.: Physiological Aspects of Human Vision and Computer Graphics. EUROGRAPHICS '91 tutorial notes, 1991

[94] Groß, M.; Seibert, F.: Visualization of Multidimensional Data Sets using a Neural Network. The Visual Computer, Vol. 10, No. 3, pp. 145– 59, 1993

[95] Groß , M.; Seibert, F.: Multispektralklassifikation von Fernerkundungsdaten mittels neuronaler Netze. Proceedings of DAGM Symposium, pp. 88–93, Berlin: Springer, 1991

[96] Groß, M.; Koglin, H.-J.: Sichtbarkeit von Freileitungen. Saarbrücken: Proceedings of the III–Forum, pp. 235–240, 1987

[97] Groß, M.; Koglin, H.-J.: Computergestützte Freileitungsplanung unter dem Aspekt der Sichtbarkeit. Elektrie, Vol. 3, pp. 101–105, 1989

[98] Groß, M.: Sichtbarkeit von Freileitungen-Erster Einsatz der Graphischen Datenverarbeitung und Bildanalyse. Saarbrücken: Universität des Saarlandes, Ph.D. thesis, 1989

[99] Groß, M.: Ein integriertes Visualisierungs– und Simulationssystem für den Umweltbereich. Informatik-Fachberichte, Vol. 256, pp. 808 – 817, Berlin: Springer, 1990

[100] Groß, M.: Effiziente Visualisierungstechniken für den Umweltschutz. Informatik-Fachberichte Vol. 274, pp. 63–75, Berlin: Springer, 1991

[101] Groß, M.; Kühn, V.: A Visualization and Simulation System for Environmental Purposes. Proceedings of the CGI '91 Conference, pp. 639–654, New York: Springer, 1991

[102] Groß, M.: Image Analysis for Advertisement Purposes - A Computational Model of Visual Perception. Computers & Graphics, Vol. 16, No. 2, pp. 213–221, 1992

[103] Groß, M.; Kühn, V.: Integrating Simulation and Visualization for Environmental Analysis. Proceedings of the German Conference on Computer Science and Environmental Protection, Informatik-Fachberichte Vol. 296, pp. 385–397, Berlin: Springer, 1991

[104] Groß, M.; Seibert, F.: Neural Network Image Analysis for Environmental Protection. Visualisierung von Umweltdaten 1991, pp. 31–42, Berlin: Springer, 1992

[105] Groß, M.; Abel, V.: Übertragung und Erkennung gestörter Zeichen mittels neuronaler Netze. Nachrichtentechnische Fachzeitschrift (NTZ) Vol. 45, No. 4 , pp. 272–279, 1992

[106] Groß, M.; Berg, A.; Clavé, S.: LISA - Ein System zur Simulation und Visualisierung von Straßenbeleuchtungsanlagen. Licht, Vol. 2, pp. 112–118, 1992

[107] Grossmann, A.; Morlet, J.: Decomposition of Hardy Functions into Square Integrable Wavelets of Constant Shape. SIAM Journal of Mathematical Analysis, Vol. 15, pp. 723–736, 1984

[108] Hagen, H.: Visualization of Large Data Sets. Proceedings of the ONR-workshop on Scientific Visualization, to appear, Academic Press, 1994

[109] Hall, L.O. ; Bensaid, A.M.; Clarke, L.P.; Velthuizen, R.P.; Silbiger, M.S.; Bezdek, J.C.: A Comparison of Neural Network and Fuzzy Clustering Techniques in Segmenting Magnetic Resonance Images of the Brain. IEEE Transactions on Neural Networks, Vol. 3, No. 5, pp. 672–682, 1992

[110] Hall, R.; Greenberg, D.: A Testbed for Realistic Image Synthesis. IEEE Computer Graphics and Applications, Vol. 3, No. 8, pp. 10–20, 1983

[111] Hall, R.: Illumination and Color in Computer Generated Imagery. Monographs in Visual Communication, New York: Springer, 1993

[112] Hancock, J.C.; Wintz, P.A.: Signal Detection Theory. New York: McGraw-Hill, 1966

[113] Hannah, M.J.: Bootstrap Stereo. Arlington, VA: Proceedings of the Image Understanding Workshop, pp. 201–208, 1980

[114] Haralick, R.M.: Statistical and Structural Approaches to Texture. Proceedings of the IEEE, Vol. 67, No. 5, pp.786–804, 1979

[115] Harmon, L.; Kahn, M.; Lasch, R.; Ramig, P.: Machine Identification of Human Faces. Pattern Recognition, Vol. 13, No. 2, pp. 97–110, 1981

[116] Heckbert, P. S.: Survey of Texture Mapping. IEEE Computer Graphics and Applications, Vol. 6, No. 6, pp. 56–67, 1986

[117] Henselder ,R.: Vorschriften zur Reinhaltung der Luft (TA-Luft). Köln: Bundesanzeiger Verlagsgesellschaft, 1986

[118] Hentschel, H.J.: Licht und Beleuchtung. 3. Ed., Heidelberg: Hüthig, 1987

[119] Hibbard, W.; Santek, D.: Visualizing Large Data Sets in the Earth Sciences. IEEE Computer, Vol. 22, No. 8, pp. 53–57, 1989

[120] Hinton, G.E.: Connectionist Learning Procedures. Artificial Intelligence, Vol. 40, pp. 185 – 234, 1989

[121] Höhne, K.H.; Bomas, M.; Pommert, A.; Riemer, M.; Schiers, C.; Tiede, U.; Wiebecke, G.: 3D Visualization of Tomographic Volume Data using the Generalized Voxel Model. The Visual Computer, Vol.6, No.1, pp.28–36, 1990

[122] Horn, B.: Robot Vision. New York: McGraw-Hill, 1986

[123] Hood, D.; Finkelstein, M.: Sensitivity to Light. In Handbook of Perception and Human Performance, Vol. I, New York: John Wiley and Sons, 1986

[124] Hubel, D.; Wiesel, T.: Receptive Fields, Binocular Interaction and Functional Architecture in the Cats Visual Cortex. J. Physiol., Vol. 160, pp. 106– 54, 1962

[125] Huss, S. A.: Automatic Performance Characterization of Analog Functional Blocks. Analog Integrated Circuits Signal Process, Vol. 1, No. 4, pp. 277–286, 1991

[126] Immel, D.S.; Cohen, M.F.; Greenberg, D.P.: A Radiosity Method for Non-Diffuse Environments. ACM Computer Graphics (SIGGRAPH 86), Vol. 20, No. 4, pp. 133–142, 1986

[127] Jacob, R.: Emerging User–Interface Media: Potentials and Challenges - Eye Tracking. SIGGRAPH '89 - Tutorial, Boston, 1989

[128] Jain, A.: Fundamentals of Digital Image Processing. Englewood Cliffs, NJ: Prentice Hall, 1989

[129] Julesz, B.; Frisch, H. L.; Gilbert, E. L.; Shepp, L. A.: Inability of Humans to Discriminate between Visual Textures that Agree in Second-Order Statistics - Revisited. Perception, Vol. 2, pp. 391–405, 1973

[130] Julesz, B.: Textons, the Elements of Texture Perception and their Interactions. Nature, Vol. 290, pp. 91–97, 1981

[131] Kajiya, J. T.: The Rendering Equation. ACM Computer Graphics (SIGGRAPH 86), Vol. 20, No. 4, pp. 143–150, 1986

[132] Kalra, D.; Barr, A. H.: Guaranteed Ray Intersections with Implicit Surfaces. ACM Computer Graphics (SiGGRAPH 89), Vol. 23, No. 3, pp. 297-306, 1989

[133] Kaneda, K.; Iriyama, H.; Kato, F.; Nakamae, E.: Realistic Image Synthesis of Complex Objects Using a Simplified Model. Proceedings of the CGI 91, pp. 277–291, New York: Springer, 1991

[134] Kaneda, K.; Okamoto, T.; Nakamae, E.; Nishita, T.: Highly Realistic Visual Simulation of Outdoor Scenes Under Various Atmospheric Conditions. Proceedings of the CGI 90, pp. 117–131, New York: Springer,1990

[135] Kasten, F.: Weather Conditions in W.-Germany. Internal Information from the Deutscher Wetterdienst

[136] Kim, N.; Takai, Y.; Kunii, T.: A Connectionist Approach to Geometrical Constraint-Solving. Proceedings of the IFIP TC5/WG 5.10 Working Conference on Modeling in Computer Graphics, pp. 367–380, Tokyo: Springer,1991

[137] Kirby, M.; Sirovich, L.: Application of the Karhunen-Loeve-Expansion for the Characterization of Human Faces. IEEE Transactions on Pattern Analysis and Machine Intelligence, Vol. 12, No.1, pp. 103–108, 1990

[138] Koch, R.: Entwicklung eines 2D und 3D Texturanalyseverfahrens basierend auf einer Merkmalsextraktion mit Wavelets. Diplom-thesis, Computer Science Department, Technische Hochschule Darmstadt, 1994

[139] Kohonen, T.: The Self-Organizing Map. Proceedings of the IEEE, Vol. 78, No. 9, pp. 1464-1480, 1990

[140] Kohonen, T.: Self-Organization and Associative Memory. 3rd ed. Springer Series in Information Sciences 8, Berlin: Springer, 1989

[141] Korn, A.: Bildverarbeitung durch das visuelle System. Fachberichte Messen - Steuern - Regeln. Berlin: Springer, 1982

[142] Kosko, B.: Neural Networks and Fuzzy Systems - A Dynamical Systems Approach to Machine Intelligence. Englewood Cliffs, NJ: Prentice Hall, 1992

[143] Kühn, V.: Towards the Simulation of the Pollution Behavior of Airplanes. Proceedings of 5th Symposium on Computer Science for Environmental Problems, pp. 583–598, Berlin: Springer, 1990

[144] Kühn, V.; Müller, W.: Advanced Object–Oriented Methods and Concepts for Simulations of Multi-body Systems. Journal of Visualization and Computer Animation, Vol. 4, pp. 95–111, 1993

[145] Kullmer, C.: Entwicklung einer graphisch–interaktiven Benutzerschnittstelle zur Datenselektion aus der EURODB. Diplom-thesis, Computer Science Department, Technische Hochschule Darmstadt, 1991

[146] Kunii, T. (Edt.): Visual Computing. Proceedings of CGI 92, Tokyo: Springer, 1992

[147] Kurihara, T.; Arai, K.: A Transformation Method for Modeling and Animation of the Human Face from Photographs. Proceedings of Computer Animation '91, pp. 45–58, Tokyo: Springer, 1991

[148] Land, E: The Retinex Theory of Color Vision. Proceedings of the Royal Institute of Great Britan, Vol. 47, pp. 23–58

[149] Lange, B.; Hornung, C.: A Solution to Global Illumination by Genetic Algorithms. Proceedings of the International Conference on Neural Nets and Genetic Algorithms, pp. 595–601, Berlin: Springer, 1993

[150] Lange, J.: Graph-Matching zur Positions- und Verzerrungsinvarianten Objekterkennung auf der Basis der Wavelet-Transformation. PhD-thesis, Georg-August Universität zu Göttingen, 1991

[151] Levoy, M.: Display of Surfaces from Volume Data, IEEE Computer Graphics and Applications, Vol. 8, No. 5, 1988

[152] Lillesand, T. M.; Kiefer, R. W.: Remote Sensing and Image Interpretation. 2nd Edition, New York: John Wiley & Sons, 1987

[153] Lippert, L.: Konstruktion und Implementierung von 2D und 3D Wavelet-Basen zur kompakten Datencodierung sowie zur Texturanalyse. Diplom-thesis, Computer Science Department, Technische Hochschule Darmstadt, 1994

[154] Lippmann, R.: An Introduction to Computing with Neural Nets. IEEE ASSP Magazine, Vol. 3, No. 4, pp. 4–22, 1987

[155] Lissner, J.; Seiderer, M.: Klinische Kernspintomographie. Stuttgart: 1990

[156] Lloyd, S.A.: Binocular Stereo Algorithm based on the Disparity-Gradient Limit and using Optimization Theory. Image and Vision Computing, Vol. 3, pp. 177–181, 1985

[157] Lohmann, G.: An Evidential Reasoning Approach to the Classification of Satellite Data. DLR Report, DLR-FB 91-29, PhD-thesis, München, 1991

[158] Lorensen, W. E.; Cline, H. E.: Marching Cubes: A High Resolution 3D Surface Construction Algorithm. ACM Computer Graphics (SIGGRAPH '87), Vol. 21, No. 4, pp. 163–169, 1987

[159] Lüke, H.D.: Signalübertragung. Berlin: Springer, 1983

[160] Luttermann, H.: Schnelle Gesichtserkennung mittels Hauptachsentransformation und neuronalen Netzen. Diplom-thesis, Computer Science Department, Technische Hochschule Darmstadt: 1992

[161] Maddox, C.: Dali. Köln: Kölnische Verlagsdruckerei, 1985

[162] Mallat, S.: A Theory for Multiresolution Signal Decomposition: The Wavelet Representation. IEEE Transactions on Pattern Analysis and Machine Intelligence, Vol. 11, No. 7, pp. 674–693, July 1989

[163] Mallat, S.; Zhong, S.: Characterization of Signals from Multiscale Edges. IEEE Transactions on Pattern Analysis and Machine Intelligence, to appear

[164] Mannaert, H., Oesterlinck, A.: A Self–Organizing Recursive Network for Object Recognition. New York: IEEE, Proceedings of the IEEE-CVPR conference, pp. II405–II408,1992

[165] Marr, D.: Vision. San Francisco: Freeman, 1982

[166] Marr, D.; Hildreth, E.: Theory of Edge Detection. Proceedings of the Royal Society, London, Vol. 207, pp. 187–217, 1980

[167] Marr, D.; Poggio, T.: A theory of Human Stereo Vision. Proceedings of the Royal Society, London, Vol. 204, pp. 301–328, 1977

[168] Mase, K.; Watanabe, Y.; Suenaga, Y.: A Realtime Head Motion Detection System. Santa Clara, CA: Proceedings of the SPIE, Vol. 1260, pp. 262 269, 1990

[169] Mason, B. J.: The Physics Of Clouds. Oxford: Clarendon Press, 1971

[170] Max, N.; Crawfis, R.; Williams, D.: Visualization for Climate Modeling. IEEE Computer Graphics and Applications, Vol. 13, No. 4, pp. 34–40, 1993

[171] McCormick, B. H.; DeFanti, T. A.; Brown, M. D. (Eds.): Visualization in Scientific Computing. ACM Computer Graphics (special issue), Vol. 21, No. 6, 1987

[172] McCulloch, W. S.; Pitts, W. H.: A Logical Calculus of the Ideas Imminent in Neural Nets. Bulletin of Mathematical Biophysics, Vol. 5, pp. 115–133, 1943

[173] Meinzer, H.P.; Meetz, K.; Scheppelmann, D.; Engelmann, U.; Baur, H.J.: The Heidelberg Ray Tracing Model. IEEE Computer Graphics and Applications, Vol. 11, No. 6, pp. 34–43, 1991

[174] Metropolis, N.; Rosenbluth, A. W.; Rosenbluth, M. N.; Teller, A. H.: Equation of State Calculations by Fast Computing Machines. Journal of Chemical Physics, Vol. 21, No. 6, pp. 1087–1092, 1953

[175] Meyer-Brötz, G.; Schürmann, J.: Methoden der automatischen Zeichenerkennung. Oldenbourg-Verlag, 1970

[176] Meyer, G. W.: Wavelength Selection for Synthetic Image Generation. Computer Vision, Graphics and Image Processing, Vol. 41, pp. 57–79, 1988

[177] Minsky, M.; Papert, S.: Perceptrons. 2nd ed., Cambridge, MA: MIT Press, 1900

[178] Moravec, H.: Visual Mapping by a Robot Rover. Proceedings of 6th International Joint Conference on Artificial Intelligence, Vol. 1, pp. 785 – 790, Tokyo: Springer, 1979

[179] Müller, H.; Stark, M.: Adaptive Generation of Surfaces in Volume Data. The Visual Computer, Vol. 9, No. 4, pp. 182–199, 1993

[180] Muraki, S.: Approximation and Rendering of Volume Data Using Wavelet Transforms. New York: IEEE Press, Proceedings of the IEEE Visualization '91 Conference, pp. 21–28, 1992

[181] Muraki, S.: Volume Data and Wavelet Transforms. IEEE Computer Graphics and Applications, Vol. 13, No. 4, pp. 50–56, 1993

[182] Murase, H.; Nayar, S. K.: Learning Object Models from Appearance. Proceedings of National Conference on Artificial Intelligence, AAAI-93, pp. 836–843, 1993

[183] Nakamae, E.; Kaneda, K.; Harada, K.; Miwa, T.; Nishita, T.; Saiki, R.: Reliability of Computer Graphic Images for Visual Assessment. The Visual Computer, Vol. 7, pp. 138–148, 1991

[184] Nakamae, E.; Kaneda, K.; Okamoto, T.; Nishita, T.: A Lighting Model aiming at Drive Simulators. ACM Computer Graphics (SIGGRAPH '90), Vol. 24, No. 4, pp. 395–404, 1990

[185] Nakamae, E.; Nishita, T.: Illumination Simulation in Interior Design. Japan Annual Reviews in Electronics, Computers & Telecommunications, Vol .18, pp. 289–300, 1988

[186] Ney, D.E.; Fishman, E.K.; Magid, D.; Drebin, A.: Volumetric Rendering of Computed Tomography Data: Principles and Techniques. IEEE Computer Graphics and Applications, Vol. 10, No. 3, pp. 24–32, 1990

[187] Nielson, G. M.: Scattered Data Modelling. IEEE Computer Graphics and Applications, Vol. 13, No. 1, pp. 60–70, 1993

[188] Nielson, G.: Visualization in Scientific and Engineering Computation. IEEE Computer, Vol. 9, pp. 58–66, 1991

[189] Niemann, H.: Pattern Analysis and Understanding. 2nd ed. Springer Series in Information Sciences 4., Berlin: Springer, 1989

[190] Nishita, T.; Okamura, I.; Nakamae, E.: Shading Models for Point and Linear Sources. ACM Transactions on Graphics, Vol. 4, No. 2, pp. 124–146, 1986

[191] Nishita, T.; Nakamae, E.; Harada, K.; Ishizaki, T.: A Montage Method: The Overlaying of the Computer Generated Images onto a Background Photograph. ACM Computer Graphics (SIGGRAPH '86), Vol. 20, No. 4, pp. 207–214, 1986

[192] Nishita, T.; Kaneda, K.; Kato, F.; Nakamae, E.; Tanaka, H.; Noguchi, T.: Three Dimensional Terrain Modelling and Display of Environmental Assessment, ACM Computer Graphics, (SIGGRAPH '89), Vol. 23, No. 3, pp. 207–214, 1989

[193] North, D.O.: An Analysis of the Factors which Determine Signal/Noise Discrimination in Pulsed Carrier Systems, Proceedings IRE 51, pp. 1016–1027, 1963

[194] Nussbaumer, H.: Fast Fourier Transform and Convolution Algorithms. 2nd ed. Springer Series in Information Sciences 2. Berlin: Springer, 1981

[195] Oja, E.: A Simplified Neuron Model as a Principal Component Analyzer. Journal of Mathematical Biology, Vol. 15, pp. 267–273, 1982

[196] Oja, E.: Neural Networks, Principal Components, and Subspaces. pp. 61–68

[197] Papathomas, T. V.; Schiarara, J. A.; Julesz, B.: Applications of Computer Graphics to the Visualisation of Meteorological Data. ACM Computer Graphics (SIGGRAPH '88), Vol. 22, No. 4, pp. 327–334, 1988

[198] Papoulis, A.: Signal Analysis. New York: McGraw-Hill, 1977

[199] Pentland, A.: Equilibrium and Interpolation Solutions Using Wavelet Bases. Proceedings of the CGI '91 Conference, pp. 507–523, New York: Springer, 1991

[200] Perry, D. F.; Nickerson, J. K.; Zobel, E. S.: An Approach to Assessing Visual Compatibility of Transmission Lines and the Landscape. Stockholm: Cigré-Symposium, Transmission Lines and the Environment, paper 210–211, 1981

[201] Philips: Prinzipien der MR-Tomographie. Philips Medical Systems, Eindhoven

[202] Pielke, R. A.: Mesoscale Meteorological Modeling. New York: Academic Press, 1984

[203] Poggio, T.: Wie Computer und Menschen sehen. In Wahrnehmung und visuelles System, 2nd. Edition, Spektrum der Wissenschaft, Sonderband, pp. 78–89, 1987

[204] Poggio, T.: Networks for Approximation and Learning. Proceedings of the IEEE, Vol. 78, No. 9, pp. 1481–1497, 1990

[205] Pokorny, J.; Smith, V.: Colorimetry and Color Discrimination. In Handbook of Perception and Human Performance, Vol. 1, New York: John Wiley and Sons, 1986

[206] Pollard, S.; Mayhew, J.; Frisby, J.: PMF: A Stereo Correspondence Algorithm using a Disparity Gradient Limit. Perception, Vol. 14, pp. 449–470, 1985

[207] Preparata, F.; Shamos, M.: Computational Geometry. An Introduction. New York: Springer, 1985

[208] Press, W. H.; Flannery, B. P.; Teukolsky, S. A.; Vetterling, W. T.: Numerical Recipes in C - The Art of Scientific Computing. New York: Cambridge University Press, 1988

[209] Radig, B.: Image Sequence Analysis using Relational Structures. Pattern Recognition, Vol. 17, No. 1, pp. 161–167, 1984

[210] Radig, B. (Edt.): Mustererkennung 1991. Informatik Fachberichte, Vol. 290, Proceedings of 13th DAGM Symposium. Springer, 1991

[211] Radig, B.: RS–Automorphisms and Symmetrical Objects. New York: IEEE-Press, Proceedings of the 7 International Conference on Pattern Recognition, pp. 1138–1140, 1984

[212] Rioul, O.; Vetterli, M.: Wavelets and Signal Processing. IEEE SP Magazine, pp. 14–38, October 1991

[213] Richter, M.: An Introduction to Colorimetry. 2nd. Ed., Berlin: de Gruyter, 1981

[214] Ritter, N.; Hepner, G.: Application of an Artificial Neural Network to Landcover Classification of Thematic Mapper Imagery. Computers & Geosciences, Vol. 16, No. 6, pp. 873–880, 1990

[215] Richter, T.: Entwicklung eines Systems zur Planung von Straßenbeleuchtungsanlagen. Diplom-thesis, Computer Science Department, Technische Hochschule Darmstadt, 1992

[216] Roache, P. J.: Computational Fluid Dynamics. Albuquerque, NM: Hermosa Publishers, 1982

[217] Rock, I.: Figuren, die man wahrnimmt, ohne sie zu sehen. In Wahrnehmung und visuelles System, 2nd. Edition, Spektrum der Wissenschaft, Sonderband, pp. 158–167, 1987

[218] Röckle, R.: Bestimmung der Strömungsverhältnisse im Bereich komplexer Bebauungsstrukturen. PhD-thesis, Technische Hochschule Darmstadt, 1990

[219] Rogers, R. R.: A Short Course in Cloud Physics, Oxford, New York, Toronto: Pergamon Press, 1076

[220] Rosenblatt, F.: The Perceptron: a Probabilistic Model for Information Storage and Organization in the Brain. Psychological Review, Vol. 65, pp. 386–408, 1958

[221] Rosenstiel, L.; Neumann, P.: Introduction to Advertisment Psychology. Darmstadt: Wissenschaftliche Buchgesellschaft, 1982

[222] Rosie, A. M.: Information and Communication Theory. London: Blackie & Son, 1966

[223] Rumelhart, D.; Hinton, E.; Williams, R.: Learning Internal Representations by Error Propagation. Parallel Distributed Processing: Explorations in the Microstructures of Cognition, Vol. 1, pp. 318–362, Cambridge, MA: MIT Press, 1986

[224] Rumelhart, D.E.; McClelland, J.L.: Parallel Distributed Processing, Explorations in the Microstructure of Cognition. Vol. 1 and 2. Cambridge, MA: MIT Press, 1986

[225] Ruskai, M.; Beylkin, G.; Coifman, R.; Daubechies, I.; Mallat, S.; Meyer, I.; Raphael, L. (Eds.): Wavelets and Their Applications. Boston: Jones and Bartlett, 1992

[226] Sakas, G.: Modeling and Animating Turbulent Gaseous Phenomena using Spectral Synthesis. The Visual Computer, Vol. 9, No. 4, pp. 200–212, 1993

[227] Schad, L.R.; Schmitt, H.P.; Oberwittler, C.; Lorenz, W.J.: Numerical Grading of Astrocytomas. Med.Inform., Vol.12, No.1, pp.11–22, 1987

[228] Schmidt, R.: Foundations of Physiology. Berlin: Springer, 1985

[229] Schnabel, A.: Integration von Landsat-TM-Bilddaten und digitalem Geländemodell. Diplom-thesis, Computer Science Department, Fachhochschule Darmstadt, 1992

[230] Schober, H.: Das Sehen. 3. Ed., Vol. I and Vol. II, Leipzig: Fachbuchverlag, 1960

[231] Seelen,von W.; Shaw, G.; Leinhos, U. M.: Organization of Neural Networks: Structures and Models. Weinheim: Verlagsgesellschaft, 1988

[232] Seibert, F.: Konzeption und Entwicklung eines Softwaresystems zur multispektralen Klassifizierung von Satellitendaten mittels neuronaler Netze. Diplom–thesis, Computer Science Department, Technische Hochschule Darmstadt, 1991

[233] Shackleton, M.; Welsh, W.: Classification of Facial Features for Recognition. Proceedings of the IEEE–CVPR conference, pp. 573–579, New York: IEEE–Press, 1991

[234] Sillion, F.; Puech, C.: A General Two-Pass Method Integrating Specular and Diffuse Reflection. ACM Computer Graphics (SIGGRAPH 89), Vol. 23, No. 3, pp. 335–344, July 1989

[235] Simoncelli, E.; Adelson, E.: Non-Separable Extensions of Quadrature Mirror Filters to Multiple Dimensions. Proceedings of the IEEE, Vol. 78, No. 4, pp. 652–664, 1990

[236] Sirovich, L.; Kirby, M.: Low-dimensional Procedure for the Characterization of Human Faces. J. Opt. Soc. Am. A., Vol. 4, No. 3, pp. 519–529, 1987

[237] Stork, A.; Groß, M.; Saradeth, S.: The Analysis of Remotely Sensed Data with Neural Networks. Proceedings of the European International Space Year's Conference, München, ESA Publication Division, pp.417–422, 1992

[238] Stummbillig, M.: Parameteruntersuchungen und Beispielanalysen mit Hilfe rechnergestützter Verfahren zur quantitativen Erfassung der Sichtbarkeit von Objekten durch Bildanalyse. Diplom-thesis, Department of Electrical Engineering, University of Saarland, 1989

[239] Stummbillig, M.: Programmierung eines Algorithmus zur Erfassung der Sichtbarkeit von Objekten durch Bildanalyse. Studienarbeit, Department of Electrical Engineering, Universität des Saarlandes, 1988

[240] Tenenbaum, A. M.; Langsam, Y.; Augenstein, M. J.: Data Structures Using C. Englewood Cliffs, New York: Prentice Hall, 1990

[241] Terzopoulos, D.; Witkin, A.; Kass, M.: Signal Matching Through Scale Space. International Journal of Computer Vision, pp. 133– 44, 1987

[242] Tufte, E., R.: The Visual Display of Quantitative Information. Cheshire, CN: Graphics Press, 1983

[243] Tumblin, J.; Rushmeier, H.: Tone Reproduction for Realistic Computer Generated Images, Internal Report No. GIT-GVU-91-13, Graphics, Visualization & Usability Center, Georgia Institute of Technology, Atlanta, GA, 1991

[244] Turk, M.; Pentland, A.: Eigenfaces for Recognition. Journal of Cognitive Neuroscience, Vol. 3, No. 1 pp. 71–86, 1991

[245] Unser, M.; Eden, M.: Multiresolution Feature Extraction and Selection for Texture Segmentation. IEEE Transactions on Pattern Analysis and Machine Intelligence, Vol. 11, No. 7, pp. 717–728, 1989

[246] Vannier, M. W.; Pilgram, T.; Bhatia, G.; Brunsden, B.: Facial Surface Scanner. IEEE Computer Graphics and Applications, Vol. 11, No. 6, pp. 72–80, 1991

[247] Väänänen, K.; Böhm, K.: Gesture Driven Interaction as a Human Factor in Virtual Environments - An Approach with Neural Networks. New York: Academic Press, Virutal Reality Systems, pp. 94–106, 1993

[248] Verbeck, C.P.; Greenberg, D.P.: A Comprehensive Light-Source Description for Computer Graphics. IEEE Computer Graphics & Applications, Vol. 4, No. 7, pp. 66–75, 1984

[249] Visa, A.; Kimmo, V.; Olli, S.: Cloud Detection Based on Texture Segmentation by Neural Network Methods. New York: IEEE Press, Proceedings of the International Joint Conference on Neural Networks, Vol. 2, pp. 1001–1006, 1991

[250] von der Malsburg, C.: Self-Organization of Orientation Sensitive Cells in the Striate Cortex. Cybernetics, Vol .14, pp. 85–100, 1973

[251] Wallace, J. R.; Cohen, J.; Greenberg , D. P.: A Two Pass Solution to the Rendering Equation: A Synthesis of Ray Tracing and Radiosity Methods. ACM Computer Graphics (SIGGRAPH 87), Vol. 21, No. 4, pp. 311–320, 1986

[252] Watanabe, Y.; Suenaga, Y.: Synchronized Acquisition of Three-Dimensional Range and Color Data and its Applications. Proceedings of the CGI 91, pp. 655–665, Berlin: Springer, 1991

[253] Whitelegg, T. M.; Gourlay, J.; Beaumont, R.; Taylor, P.; Aylward, G.; Turnbull, M.: An Environmental Assessment Methodology and Computer-Aided Design Techniques for the Visual Analysis of Transmission Line Routes. Stockholm: Cigré-Symposium, Transmission Lines and the Environment, paper 210–11, 1981

[254] Whitted, T.: An Improved Illumination Model for Shaded Display. Communications of the ACM, Vol. 23, No. 6, pp. 343–349, 1980

[255] Widrow, B.; Michael, A.: 30 years of Adaptive Neural Networks: Perceptron, Madaline and Backpropagation. Proceedings of the IEEE, Vol. 78, No. 9, pp. 1415–1442, 1990

[256] Willis, P. J.: Visual Simulation of Atmospheric Haze. Computer Graphics Forum, Vol. 6, No. 1, pp. 35–42, 1987

[257] Winkel, R.: Ein stochastisches Verfahren zur automatischen Korrelation stereoskopischer Bilder. Diplom-thesis, Computer Science Department, Technische Hochschule Darmstadt, 1992

[258] Wolter, F. E.; Tuohy, S. T.: Curvature Computations for Degenerate Surface Patches. Computer Aided Geometric Desing, Vol. 9, pp. 241–270, 1992

[259] Wong, K.; Law, H.; Tsang, P.: A System for Recognizing Human Faces. New York, IEEE-Press, Proceedings of the IEEE-ICASSP, pp. 1638–1642, 1989

[260] Wyszecki, G.: Color Appearance. In Handbook of Perception and Human Performance, Vol. 1, New York: John Wiley and Sons, 1986

[261] Wyszecki, G.; Stiles, W.: Color Science. Concepts and Methods, Quantitative Data and Formulae., 2nd ed., New York: John Wiley & Sons, 1991

[262] Yan, J. K.: Advances in Computer-Generated Imagery for Flight Simulation. IEEE Computer Graphics and Applications, Vol. 8, No. 4, pp. 37–50, 1985

[263] Young, F.; Rheingans, P.: Visualizing Structure in High-Dimensional Multivariate Data. IBM Journal of Research and Development, Vol. 35, No. 1/2, pp. 97–107, 1991

[264] Young, T. Y.; Fu, K. S. (Eds.): Handbook of Pattern Recognition and Image Processing. Orlando, FL: Academic Press, 1986

[265] Yuille, A.; Cohen, D.; Hallinan, P.: Feature Extraction From Faces Using Deformable Templates. New York, IEEE Press, Proceedings of the IEEE–CVPR conference, pp. 104–109, 1989

[266] Zhang, Q.; Benveniste, A.: Wavelet Networks. IEEE Transactions on Neural Networks, Vol. 3, No. 6, pp. 889–898, 1992

[267] Zindler, M.: Konzeption und Entwicklung einer X/Motif Benutzeroberfläche für das Gelände- und Umweltvisualisierungssystem TERRA. Diplom-thesis, Computer Science Department, Technische Hochschule Darmstadt, 1991

[268] Zyda, M.; Jones, A.; Hogan, P.: Surface Construction from Planar Contours, Computer and Graphics, Vol. 11, No. 4, pp. 393–408, 1987

Index

Chapter 2

f	:	function
x	:	value / activity
w	:	weight value
l, j, i, k	:	index
D	:	diopters
r	:	distance
I	:	(luminous) intensity of light
α	:	visual angle
d	:	pupil's diameter
J_1	:	first order Bessel function
λ	:	wavelength
E	:	energy
h	:	Planck's constant
c	:	speed of light
$V(\lambda)$	:	relative spectral sensitivity for daytime vision
$V'(\lambda)$	:	relative spectral sensitivity for nighttime vision
$P(\lambda)$	:	spectral power distribution
F	:	luminous flux
$const$	:	constant 683 lm/W
Ω	:	solid angle
A	:	surface area
P	:	patch
E_A	:	illumination
δ	:	angle
Y	:	luminance

x, x', x'' : points in space
$g\,(x, x')$: geometry term
$\varepsilon\,(x, x')$: emitted light term
$\varrho\,(x, x', x'')$: reflexion term
θ : angle (light source) to the C-plane
β : angle between the illumination axis and the lighting ray
C : C - plane
T : unit time
$\Delta\lambda$: resolution of the spectral sampling methods
K : specific index
M : number of light sources
$\overline{N}$: surface normal
Γ : form-factor
B_i : radiosity of a patch i
N : number of patches

Chapter 3

Y_A : adaptation luminance
d . pupil's diameter
C : contrast
C_{min} : contrast sensitivity
B : brightness (physiologically)
Y_s : scattered luminance
N : number of slits in a grating
θ : diffraction angle
I : intensity (distribution of light)
α, β : angles
a : width of a slit of a grating
b : length of a period of a grating
Φ : rotation angle
V : visual acuity
α_{min} : minimun visual angle
r : distance, radius
g : DOG function
E_0, I_0, R_1, R_2 : parameters of the DOG
t : time
Y_{min} : threshold luminance

Y_{min}	:	threshold luminance for infinite observation time
$\overline{Y}$	:	mean luminance
f_v	:	threshold frequency for flickering
d	:	disparity
m,n	:	distances on the retina
$R(\lambda),G(\lambda),B(\lambda)$	:	chromatic response functions
YE	:	yellow channel
$x(\lambda),y(\lambda),z(\lambda)$	:	CIE spectral response functions
X, Y, Z	:	CIE primaries
x, y, z	:	CIE primaries (normalized)
$P(\lambda)$	:	spectral energy distribution
g_{11}, g_{12}, g_{22}	:	constants used to describe the McAdams ellipsoids
$[X_{RGB}]$	:	CIE transformation matrix
ΔE	:	color difference
L^*, u^*, v^*	:	perceptual color space
L^*, a^*, b^*	:	perceptual color space
u, v	:	color coordinates
X_W, Y_W, Z_W	:	nominally white color
A, C_1, C_2	:	Meyer's color space
$\gamma_R, \gamma_G, \gamma_B$	:	values for the γ-correction
$R_\gamma, G_\gamma, B_\gamma$	:	γ-corrected R, G, B values
C_R, C_G, C_B	:	constants

Chapter 4:

r	:	distance
Ω	:	solid angle
V	:	visual acuity
α	:	visual angle
c_1, c_2, c_3	:	parameters
$\Delta\Omega$	:	solid angle segment
Y, x, y	:	color coordinates
r, ϕ	:	polar coordinates
$C(r)$	:	contrast function
$\Delta x, \Delta y$	:	color shifts
Z	:	atmospheric extinction coefficient
ΔE	:	color difference
S''	:	specific visibility

S	:	visibility
S''_{max}	:	maximum specific visibility
S_{max}	:	maximum visibility
η''	:	efficiency of camouflage for S″
η	:	efficiency of camouflage for S
b_A	:	ratio to moderate the visibility
X,Y,Z	:	spatial cartesian coordinates
P	:	point in space
X_P,Y_P,Z_P	:	coordinates of a point in space
$\Delta r,\Delta\phi$	:	spatial resolution of the polar coordinate system
m,i,j,k,n	:	index
K	:	resolution of the discrete surface segments
ΔA	:	surface segment
F	:	variational integral
u,v,w	:	velocity components
α_h,α_v	:	control parameters
u_0, v_0, w_0	:	initial velocties
λ	:	variation parameter
u_x,v_y,w_z	:	characterizes the constraint div($\mathbf{v}$) = 0
C	:	concentration
P, D	:	parameters
K_x,K_y,K_z	:	diffusion parameters
V_A	:	counting volume
$N(x_i,y_j,z_k)$	:	number of particles in a counting volume

Chapter 5:

Y	:	luminance
l,i,j,k,m,n,p	:	index
R_k	:	retinal image description of filter k
C_l	:	cortical image description of filter l
K	:	number of retinal filters
L	:	number of cortical filters
$g(r)$	:	Gaussian function
w_{2D}	:	central panel width
σ	:	variance of $g(r)$
∇^2	:	Laplace operator
x,y,z	:	spatial coordinates
$\nabla^2 g$	:	Marr–Hildreth operator

$i(x,y)$	: image intensity function
α,β	: coordinates
M,N	: resolutions of the image
I	: discrete image intensity fuction
i^F	: Fourier transform of the image intensity function
I^F	: discrete FT of the image intensity function
H^F	: FT of the impulse response of a filter h
u,v	: spatial frequencies
I_{Oi}	: pixel intensities of an object by filter i
I_{Ui}	: pixel intensities of the environment by filter i
P_O	: total number of object pixels
P_U	: total number of environment pixels
O	: optical conspicuousness
$w_1,..,w_5$	: number for the analyzed industry logos
$L^2(\mathbf{R})$	: Hilbert space of functions of finite energy
WT	: Wavelet transform
GT	: Garbor transform
$STFT$	: Short-Time Fourier Transform
τ, t	: time
f, ω	: frequency
$x(t)$	: signal
$g(t)$	: Gaussian window function
j	: complex number operator
Q	: quality
a	: scaling factor of the WT
$\psi(x)$	: wavelet basis function
$f(x)$	: measurable, square integrable, one–dimensional function
$A_{2^j}f$	: onthonormal projection on a vector space V_{2^j}
V_{2^j}	: set of possible approximations of $L^2(R)$ at resolution 2^j
k	: integer number
$\phi(x)$	: scaling function
$A_{2^j}f(x)$	: discrete approximation of f at resolution 2^j
$<f,g>$	: inner product of f and g
n	: variable
$h(n)$	: impulse response of a discrete filter
$H(\omega)$	: Fourier transform of the filter
$\overline{\Phi}(\omega)$	: Fourier transform of a scaling function

Index

$\boldsymbol{O}_{2^j}$	:	orthogonal complement of V_{2^j} in $V_{2^{j+1}}$
$G(\omega)$	:	quadrature mirror pair to $H(\omega)$
$\psi(\omega)$	:	Fourier transform of a wavelet function
$D_{2^j} f$	:	detail signal at resolution 2^j
J	:	upper resolution limit
$P_{\boldsymbol{O}_{2^j}} f$	:	orthogonal projection
$\boldsymbol{L}^2(\boldsymbol{R}^2)$	:	2D extensions of $\boldsymbol{L}^2(\boldsymbol{R})$
$\boldsymbol{L}^2(\boldsymbol{R}^3)$	:	3D extension of $\boldsymbol{L}^2(\boldsymbol{R})$
$\Phi(x,y)$	:	2D scaling function
$\Psi(x,y)$	:	2D wavelet
$\Phi(x,y,z)$	:	3D scaling function
$\Psi(x,y,z)$	:	3D wavelet
$h(x)$	:	Gabor function
ς	:	phase angle
L	:	discretization in phase
N	:	spatial resolution
$g_{WT}(x)$	:	Gabor wavelet
c_j	:	coefficients of the wavelet transform
τ_j	:	corresponding wavelet or scaling function
$\boldsymbol{x}(x,y)$	:	vectorial representation
X_w, Y_w, Z_w	:	world coordinates
d	:	disparity
L	:	baseline
f	:	focal length
x_{Pl}, y_{Pl}	:	coordinates of a point in the left image
x_{Pr}, y_{Pr}	:	coordinates of a point in the right image
Δd	:	disparity range
P	:	state probability
E	:	energy
T	:	temperature
∇d	:	disparity gradient
$N(k)$	:	local neighborhood
r	:	radius, distance
$r_{\max}$	:	$1/e$-radius
$d_{\max}$	:	maximum disparity
$d_{\min}$	:	minimum disparity

ΔE	:	energy difference
I_L	:	left image intensity
I_R	:	right image intensity
λ	:	variational parameter

Chapter 6:

$\boldsymbol{x}$	:	data vector
$\boldsymbol{m}$	:	mean vector
l,k	:	specific index
$p(x)$	:	data density distribution
c	:	number of clusters
N	:	dimension of the data vector
E	:	energy, cost function
j,i	:	index
Φ	:	set of data vectors
s	:	number of data samples in Φ
$\bar{\boldsymbol{x}}$	:	specific data sample
a,b	:	markers
$P(\boldsymbol{x})$	:	probability of $\boldsymbol{x}$
ΔV	:	hypervolume element of an N-tree cell
$\delta_{\max}$	:	threshold for subdivision
E_D	:	cost function for dimensionality scaling
∇	:	gradient operator
g	:	number of dissimilarities
d_{ij}	:	inter-point distance in subspace
δ_{ij}	:	inter-point distance
$\bar{d}_{ij}$	:	ranked numbers
E_{mon}	:	monotonicy cost function
$\boldsymbol{d}_j$	:	difference vectors
$\boldsymbol{u}_k$	:	eigenvector k
λ_k	:	eigenvalue k
$\boldsymbol{C}$	:	covariance matrix
$\boldsymbol{A}$	:	matrix
$\boldsymbol{v}_i$	:	eigenvector
ω_i	:	coordinates in eigenspace
Ω	:	coordinate vector in eigenspace
K	:	number of classes
$g(x)$	:	discriminante function

P_E	:	error probability
b	:	minimum error boundary value
C	:	class
d	:	distance
z_i	:	target value for the discriminant function
$P(C_i\|\mathbf{x})$	:	a posteriori probability
$p(\mathbf{x}\|C_i)$	:	state conditional probability density function
$P(C_i)$	:	a priori probability of class C_i
w	:	weights in neural networks
S	:	sum
T	:	target value
η	:	learning rate
a	:	output of a neuron
d	:	(Euclidian) distance
$N_e(t)$	:	time-dependent neighborhood
$T_{\max}$	:	upper training time limit
L	:	subspace dimension
ε	:	small constant
α	:	LVQ-training rate
δ	:	window factor (LVQ)
$V(j)$	:	set of predecessor neurons of neuron j
net_j	:	overall activation function
$N(j)$	:	set of successor neurons of neuron j
n_p	:	number of training vectors
n_j	:	number of output neurons
E_{RMS}	:	root mean square error
n_a	:	number of active neurons in the preceding layer
ΔE	:	energy difference
$A(j)$	:	set of neurons connected with neuron j
P_{ij}	:	state probabilities for both neuron i and neuron j being "on"
$\mathbf{W}$	:	connection weight matrix
$\mathbf{a}$	:	output vector
ξ	:	internal feedback

Chapter 7:

s	:	signal
$y(t)$	:	output signal

$n(t)$	:	noise signal
$h(t)$	:	impulse response function
t	:	time
T	:	sampling time
$g(t)$	:	signal of the decomposition
$n_e(t)$	:	noise of the decomposition
S_a	:	signal power at T
N	:	noise power at T
N_0	:	power spectrum of a white noise signal
p_{sh}^E	:	normalized cross correlation coefficient
$\bar{h}(t)$	:	optimal impulse response
E	:	signal energy
$const$	:	generic constant
p_{sh}^E	:	optimum of p_{sh}^E
$\phi_{ss}^E(t)$	:	autocorrelation function of a signal $s(t)$
τ	:	threshold
ξ	:	variable
π_0, π_1	:	probabilities
$\bar{P}_E$	:	minimum total error probability
M	:	number of false characters
M_{tot}	:	total number of characters
Z	:	number of learning cycles
B_0	:	constant magnetic field
ω_L	:	Larmor frequency
$\boldsymbol{M}$	:	magnetic momentum
$\boldsymbol{M}_z$	:	z-component of $\boldsymbol{M}$
$\boldsymbol{M}_{xy}$	:	x,y-component of $\boldsymbol{M}$
T_1	:	longitudinal relaxation
T_2	:	transversal relaxation
T_e	:	echo time
T_R	:	pulse repetition time
N	:	data dimension
K	:	dimension of a subspace
$class(j)$	:	class assignment of vertex j
k,n,i,j	:	index
s_j	:	distance of the voxel to vertex j
(x_v, y_v, z_y)	:	voxel coordinates
Q	:	number of persons
P	:	number of face pictures

ε_{in}	:	Euclidian distances of face *i* and *n* in eigenspace
$\overline{\varepsilon}$	:	minimum distance in eigenspace
τ	:	threshold
σ	:	standard deviation
x_{ink}	:	test rating of person *k* for face *i* and face *n*
σ_{PCA}	:	standard deviation to the PCA distance
$\overline{\Omega}_i$	:	mean coordinate vector of a person *i* in eigenspace
$\omega_{ij}{}^{(k)}$	:	*k*-th coordinate of face *j* of person *i*
m_{in}	:	mean rating of face pair *i* and *n*

Springer-Verlag and the Environment

We at Springer-Verlag firmly believe that an international science publisher has a special obligation to the environment, and our corporate policies consistently reflect this conviction.

We also expect our business partners – paper mills, printers, packaging manufacturers, etc. – to commit themselves to using environmentally friendly materials and production processes.

The paper in this book is made from low- or no-chlorine pulp and is acid free, in conformance with international standards for paper permanency.

Printing: Saladruck, Berlin
Binding: Buchbinderei Helm, Berlin